A GEOLOGY OF
IRELAND

Gweedore, County Donegal in September, looking towards the 'Poisoned Glen'—blanket bog with pools in foreground; the Donegal granite mountains under cloud.

Frontispiece

Photograph by M. C. F. Proctor

A GEOLOGY OF
IRELAND

Edited by

C. H. HOLLAND

1981

SCOTTISH ACADEMIC PRESS
EDINBURGH

Published by
SCOTTISH ACADEMIC PRESS LTD
33 Montgomery Street
Edinburgh EH7 5JX

First published 1981

ISBN 0 7073 0269 2

Designed by: T. L. Jenkins, Edinburgh
Printed in Great Britain by
Clark Constable Ltd, Edinburgh

CONTENTS

CONTRIBUTING AUTHORS

Gordon L. Herries Davies — Department of Geography, Trinity College, Dublin

C. H. Holland — Department of Geology, Trinity College, Dublin

G. F. Mitchell — Department of Geology, Trinity College, Dublin

T. Murphy — School of Cosmic Physics, Dublin Institute of Advanced Studies

W. E. A. Phillips — Department of Geology, Trinity College, Dublin

J. Preston — Department of Geology, Queen's University, Belfast

G. D. Sevastopulo — Department of Geology, Trinity College, Dublin

C. J. Stillman — Department of Geology, Trinity College, Dublin

H. E. Wilson — *Formerly*: Geological Survey of Northern Ireland, Belfast; *presently*: Institute of Geological Sciences, Keyworth, Nottingham, England

PREFACE

The late Professor J. K. Charlesworth's substantial compilation of the historical geology of Ireland was published seventeen years ago and since then much has happened in Irish geological research. Several, more recent, books on the stratigraphy of the British Isles have devoted a relatively small proportion of their pages to Ireland. But additionally, and more positively, we have felt the need for a treatment of Irish geology which is at once broad and concise, in which it is hoped that some loss of detail and of a comprehensive statement of bibliographical control are compensated by freshness and readability.

It is intended that the book will be of value not only to students of Irish and British geology, of all ages, professional and amateur alike, but also to those many earth scientists abroad who must take interest in this island, poised on the edge of Europe and yet linked in so many ways with North America. Our treatment is in terms of historical geology, but included also are a short survey of geophysical evidence, an account of Ireland's now very important economic geology, and a review of the fascinating history of Irish geology itself.

Although numerous names are mentioned in the text, this book depends upon the work of very many more whom it has not been possible to acknowledge. Sources of illustrations are given more fully. Colleagues in the Department of Geology at Trinity College, Dublin have helped immensely, not least in the preparation of a succession of manuscripts and of the illustrations. The Editor is grateful to them and to his fellow authors for their kind patience and co-operation.

CHARLES HEPWORTH HOLLAND

Trinity College
Dublin

August 1979

Time past and time future
Allow but a little consciousness.
To be conscious is not to be in time
But only in time can the moment in the rose-garden,
The moment in the arbour where the rain beat,
The moment in the draughty church at smokefall
Be remembered; involved with past and future.
Only through time time is conquered.

T. S. ELIOT
'*Four Quartets : Burnt Norton*'

I

INTRODUCTION

C. H. Holland

The geological sciences know no national frontiers. This book is about the island of Ireland as a physical whole. Studies of marine geology and geophysics, stimulated by the search for oil and natural gas, have shown that the Irish coastline, like that of mainland Britain, does not, as was once believed, capriciously cut off from observation a solid geology continuous in character from that of the land. The configuration of the coastline in places parallels the margins of submarine subsided basins of thick Mesozoic and Tertiary rocks (Fig. 184). It would have been reasonable to extend our systematic treatment of Irish geology throughout the continental shelf of this island, eastwards as far as the median line of the Irish Sea and into deeper waters from the Atlantic shore. However, it is true that information is limited in availability and, in any case, there must be constraint upon the length of this book. Accordingly the offshore is treated in Chapter 18, where its economic importance is also brought out.

The land of Ireland, then, is largely of Palaeozoic rocks, amply covered in places by the drift deposits of the very latest episodes of geological history. Clearly there were earlier connections between the environments represented by the Irish Palaeozoics and those recorded in rocks of the same age in mainland Britain and even in the New World. Evidence of these past connections is to some extent concealed by the younger rocks of the marginal basins and has been made more elusive by the effects of ocean floor spreading and perhaps by earlier episodes of subduction. Certainly, as always in geology, the international context must be kept in sight. The details of the Irish landscape, rural and urban; the distribution of bog and forest; the nature of the present day vegetation; all depend upon the activities of man during his short occupancy of this island. The scenery of both lowland and upland Ireland (Fig. 1) is also much affected by the climatic events of the Quaternary Period discussed by G. F. Mitchell later in this book. We lack the relatively large areas of Mesozoic rocks which William Smith, 'The Father of English Geology' saw in succession in southern and eastern England, inclined to the south-east 'like slices of bread and butter'. Except for the relatively small area of the Lough Neagh basin, we lack, too, the Tertiary basins as of London and Hampshire. The exceedingly varied and sometimes very beautiful landscape of Ireland is controlled, regionally at least, by a largely Palaeozoic solid geology (Fig. 2), the skeleton of its anatomy. The splendid coastline is cut largely in Palaeozoic rocks: the coastline of the Burren in County Clare* in Lower Carboniferous limestones, the famed Cliffs of Moher (Fig. 4) in Namurian sediments, the peninsulas of Kerry and Cork in Old Red Sandstone; and so on. An exception is County Antrim with its Giant's Causeway in columnar basalts of Tertiary age (Fig. 142) and where white Chalk and dark igneous rocks can be seen juxtaposed in striking contrast. The mountain rim of Ireland and the mountainous 'islands' which arise from the central plains are largely of Old Red Sandstone or of older Palaeozoic rocks. Within the rim the Lower Carboniferous widely provides the concealed floor to the Quaternary blanket.

In what follows we trace the geological history of what is now Ireland from earlier Pre-Cambrian times to the present. The period of time (Table 1) is immense. The basis of historical geology has itself oscillated over the years between an extreme uniformitarianism and a kind of all-embracing cyclicity of varied physical and organic processes. A modern view would probably lie between the two, recognising a large-scale cyclicity in the grand pattern of crustal evolution. A pre-Caledonian basement is recognised

---

* The names of the Irish counties and provinces shown in Figure 3 are much used in scientific as well as more general literature.

but sparsely in Ireland, though larger areas of later Pre-Cambrian rocks are involved together with Lower Palaeozoics in the orthotectonic belt of the Irish Caledonides. The earlier Pre-Cambrian is best seen against vaster backcloths such as that of the African continent. In Zimbabwe, for example, the swirling patterns of greenstone terranes around granitic masses themselves give a vivid impression of a once more mobile state. Evolution of Pre-Cambrian crust remains a matter for debate but Professor J. Sutton of Imperial College, London, in particular, has done much to clarify our picture of these earlier phases of geological history.

At the other end of the scale, in consideration of Mesozoic and later times, the advent of the science of palaeomagnetism, followed by the accumulated evidence for ocean floor spreading, have lent much support to the idea that there has been continental drifting apart of what are now regarded as Eurasian and American plates from a spreading axis along the Mid-Atlantic ridge. There remain few dissidents. The Antrim Tertiary igneous rocks described in Chapter

13 are but part of a much larger North Atlantic province associated with this process of break up and separation. This closely understood latest episode of continental drift now provides a background to the better understanding of such matters as palaeobiogeography.

A contrasting situation exists if we return to the Palaeozoic, where the results of stratigraphy, palaeontology, and structural geology must themselves be used as evidence in suggesting the original disposition of continents and oceans. Figure 5 shows a map modified by H. B. Whittington and C. P. Hughes on the basis of Ordovician trilobite distribution. Such maps for the Lower Palaeozoic show north-western Ireland attached to a North American plate and the remainder of the island associated as now with Europe. The *Proto-Atlantic* (the name *Iapetus* does not seem an improvement) lay between the two, and evidence from Irish Lower Palaeozoic rocks is consistent with the picture of a gradual closing of the Proto-Atlantic to be completed in Devonian times. Positive evidence for operation of a mechanism of

Fig. 1. Connemara blanket bog from the Twelve Bens: looking south-eastwards from Derryclare Mountain to Recess and Screeb. The blanket bog (see Chapter 17) overlies schists and gneisses of the Dalradian, in contrast to the quartzites of the Twelve Bens.

Photograph by M. C. F. Proctor

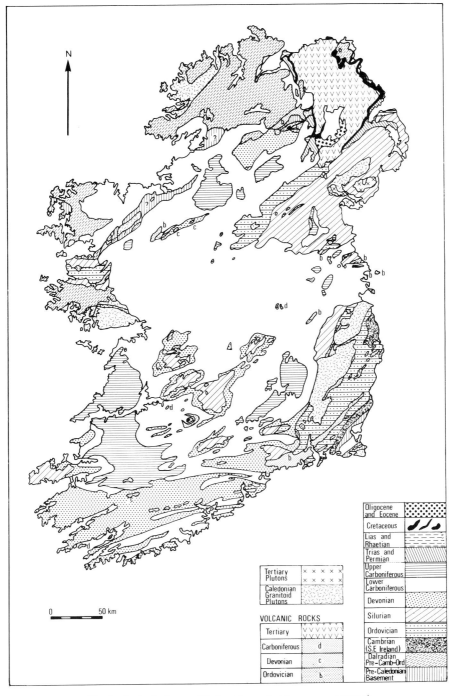

Fig. 2. Geological map of Ireland (compiled from many sources).

ocean floor creation, spreading, and complementary subduction is not so easily obtained, though the Caledonian igneous rocks described in Chapter 6 may be helpful in this respect.

During the Upper Palaeozoic, Ireland as a whole formed part of a Laurasian plate and our splendid display of Carboniferous rocks can be clearly linked with their counterparts elsewhere in Europe. The presence or otherwise of a late Palaeozoic ocean across southern Europe is controversial but outside our terms of reference.

If order is to be maintained in the study of this long geological history use of a reasonably consistent and agreed stratigraphical nomenclature is essential. Geologists in western Europe, where so much of the early stratigraphical work was done, have the problem of operating under a long established but very varied terminology. They must steer a course between the maintenance of well known and well tried terms, which do not fit into modern rules, and the provision of a stratigraphical nomenclature which is understandable from one worker to another and, above all, is understandable internationally. The old and the new are inevitably intermingled in the stratigraphy

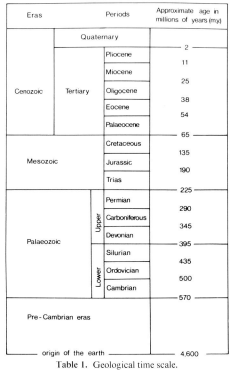

Eras	Periods		Approximate age in millions of years (m.y.)
Cenozoic	Quaternary		
	Tertiary	Pliocene	— 2 —
			11
		Miocene	
			25
		Oligocene	
			38
		Eocene	
			54
		Palaeocene	
			— 65 —
Mesozoic	Cretaceous		
			135
	Jurassic		
			190
	Trias		
			— 225 —
Palaeozoic	Upper	Permian	
			290
		Carboniferous	
			345
		Devonian	
			— 395 —
	Lower	Silurian	
			435
		Ordovician	
			500
		Cambrian	
			— 570 —
Pre-Cambrian eras			
— origin of the earth —			— 4,600 —

Table 1. Geological time scale.

which follows. We have been as consistent as possible, but not to the extent of using this opportunity for the wholesale revision of stratigraphical nomenclature.

A concise guide to stratigraphical classification is that of the Geological Society of London referred to in the short bibliography for this chapter. Though we have tried to keep the text clear by avoiding the otherwise necessarily very numerous scattering throughout of references to the literature, the short chapter bibliographies do provide an access at one remove to many of the relevant sources. The various *Special Reports* of the Geological Society of London are especially useful in this respect, as is the *Regional Geology of Northern Ireland* by H. E. Wilson. The Geological Society of London's volume, *The Caledonides of the British Isles — reviewed*, contains many papers on Irish geology and a wealth of bibliographical material. Useful geological maps of Ireland are the 1:750,000 sheet published by the Irish Ordnance Survey based upon the work of the Geological Survey of Ireland, and the 1:250,000 map of Northern Ireland published by the British Ordnance Survey on behalf of the Institute of Geological Sciences, but extending south to the 54th parallel and incorporating the work of the Geological Surveys of both Northern Ireland and the Republic. Professor W. S. Pitcher of the University of Liverpool has compiled all the data for Donegal.

Fig. 3. County map of Ireland. Provinces are also indicated. The name Connacht shown on the map and based upon the Irish spelling is widely used. though the version Connaught is commonly found in the literature. for instance of the coalfields.

Fig. 4. Cliffs of Moher, County Clare, looking towards O'Brien's Tower. These steep Atlantic cliffs and sea stacks are cut in Namurian (R_1) sediments, here almost flat lying. The upper part of the cliff shows the lowest cyclothem of the Namurian (Chapter 10), capped by the *Reticuloceras* aff. *stubblefieldi* Marine Band.   Bord Failte Photograph

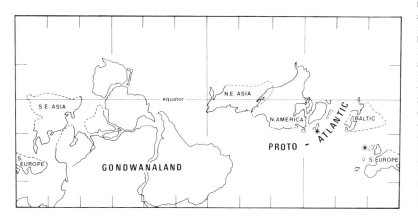

Fig. 5. Palaeogeographical map for Lower Ordovician times amended by Whittington and Hughes (*in* Hughes 1973) on the basis of trilobite distributions. Dashed lines indicate 'gross approximation'. Western Ireland, indicated by an asterisk, is grouped with western Newfoundland and Scotland on the north-western side of the Proto-Atlantic Ocean; eastern Ireland, indicated by the other asterisk, is grouped with England and Wales on the south-eastern, European, side of the Proto-Atlantic. Symbols for trilobite faunal provinces are here omitted.

BIBLIOGRAPHY

AGER, D. V.   1970 On seeing the most rocks. *Proc. Geol. Ass.*, **81**, 421–427.

DAVIS, G. L. H. & STEPHENS, N.   1978 *The Geomorphology of the British Isles: Ireland*. Methuen & Co. Ltd., London, pp. 250.

HARRIS, A. L., HOLLAND, C. H., & LEAKE, B. E. (Eds.).   1980 *The Caledonides of the British Isles – reviewed*. Geological Society of London, pp. 768.

HOLLAND, C. H. *et al.*   1978 A guide to stratigraphical procedure. *Geol. Soc. Lond. Spec. Rep.*, **11**, pp. 18.

HUGHES, N. F. (Ed.)   1973 Organisms and continents through time. *Spec. Pap. Palaeont.*, **12**, pp. 334.

MATTHEWS, S. C.   1977 The Variscan foldbelt in southwest England. *N. Jb. Geol. Paläont. Abh.*, **154**, 94–127.

MITCHELL, G. F.   1976 *The Irish Landscape*. Collins, London, pp. 240.

NAYLOR, D. & MOUNTENEY, S. N.   1975 *Geology of the North-West European Continental Shelf*. Volume 1. Graham Trotman Dudley Publishers Ltd., London, pp. 162.

READ, H. H. & WATSON, J.   1975 *Introduction to Geology. Volume 2. Earth History. Part 1. Early stages of Earth History*. The Macmillan Press Ltd., London, pp. 221.

READ, H. H. & WATSON, J.   1975 *Introduction to Geology. Volume 2. Earth History. Part 11. Later Stages of Earth History*. The Macmillan Press Ltd., London, pp. 371.

SUTTON, J. & WINDLEY, B. F.   1974 The Precambrian. *Sci. Prog. Oxf.*, **61**, 401–420.

WHITTOW, J. B.   1974 *Geology and scenery in Ireland*. Penguin Books Ltd., Harmondsworth, pp. 301.

WILSON, H. E.   1972 *Regional geology of Northern Ireland*. Ministry of Commerce, Geol. Surv. Northern Ireland. Belfast, H.M. Stationery Office, pp. 115.

2

THE PRE-CALEDONIAN BASEMENT

W. E. A. Phillips

The thick successions of sedimentary and volcanic rocks of the Irish Caledonides possess distinctive characters impressed upon them in the form of an orderly sequence of igneous rocks (Chapter 6) and a distinctive assemblage of major tectonic structures and metamorphic minerals and textures (Chapters 3 and 7). At various levels in the Caledonian stratigraphical successions, these distinctive impressed characters can be seen to *overprint* those of earlier and therefore Pre-Caledonian thermotectonic cycles. Recognition of the Pre-Caledonian basement has depended largely upon evidence of overprinting, for the contacts which can be seen between basement and Caledonian cover rocks are all tectonic in origin. In some cases the original unconformities can be inferred from the presence of clasts of basement lithologies in the sedimentary rocks of the Caledonian cover. A limited number of radiometric age determinations in the range from about 2,400 m.y. to 551 ± 10 m.y. confirms the recognition of Pre-Caledonian basement rocks. Four quite different zones of basement have been recognised, using these methods.

In south-east County Wexford, an angular unconformity is inferred between a Caledonian cover of Cambrian sediments and a basement of metasediments, gneisses, and intrusive rocks in which possibly four Pre-Caledonian thermo-tectonic cycles have been recognised. In the Ox Mountains, and probably in the Lough Derg inlier as well as in Tyrone, there is a second zone of probable Pre-Caledonian basement consisting largely of high grade metasedimentary rocks in which the effects of two thermo-tectonic cycles have been recognised. An unconformity with overlying Lower Palaeozoic rocks of the upper part of the Dalradian Supergroup (Southern Highland Group) has been inferred. The third zone is seen in North Mayo where late Pre-Cambrian gneisses (1,070 ± 20 m.y.) are tectonically overlain by a Cale-

donian metasedimentary cover with at least 8 km of late Pre-Cambrian sediments. A fourth zone is seen in the island of Inishtrahull, where gneisses older than 1,500 m.y. are correlated with the gneisses of the Lewisian Complex of North West Scotland.

County Wexford

A Pre-Caledonian basement can be recognised in the Rosslare Complex and Cullenstown Formation of south-east County Wexford. The Rosslare Complex of south-east Wexford (Fig. 6) consists of an interbanded series of grey plagioclase-biotite-quartz gneisses of probable metasedimentary origin and dark amphibole-rich gneisses of probable igneous origin. Dr M. D. Max has recognised four thermo-tectonic cycles within the complex, using the criteria of superposed structures and metamorphic textures, and of igneous cycles starting with the formation of syntectonic granitic migmatite and terminating with the intrusion of fine grained basic dykes (Table 2, Fig. 7). Preliminary results from Rb/Sr dating may indicate that the first cycle is no older than 2,400 m.y. The second cycle, of minimum age about 1,700– 1,600 m.y., and the third cycle involved the intrusion of granitoid rocks followed by basic and intermediate dykes. Both cycles were associated with the development of schistosities, minor folds, and recrystallisation under amphibolite facies conditions.

Prior to the intrusion of the Carnsore Granite, of minimum age 551 ± 10 m.y., all the components of the Rosslare Complex were locally affected by intense cataclasis and low grade recrystallisation producing mylonitic and blastomylonitic schists. Mylonitic bands become more widespread towards the north-western side of the complex, where they coalesce to form a continuous belt. Farther to the north-west, across a gap formed by an outlier of Lower Carboniferous rocks, lies the Cullenstown Formation consisting of pale green and red albite-chlorite-sericite schists with ripple-drift cross-stratification, quartzites, and psammitic greywackes containing clasts of unmylonitised Rosslare Complex lithologies. Growth of chlorite, sericite, and albite was associated with an S1 schistosity which is axial planar to F1 isoclinal folds. Later north-south trending easterly verging F2 folds have a non-penetrative axial planar S2 cleavage. It is very likely that these events and D5 and D6 of

the near-by mylonitic parts of the Rosslare Complex belong to the same thermo-tectonic cycle. A Pre-Cambrian age for this cycle is indicated by the presence of metamorphic clasts of Cullenstown Formation lithologies in the Cambrian sediments downfaulted to the west. A late Pre-Cambrian age is also implied by Crimes and Dhonau's comparison of the Cullenstown Formation with the lower part of the Mona Complex of Anglesea, where the minimum age of metamorphism is about 620 m.y.

The available radiometric dates are as yet in-

Thermo-tectonic cycles	Deposition	Deformation	Metamorphism	Igneous intrusion
CYCLE 4 cf. Cadomian of Brittany (700–590 m.y.)	deposition of greywacke, pelite, and quartzite of Cullenstown Formation	D6 ENE-WSW minor folds verge SE ≡ D2 Cullenstown Formation D5 ENE-WSW mylonite zones ≡ Cullenstown Formation	low greenschist facies low greenschist facies	Carnsore Granite (551 ± 10 m.y.)
CYCLE 3 cf. Late Pentevrian of Brittany (1,100–900 m.y.)		D4-F4 minor folds and S4	amphibolite facies	basic dykes Saltees Granite
CYCLE 2 (min. c. 1,700– 1,600 m.y.) cf. Lihouan of Brittany (2,000–1,900 m.y.)		D3-F3 minor folds and S3	amphibolite facies	basic dykes granodiorite sheets intermediate dykes St Helens Amphibolite (c. 2,400 m.y.)
CYCLE 1 (c. 2,400 m.y.) cf. Icartian of Brittany (2,700–2,550 m.y.)		D2-F2 minor folds and S2 D1-F1 minor folds and S1	amphibolite facies	basic dykes granodioritic migmatite
		formation at amphibolite-granulite (?) facies of the initial dark and grey gneiss complex		

Table 2. Summary of geological events recognised in the Rosslare Complex and Cullenstown Formation.

adequate to establish the minimum ages of the four recognisable thermo-tectonic cycles in south-east Wexford; however the geological history and available dates make it likely that the Rosslare Complex can be correlated with the Pentevrian Complex of north-western France and the Channel Islands.

The Ox Mountains, Rosses Point, Lough Derg, and Tyrone inliers

The Ox Mountains inlier is a narrow ridge of metamorphic and igneous rocks which can be traced from Clare Island in West Mayo to Manorhamilton in County Leitrim (Fig. 8). Most of the inlier is formed of metasedimentary rocks, informally known as the Ox Mountains sequence, which have reached at least amphibolite facies conditions of metamorphism. In the central and south-western part, these high grade metasedimentary rocks are tectonically overlain by a Caledonian cover of coarse proximal turbidites of the upper Dalradian.

This upper Dalradian cover shows a characteristic polyphase deformational history and low greenschist facies metamorphism. These Caledonian textures and structures have overprinted earlier amphibolite facies metamorphism and D1–D4 structures within the adjacent Ox Mountains sequence (Fig. 8B). The Slieve Gamph Igneous Complex was intruded at 487 ± 6 m.y. (Rb/Sr W.R.), after D4 in this part of the Ox Mountains sequence but during the Caledonian deformation of the local upper Dalradian. The age of the early metamorphism and deformations prior to 487 ± 6 m.y., and hence of the Ox Mountains sequence here, is uncertain. The writer prefers a Pre-Caledonian age for these rocks and these early events because there is no record elsewhere of the first Caledonian deformation of the upper Dalradian overprinting earlier metamorphism and structures of Caledonian age in the Dalradian Supergroup. Dr B. Long of the Geological Survey prefers a correlation with the Dalradian for the Ox Mountains sequence of the central Ox Mountains, and hence a Caledonian age for all their deformation and metamorphism. Table 3 summarises what is known of the history of the inlier. The earliest recognised event is the deposition of the Ox Mountains sequence of the north-east

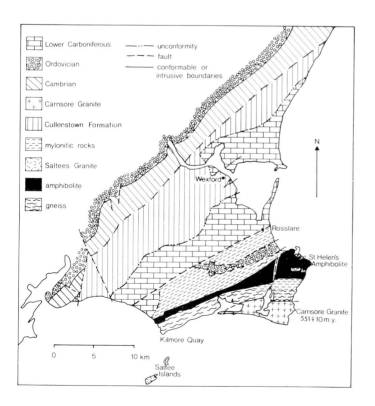

Fig. 6. Geological map of south-east County Wexford (modified after Max 1975).

Ox Mountains (Fig. 8A), which consists of thick units of psammite with local calc-silicate and marble lenses; there are also semipelitic and pelitic metasediments. The lithologies can be compared both to the Moine north-west of the Great Glen Fault in Scotland, and to parts of the younger Dalradian Supergroup. Primary sedimentary structures, indicating the original stratigraphical succession, have not survived the intense deformation, the earliest event of which (D1) produced a strong planar fabric of flattened quartz in the metasediments, a generally north-west to south-east trending foliation, and intense boudinage of early minor basic intrusions. During and after this 'D1' deformation, itself probably polyphase, recrystallisation produced a granulite facies metamorphic mineral assemblage of kyanite and potash feldspar in the pelitic lithologies and mesoperthite in the psammites, indicating minimum temperature and pressure conditions of about 700° C and 8kb. The assemblage of garnet-plagioclase-clinopyroxene-brown hornblende developed in the boudinaged early basic intrusive rocks. These early events were followed by a series of ultrabasic and basic intrusions which may have been affected by the granulite facies metamorphism. They are now represented, as a result of the later Pre-Caledonian (?) metamorphism, by partly serpentinised ultramafic rocks and associated amphibolites. These intrusions may mark the end of an early Pre-Caledonian thermo-tectonic cycle.

In the central and south-western parts of the inlier, this first cycle is not recognised.

Early basic and ultrabasic intrusions in the central

Ox Mountains and the Clew Bay area, which post-date the local D1, may be of the same age as those in the north-east Ox Mountains. In the north-eastern part of the inlier and in the Clew Bay area, the development of S2 as a hornblende oligoclase striping in the basic intrusions and a talc-antigorite fabric in the margins of ultrabasic ones, marks continued probably Pre-Caledonian activity. In the north-eastern part of the inlier, this amphibolite facies recrystallisation (MS2–MP2) becomes more intense towards the south-west, where MP2 green hornblende from an early basic boudin has given a Pre-Caledonian minimum age component of about 700 m.y. and a younger Caledonian one of 437 ± 2 m.y. using the $^{40}Ar/^{39}Ar$ step heating method. This is consistent with a Pre-Cambrian age for the amphibolite facies MP2 event. A strong D3 deformation is shown by augening of MP2 porphyroblasts and by the development of MS3 muscovite and biotite on a penetrative schistosity; later MP3 hornblende is also developed. In the central part of the Ox Mountains inlier (Fig. 8B), the Ox Mountains sequence contains psammites which are comparable to those of the north-eastern region, but they lie within a more varied series of semipelites, pelites, and lenses of marble. A D1–D4 structural sequence with kyanite (MP2) and staurolite (MP3) in pelites has been recognised. These metasediments have never been above lower amphibolite facies conditions and their relationship to the granulite facies metasediments to the north-east is obscured by a substantial fault. Pankhurst and others have shown that the granitoid rocks, appinites, and diorites of the

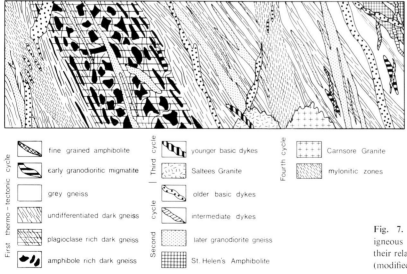

First thermo-tectonic cycle

fine grained amphibolite	
early granodioritic migmatite	
grey gneiss	
undifferentiated dark gneiss	
plagioclase rich dark gneiss	
amphibole rich dark gneiss	

Second cycle / Third cycle

younger basic dykes	
Saltees Granite	
older basic dykes	
intermediate dykes	
later granodiorite gneiss	
St. Helen's Amphibolite	

Fourth cycle

Carnsore Granite	
mylonitic zones	

Fig. 7. Diagrammatic representation of igneous and metamorphic lithologies and their relationships in the Rosslare Complex (modified after Max and Dhonau 1971).

Slieve Gamph Igneous Complex were intruded after D4 at 487 ± 6 m.y. (mid-Ordovician). This provides a minimum age for D1–D4 and also dates the Caledonian deformation of the local upper Dalradian, for this was taking place during emplacement of the pluton. Caledonian structures in the proximal turbidites of the overlying upper Dalradian start with recumbent south-easterly facing folds Fc1 and an axial planar slaty cleavage associated with fine-grained sericite and chlorite. This Sc1 fabric becomes a mylonitic fabric in the adjacent Ox Mountains sequence, overprinting, and so younger than, D1–D4 structures and textures. Minor veins from the Slieve Gamph Igneous Complex are also deformed by this event. The contact between the Ox Mountains sequence and the upper Dalradian is now a (Dc1) Caledonian slide zone, equivalent to D5 of the underlying sequence. In the coarse proximal turbidites of the upper Dalradian, abundant metamorphic clasts of lithologies known in the Ox Mountains sequence provide some evidence for an original unconformable contact between the two units.

The single ^{40}Ar/^{39}Ar age determination of about 700 m.y. for the Pre-Caledonian amphibolite facies metamorphism can be compared with the well established group of ages of 700–800 m.y. obtained from part of the Moine succession in Scotland affected by the Morarian orogeny.

In the small inlier at Rosses Point (Fig. 8), and in the larger Lough Derg inlier (Fig. 10), the Ox Mountains sequence reappears to granulite facies with early basic boudins. In the Lough Derg inlier, these rocks are overlain to the north-east by an inverted cover of upper Dalradian rocks. The contact is probably a tectonic slide, but relationships between the structures and textures on either side of the slide have not as yet been established.

In Tyrone (Fig. 10), the psammites and sillimanite-garnet pelitic schists of the central inlier may also be a continuation of the Ox Mountains sequence. The penetrative deformation and amphibolite facies metamorphism of these rocks is earlier than the emplacement of gabbros correlated with the upper Dalradian of the Tyrone Igneous Group (Chapter 3).

North Mayo

A rather different kind of Pre-Caledonian basement is seen in the Annagh Gneiss Complex of North Mayo (Table 4). Sutton and Max have recognised that the oldest components are grey and dark quartz-plagioclase-microcline-amphibole gneisses (Fig. 9) of uncertain origin, with minor lenses of probable meta-sedimentary epidosite. These rocks are cut by an early set of basic dykes. Later intrusion of granitic

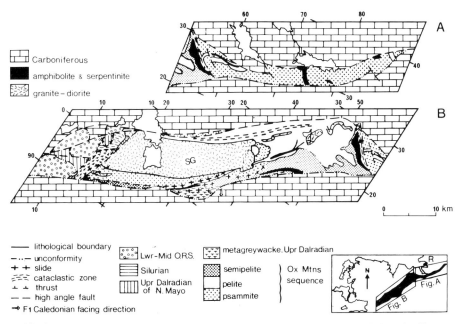

Fig. 8. Geological map of the north-eastern and central parts of the Ox Mountains inlier. SG = Slieve Gamph Igneous Complex, R = Rosses Point inlier.

sheets, dated by D. van Breemen and D. R. Bowes at 1,070 ± 30 m.y. (U/Pb zircon), associated with local potash feldspar metasomatism and followed by polyphase deformation and amphibolite facies metamorphism, have produced a composite gneissose banding. The subsequent intrusion of small sheets of granite dated at 1,000 ± 30 m.y. (U/Pb zircon), and a general static metamorphic coarsening of the texture are earlier than the Caledonian deformation of Dalradian cover. Upward movement of the Pre-Caledonian basement produced early Caledonian mylonites along its margins.

Thermo-tectonic cycles	Deposition	Deformation	Metamorphism	Igneous intrusion
Caledonian cycle (500–430 m.y.?)	deposition of Upper Dalradian proximal turbidites probably Lower Ordovician	D_c3 minor NE-SW upright F_c3 monoclines D_c2 major NE-SW upright F_c2 buckle folds and S_c2 fracture cleavage D_c1 SE facing recumbent folds, S_c1 slaty cleavage, mylonites, and slides	MP_c2 low greenschist facies MS_c2 low greenschist facies MS_c1 low greenschist facies	granites, diorites, appinites of the Slieve Gamph Igneous Complex (487 ± 6 m.y.)
Pre-Caledonian cycle (late Pre-Cambrian : Grenville?) Moravian?	Ox Mountains sequence deposition of psammites with calcareous lenses semipelites, and pelites	D4 NE-SW F4 minor folds S3 crenulation cleavage D3 NE-SW F3 isoclines, strong S3 schistosity, slides D2-S1 schistosity D1 intense flattening on S1 fabric	MP3 amphibolite MS3 facies MP2 amphibolite MS2 facies (c. 700 m.y.?) granulite facies in NE amphibolite facies in SW centre?	basic and ultrabasic intrusions minor basic and ultrabasic intrusions

Table 3. Summary of the geological history of the Ox Mountains inlier.

Caledonian	11	Penetrative deformation with sub-isoclinal folds and amphibolite facies metamorphism (D2, MS2)	
	10	Amphibolite facies metamorphism (MP1)	
	9	Formation of slides, penetrative (D1) deformation, and greenschist facies metamorphism (MS1)	
	8	Intrusion of dolerite dykes	
	7	Early D1 reconstitution of basement along slide zones with the cover	
Pre-Caledonian : (Grenville?)	6	Porphyroblastic growth of plagioclase, microcline, biotite, amphibole, epidote, and garnet	
	5	Intrusion of small granite sheets	$1,000 \pm 20$ m.y.
	4	Polyphase deformation and amphibolite facies metamorphism with development of a composite gneissose banding, boudinage of basic dykes	$1,070 \pm 20$ m.y.
	3	Intrusion of granite with marginal potash metasomatism of the country rock	
	2	Intrusion of basic dykes	
	1	Formation of Grey Gneisses - probably of mixed sedimentary and igneous origin. It is uncertain whether gneissose banding was produced at this stage or later.	

Table 4. Summary of the geological history of the Annagh Gneiss Complex (based on Sutton 1972).

Inishtrahull

Pre-Caledonian gneisses form the island of Inishtrahull, off the north coast of Donegal (Fig. 10). The dominant lithology is quartz-plagioclase-microcline-biotite gneiss, with local epidote rich layers probably derived from calcareous metasediment. Minor layered basic intrusions were emplaced before a D1 deformation and amphibolite facies metamorphism which produced the gneissose banding. The subsequent history of polyphase deformation, cataclasis, and minor intrusions is summarised in Table 5. On the basis of lithological similarities, McCallien in 1930 suggested a Lewisian age for these rocks. This has recently been supported by Bowes with detailed comparison of their structural history with the radiometrically dated histories of Lewisian areas in western Scotland, and Rb/Sr whole rock dating of more than 1,500 m.y. for the gneisses of Inishtrahull. Younger Rb/Sr and K/Ar ages in the range of 520 ± 50 m.y.–370 m.y. indicate strong Caledonian overprinting which may be represented by some of the late more brittle structures.

Fig. 9. Grey gneisses of the Annagh Gneiss Complex at the western end of Annagh Head. Mullet peninsula. showing gneissose banding augening a large and many small amphibolite boudins. The banding is cut by a flat lying schistose Caledonian metadolerite.

Photograph by W. E. A. Phillips

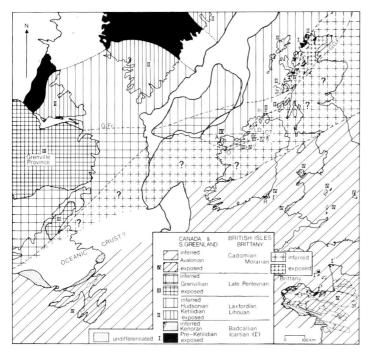

Fig. 10. Continental refit map for the North Atlantic, showing the probable distribution of the Pre-Cambrian age provinces forming the Pre-Caledonian basement.

A = Annagh Gneiss Complex

CT = central inlier of Tyrone

GFr = Grenville Front

GGF = Great Glen Fault

In = Inishtrahull

LD = Lough Derg inlier

MT = Moine Thrust

O = Ox Mountains inlier

R = Rosslare Complex

13	D8	: Caledonian shear zones
12	F7	: Open folds with vertical axial planes striking NNE-SSW
11	F6	: Open folds with vertical axial planes striking E-W
10	F5	: Open folds with vertical axial planes striking NW-SE, cleavage
9	F4	: Open folds with vertical axial planes striking NNE-SSW, cleavage
8		Emplacement of minor acid and intermediate intrusions
7		Intrusion of pegmatites
6	F3	: NE-SW trending upright folds and shear zones
5		Minor basic igneous intrusions
4		NNE-SSW trending F2 folds
3		Isoclinal F1 folds with axial planar S1 foliation and amphibolite facies metamorphism
2		Emplacement of mafic igneous masses
1		Formation of lithological layering (sedimentary ^{and}/or igneous)

Table 5. Summary of the geological history of Inishtrahull (based on Bowes and Hopgood 1975).

Regional correlations

As a result of the application of radiometric dating methods, understanding of the history of the Pre-Caledonian basement in Ireland has reached a stage where it is worth considering large-scale regional correlations within the North Atlantic area (Fig. 10). The gneisses of Inishtrahull are established as the most southerly outcrop of the Lewisian Complex of north west Scotland. It is likely that the Rosslare Complex is the most northerly outcrop of the Pentevrian Complex of north-western France and the Channel Islands. There is a zone approximately 350 km wide between these two complexes, and it is here that the Grenville gneisses of North Mayo lie along strike from the Grenville Province of eastern Canada and southern Rockall Bank. These rocks continue eastwards to the Sveconorvegian province of the Baltic Shield. It is possible that some of the Pre-Caledonian metamorphism and deformation of the Ox Mountains sequence are also of Grenville age. Crustal shortening produced by this cycle, and by the later Caledonian one, was probably responsible for the narrowing, in comparison with Canada, by at least 50 per cent of the Grenville belt in Ireland (Fig. 10).

BIBLIOGRAPHY

BISHOP, A. C., ROACH, R. A., & ADAMS, C. J. D. 1975 Precambrian rocks within the Hercynides. *In* Harris, A. L. *et al.* (Eds.). A correlation of the Precambrian rocks in the British Isles. *Geol. Soc. Lond. Spec. Rep.,* **6,** 102–107.

BOWES, D. R. & HOPGOOD, A. M. 1975 Structure of the gneiss complex of Inishtrahull, Co. Donegal. *Proc. R. Ir. Acad.,* **75B,** 369–390.

MACINTYRE, R. M., VAN BREEMAN, O., BOWES, D. R., & HOPGOOD, A. M. 1975 Isotopic study of the gneiss complex, Inishtrahull, Co. Donegal. *Scient. Proc. R. Dubl. Soc. Ser. A,* 5, 301–309.

MAX, M. D. 1970 Mainland gneisses southwest of Bangor in Erris, Northwest County Mayo, Ireland. *Scient. Proc. R. Dubl. Soc. Ser. A,* 3, 275–291.

1975 Precambrian rocks of South-east Ireland. *In* Harris, A. L. *et al.* (Eds.). A correlation of the Precambrian rocks in the British Isles. *Geol. Soc. Lond. Spec. Rep.,* **6,** 97–101.

MAX, M. D. & DHONAU, N. B. 1971 A new look at the Rosslare Complex. *Scient. Proc. R. Dubl. Soc. Ser. A.* 4, 103–120.

PANKHURST, R. J., ANDREWS, J. R., PHILLIPS, W. E. A., SANDERS, I. S., & TAYLOR, W. E. G. 1976 Age and structural setting of the Slieve Gamph Igneous Complex, Co. Mayo. Eire. *Jl. geol. Soc. Lond.,* **132,** 327–334.

PHILLIPS, W. E. A., TAYLOR, W. E. G., & SANDERS, I. S. 1975 An analysis of the geological history of the Ox Mountains Inlier. *Scient. Proc. R. Dubl. Soc. Ser. A,* 5, 311–329.

SUTTON, J. S. 1972 The Pre-Caledonian rocks of the Mullet Peninsula, County Mayo, Ireland. *Scient. Proc. R. Dubl. Soc. Ser. A,* 4, 121–136.

3

THE ORTHOTECTONIC CALEDONIDES

W. E. A. Phillips

In the northern half of Ireland the orthotectonic Caledonides are represented in four major inliers (north-east Antrim, Donegal-Tyrone-Derry, north Mayo, and Connemara) where there are continuous thick successions of late Pre-Cambrian and early Palaeozoic sediments. Major contributions to the knowledge of these inliers have been made by the work of R. M. Shackleton, W. S. Pitcher, B. E. Leake, and their many associates.

Towards the base of the succession in north Mayo lies a monotonous sequence of psammitic meta-sediments, comparable with the oldest part of the Dalradian Supergroup in Scotland. Above this lies a more diverse sequence of quartzites, pelites, lime-stones, meta-volcanic rocks, and turbidites. The upper part of the Dalradian includes Cambrian sediments and in Tyrone may even include rocks as young as Caradoc. In the orthotectonic belt the main defor-mation and metamorphism were completed by the end of the Ordovician at the latest. The orthotectonic belt is also distinctive in having large-scale recumbent folds as opposed to the more upright folds of the para-tectonic belt, a more complex polyphase history of deformation, and amphibolite-greenschist facies regional metamorphism.

Stratigraphy

The early development and large-scale structure of the orogen can best be studied by stratigraphical methods. Unfortunately the virtual absence of fossils means that only lithological correlation can be used. In the Dalradian the only lithologies which may define approximate time-planes are the tillite and the wide-spread limestone correlated with the Loch Tay Lime-stone of Scotland.

Dalradian Supergroup

Nomenclature for sub-division of the Dalradian Supergroup here follows that of A. L. Harris and W. S. Pitcher. The succession is listed in the key to Figure 11.

Grampian Group. It is only the north Mayo inlier that the lowest, Grampian Group part of the succes-sion is seen, these rocks appearing in a number of isolated tectonic slices, some of which are tectoni-cally underlain by Pre-Caledonian basement gneisses. The predominant lithology of the Grampian Group rocks is a banded quartz-plagioclase-mica psammite with abundant cross-stratification, heavy mineral bands, and thin calc-silicate lenses. Locally these psammites, which are up to 4 km in thickness, are underlain by semipelitic schists with dolomitic lenses. It is probable that the sediments were laid down in fluviatile to marginal marine environments. The high content of hematite and magnetite may be an indication that the original succession included red beds.

Appin Group – Lochaber Subgroup. The base of the Appin Group is generally drawn at the base of the first major quartzite. Such a boundary can be drawn between the Grampian Group psammites and an overlying quartzite in Achill Island and in the north-east part of the north Mayo inlier (Fig. 11). In Achill Island the lowest quartzite of the Appin Group is over-lain by at least 4 km of cross-stratified psammites with semipelitic bands and quartzites becoming more abundant upwards (Fig. 12). Above this lies up to at least 1 km of slightly calcareous pelite and semipelite with local bands of marble and quartzite, which are correlated with the lithologically similar Creeslough Formation which forms the lowest part of the Dal-radian succession exposed in north-west Donegal. This Lochaber Subgroup is clearly a lithological transition zone from the Grampian Group to the better sorted and more diverse overlying lithologies. It may mark a transition into stable marine shelf conditions.

Ballachulish Subgroup. The Ballachulish Subgroup is best exposed in north-west Donegal where it com-

prises a limestone followed by graphitic pelites with dolomitic limestone bands. This sequence can be correlated with similar formations in Achill and in the Ballachulish area of Scotland and indicates a widespread development of stagnant starved basinal con-

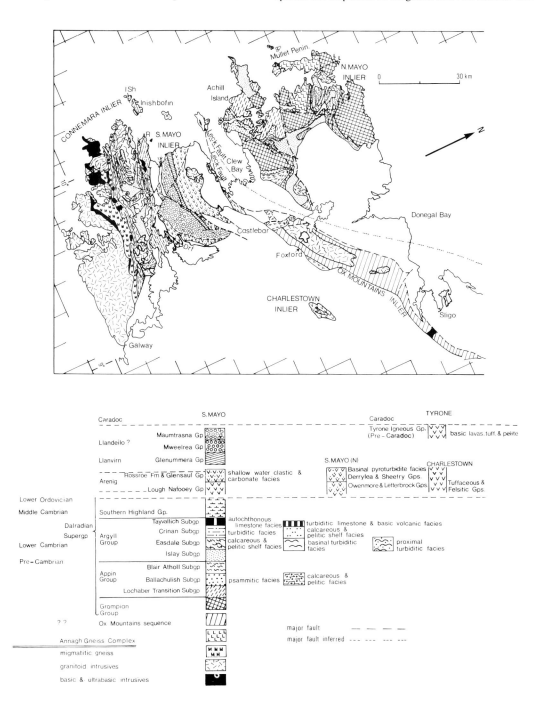

ditions at this time. These conditions were terminated by a progressive influx of sand producing a transition up into the Ards Quartzite of Donegal and its equivalents in Achill and Scotland (Appin Quartzite). In Donegal the Ards Quartzite shows possible tidal lamination, pebble lenses, channels, and small-scale slumps, suggesting deposition in shallow water. Above this there is a sharp change to a variable assemblage of pelites, quartzites, and calcareous rocks known as the Sessiagh-Clonmass Formation. In general there

Fig. 11—Facing page and below:
Geological maps showing lithostratigraphical units of the orthotectonic Caledonides in Ireland. National Grid and longitude lines are shown.

Drf = Doon Rock Fault

ISh = Inishshark

R = Renvyle

Rm = Rathmullen

Sp = Sperrin Mountains.

The geology of Connemara is based on information kindly given by Dr M. E. Badley.

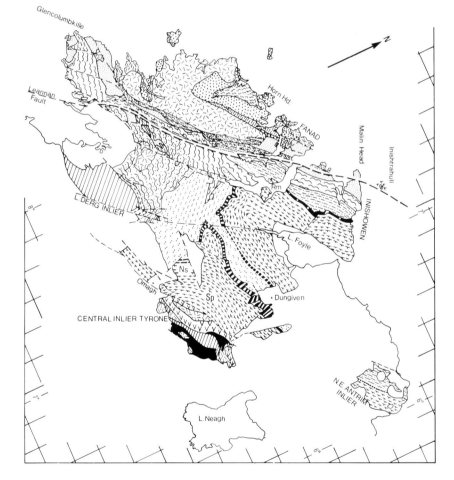

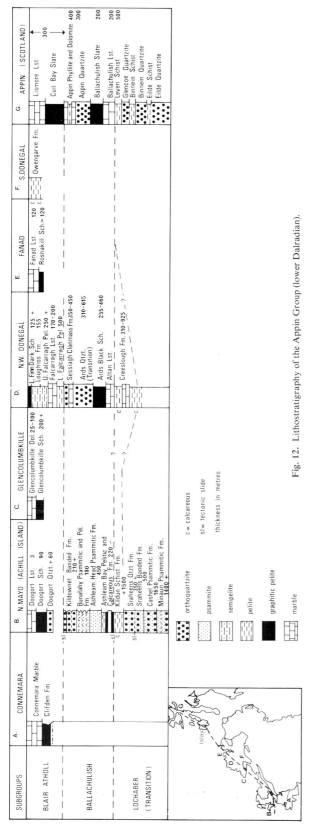

Fig. 12. Lithostratigraphy of the Appin Group (lower Dalradian).

appears to be a facies change within the formation involving the development of more quartzites, with local mud cracks, to the north and north-west of the Main Donegal Granite, while finer grained more calcareous sediments are seen to the south and south-east. If large-scale sinistral displacement has taken place on the Leannan Fault (see Chapter 7), then the Sessiagh-Clonmass Formation must have lain to the west or north-west of Islay in Scotland, and the south-easterly transition into more calcareous rocks seen in Donegal is continued in Scotland, where the equivalent formation is the relatively thin and probably more off-shore Appin Phyllite and Dolomite.

Blair Atholl Subgroup. The Blair Atholl Subgroup in north-west Donegal starts with the Lower Falcarragh Pelites of up to 600 m of grey and black graphitic and pyritous pelites with some semipelitic and calcareous bands. The Falcarragh Limestone, up to 200 m thick, separates these pelites from the overlying, less graphitic, silty banded Upper Falcarragh Pelites, which show graded bedding and small-scale cross-stratification. The overlying Loughros Formation is a rather varied sequence of quartzites and semipelites. A notable facies change to the south-east is again indicated if large-scale sinistral strike-slip displacement on the Leannan Fault is accepted, for the mixed clastic sediments of the Loughros Formation appear to be equivalent to the upper part of the Lismore Limestone of the Appin and Islay areas of Scotland. Such a reconstruction would be consistent as before with a north-westerly littoral facies to the basin at this time. East of the Knockateen slide (page 29), the remainder of the Subgroup in Donegal consists of the dark graphitic pelites and thin limestones of the Lough Finn Dark Schist, overlain by the Glencolumbkille Limestone of up to 100 m of grey limestone with a paler, locally dolomitic, top. The upper dolomite is oolitic in Fanad indicating very shallow water conditions of deposition there. This dark schist-limestone sequence is the oldest recognised part of the Connemara succession, where a lower dolomite formed the well-known green serpentinous marble. A similar sequence (Inver Group) is seen in north Mayo, the more quartzitic parts of which may be equivalent to the Loughros Formation of Donegal.

Argyll Group – Islay Subgroup. The Argyll Group occupies a major part of all the Irish Dalradian inliers. Its base is marked by the well-known boulder bed which is generally accepted to be of glacial origin and therefore a tillite. The greatest thickness (525 m) of boulder bed is seen in Fanad (north Donegal) where there is a succession with 12 separate tillites. In Glencolumbkille the boulder bed is up to 120 m thick and includes 13 tillites; at Cleggan Head in Connemara it is 145 m thick with at least 7 tillites. There are many other localities where lesser thicknesses of boulder

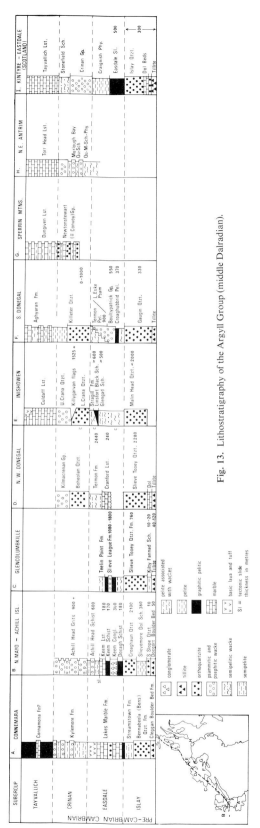

Fig. 13. Lithostratigraphy of the Argyll Group (middle Dalradian).

bed are exposed. The boulder bed consists of unsorted clasts, up to 2 m in diameter, scattered through a rather homogeneous matrix of semipelite, psammite, or quartzite. There is a distinctive stratigraphy with lower boulder beds with a calcareous semipelitic matrix and few granitic but abundant dolomitic intra-basinal clasts, probably derived from the underlying limestones. The middle boulder beds are more aren-aceous and contain mostly granitic fragments with minor amounts of psammitic and semipelitic gneiss and metabasic rocks of extrabasinal origin. The upper boulder beds have a quartzitic matrix and again con-tain mostly granitic fragments. The case for a glacial origin for these deposits rests primarily upon their extraordinarily widespread distribution from western Ireland through Scotland, Norway, Spitzbergen, and East Greenland, even the stratigraphical sub-division being recognisable in these places. The identification of drop-stones and probable subaerial permafrost polygons at some of the Irish localities supports the glacial hypothesis. R. J. Howarth has interpreted the boulder bed in Donegal as a subaerial flow till laid down in a coastal environment. Where the tills came from is uncertain. Unlike the underlying Dalradian clastic sediments, derivation from a north-western land mass is unlikely, for Lewisian gneissic lithologies do not appear amongst the clasts. It seems more probable that there was an extensive source area to the south-east formed of granitic rocks intruding psammitic gneisses.

The boulder bed is overlain in north-west Donegal and Achill by up to 360 m of pelites with a variable dolomite content, followed by a major development of quartzite. The quartzite is everywhere rather felds-pathic with a notable concentration of heavy mineral bands near the base and quartz pebble bands near the top. The formation can be traced for over 700 km along strike from Connemara to Banffshire in north-east Scotland. There is considerable variation in thickness in Ireland. Though some of this is of tec-tonic origin, some may be original for it is associated with notable facies changes in the overlying sediments (Fig. 13). In the lower part of the quartzite in Islay (south-west Scottish Highlands), there is evidence for intertidal conditions of deposition with deeper water to the north-west and current flow from the south. A similar current flow pattern has been found in the Glencolumbkille area of Donegal. The quartzites as a whole may well represent tidally reworked post-glacial outwash sands derived from the south-east land area, with the addition of sand reworked from the tills themselves.

Easdale Subgroup. In Glencolumbkille, south Donegal, Achill, and Connemara, the appearance of pelites and semipelites, which are often graphitic, marks the base of the Easdale Subgroup. These pelites are followed by a varied sequence of pebbly often graded quartzites, limestones, and further dark pelites. In contrast to the Islay Subgroup, there are major facies changes both along and across the strike (Fig. 13). North-west of the Leannan Fault there appears to be a considerable unconformity between the Cranford Limestone and the underlying Slieve Tooey Quartzite. The missing lower, mostly pelitic, part of the Easdale Subgroup reappears to the south-west in Glencolumbkille and in Achill where it includes a shallow water conglomerate. Above the Cranford Limestone of Donegal lies up to 2·4 km of pelites (Termon Formation), with a more graphitic lower part and local psammites and pebbly grits of turbiditic origin in the middle. A similar but tectonically reduced succession is seen above the Keem Limestone of Achill. Southeast of the Leannan Fault (Fig. 11) in Inishowen, the Easdale Subgroup consists of up to 0·6 km of predominantly pelitic rocks with bands of cross-stratified quartzite and limestone. When traced south-westwards into south Donegal, this shelf type of succession with some distal pelitic turbidites, passes laterally into a more proximal turbidite sequence (Boulypatrick Grits), overlain by somewhat finer grained turbidites of the Lough Eske Psammites. These clastic rocks contain granitic and quartzitic (including blue quartz) clasts. This southern turbidite basin probably reflects continued derivation from the southern granitoid basement which may have supplied detritus to the upper part of the boulder bed and the Slieve Tooey Quartzite.

In Connemara the Bennabeola Quartzite, near the top of the Islay Subgroup, is overlain by semipelites and pelites with limestones and local pebbly quartzites. These rocks are probably the equivalent of the Easdale Subgroup and appear to be of the relatively shallow water shelf facies also seen in Achill, Glencolumbkille, and Inishowen. On the basis of microfossils obtained by C. Downie and T. R. Lister from the Argyll Group in Scotland, and of the first appearances of calcareous algae there, the base of the Cambrian probably lies within the Easdale Subgroup.

Crinan Subgroup. The Crinan Subgroup is generally marked by rather coarse-grained graded quartzites and psammitic wackes of turbiditic origin. To the north-west of the Leannan Fault in Donegal, the subgroup consists of thin-bedded, fine grained, and locally graded quartzite and semipelite (Boheolan Quartzite). These are followed by coarser grained proximal turbidites (Kilmacrenan Grit) with lenses of dark pelite and limestone. To the south-west in Achill the equivalent rocks are the turbiditic quartzites and pelites of the Achill Head Grits, probably representing a more basinal facies. On the south-east side of the Leannan Fault in Inishowen the Crana Quartzite is a typical proximal turbidite sequence of at least 1·5 km

of coarse-grained, graded, psammitic wackes with some interbeds of pelite and impure limestone, sole structures indicating current flow to the south-west. In north-east Antrim the Murlough Bay Quartz-Schists represent a more pelitic and probably more distal turbiditic facies of the subgroup. In the Rathmullen area, south-west of Inishowen, the Crana Quartzite can be subdivided into a lower fine-grained psammitic and semipelitic unit, a central one with thinly bedded psammites and limestones, and an upper one with coarse graded psammitic wackes. This change from proximal to distal turbidites spreads upwards through the subgroup as it is traced farther south-westwards into central and south Donegal, where the base is marked by up to 1 km of massive quartzite followed by pelites. South-eastwards around Newtownstewart in the Sperrin Mountains, the quartzites with pelites and limstones of the Newtown-stewart Group are further representatives of a southern shelf facies. Clearly there was a reversal of the palaeogeography from that of the Easdale Subgroup, for the shelf facies appears in central and southern Donegal and in Tyrone, while the turbidite trough lay to the north-west. Farther to the southwest, in Connemara, one might expect to find a continuation of this shelf facies. This is not so, for the thick sequence of coarse psammitic wackes with interbedded pelites seen on Inishbofin and Inishshark, at Renvyle, and farther east represent a turbiditic facies comparable to those of Achill, north-west Donegal, and Inishowen. As before, the Connemara succession appears to fit the palaeogeography of the central part of the Dalradian outcrop. In the southwest Scottish Highlands, palaeocurrent data and distribution of facies within the Crinan Subgroup suggest that sediment was derived from the north-west, though with some axial transport along the north-east to south-west trending trough. This palaeogeography would also fit in with the suggestion that the subgroup can be broadly correlated with the basal Cambrian quartzites in north-west Scotland. The southern shelf facies and the persistence of granitic and blue quartz clasts may also reflect some sediment supply from the southern side.

Tayvallich Subgroup. The Tayvallich Subgroup consists of limestones with local dark pelites and basic volcanic rocks interbedded with them. Work by P. J. Gower on the subgroup in Ireland and Scotland has shown that the deposition of limestone and the onset of widespread basic volcanicity were contemporaneous. Three different facies are recognised. The first, autochthonous limestone facies is seen in Inishowen (Culdaff Limestone) and north-east Antrim (Torr Head Limestone), where limestones 80–100 m thick are interbedded with some thin tuffaceous bands. In south-west Inishowen the Culdaff Limestone becomes interbedded with turbidites (Inch Lime-stone Group), showing a transition towards the second facies of allochthonous limestone deposited from turbidity currents. This facies is well developed farther south in the Sperrins where the Dungiven Limestone consists of up to 80 m of interbedded limestones and dark pelites. The pelitic element becomes more abundant at the expense of limestone as the subgroup is traced westwards through Tyrone into southern Donegal, where limestone is quite subordinate to turbiditic pelite and quartzite (Aghyaran Formation).

A similar basinal facies is seen in Connemara where graphitic schists with a graphitic marble (Cornamona Formation) may represent either the Crinan or Tayvallich subgroups.

No definite representative of the subgroup has been found north-west of the Leannan Fault, though calcareous schists, graded quartz wackes, and basic volcanic rocks at the base of the Lough Feeagh Group in north Mayo (Glandavoolagh Formation) may represent the third facies previously mentioned, deposited from turbidity currents in areas of volcanicity. According to J. L. Knill, the palaeogeography at this time seems to conform with that in Scotland, where a north-western carbonate shelf facies, possibly a continuation of the Lower Cambrian Durness Limestone of the north-west foreland, passes south-eastwards into a basinal turbiditic facies locally associated with basic volcanicity. It is likely that these widely distributed limestone facies are broadly of the same age.

Southern Highland Group. The succession within the Southern Highland Group is one of turbidites of varied proximality, interbedded locally with volcanic rocks, lenses of limestone, and graphitic pelites. The lack of reliable marker horizons and the likelihood of rapid facies changes makes it difficult to subdivide the group into anything but local formations (Fig. 14).

In Inishowen the group consists of about 1·3 km of turbidites including turbidite conglomerates; there are two epidote rich horizons (Cloghan and Greencastle Green Beds) which probably represent tuffaceous sediment. In general the turbidites become more proximal towards the top of the succession and contain abundant clasts of quartz, blue quartz, quartzite, and feldspar. In north-east Antrim, the group shows no notable concentration of coarser grained more proximal turbidites at any point in the succession. There are two separate hornblende – epidote and chlorite rich 'Green Beds' within a succession of quartz mica schists, with bands of psammitic wacke with the usual clasts of blue quartz. In the Sperrin Mountains, two horizons up to 100 m thick of basic pillow lavas lie near the base of the group. In contrast to Inishowen, these are overlain by the coarse proximal turbidite facies, and the upper part of the succes-

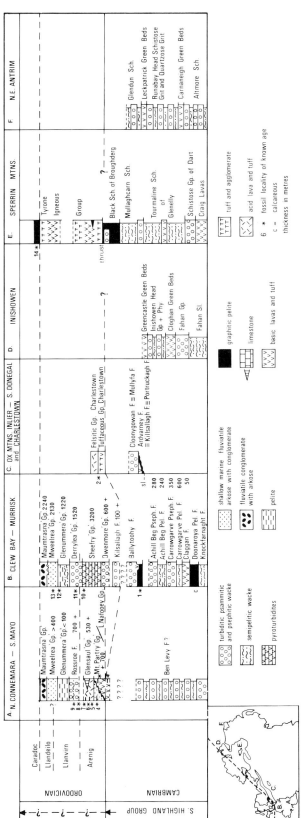

Fig. 14. Lithostratigraphy of the upper Dalradian.

sion becomes one of finer grained distal turbidites with a local 'Green Bed' in the middle. The Black Schists of Broughderg were taken by J. J. Hartley to form the highest unit of the Dalradian of the Sperrin area.

In south Donegal and west Tyrone, the micaceous quartz-feldspar psammites with coarse pebbly bands of the Mullyfa Formation, assigned to the Southern Highland Group, are inverted, younging downwards to the south towards the probable Pre-Caledonian metasediments of the Lough Derg inlier (Chapter 2). Unfortunately it is uncertain where the main slide boundary lies between these two units. On the basis of comparison with the Ox Mountains, the contact is tentatively placed at the stratigraphical top of the Mullyfa Formation, and the Shannaghy Green Beds and pelites of the Groagharrow Formation are provisionally assigned to the Pre-Caledonian basement. Irrespective of where the boundary is finally established here, it is clear the situation is comparable to that in south Tyrone, for in both areas coarse-grained proximal turbidites immediately overlie the Tayvallich Subgroup. In the central and south-western parts of the Ox Mountains inlier, very coarse-grained proximal turbidites rest with slide contact upon the high grade rocks of the Ox Mountains sequence. These isolated outliers of turbidite are assigned to the Southern Highland Group because of their close lithological similarity to the Mullyfa Formation of south Donegal and the Ballytoohy Formation of Clare Island. As elsewhere in the group these coarse-grained turbidites contain clasts of quartz which is often blue with rutile inclusions, plagioclase, pegmatite, granite, quartzite, and semipelitic schist. All these clasts could have been derived from the Ox Mountains sequence. This factor together with the occurrence of these proximal turbidites immediately above varied members of the Ox Mountains sequence suggests that the slide contact between the two units could have eliminated an original unconformity. It is therefore possible that part of the southern source of high-grade metamorphic and plutonic igneous detritus inferred for the Southern Highland Group may actually be seen now in the Ox Mountains sequence and its continuation in the Lough Derg and central Tyrone inliers. Similar detritus can be recognised in the Boultypatrick Grits of the Easdale Subgroup for which a comparable southern source area has already been proposed, and at other horizons down to the tillite.

In north Mayo the Southern Highland Group occurs in a number of tectonic slices. It consists of at least 2 km of turbiditic sediment with several local horizons of basic lavas and tuffs with minor lenses of limestone and of serpentinised ultrabasic rock. Unfortunately there is no widespread limestone to define the base of the group as elsewhere. The succession as a whole resembles that of Inishowen being more pelitic near the base and containing more coarse-grained proximal turbidites towards the top. On the north side of Clare Island a specimen of *Protospongia hicksi*, of probable Middle Cambrian age, has been collected from dark cherty pelites. These rocks are overlain by at least 1 km of younger coarse-grained proximal turbidites, for which a southerly derivation from a continuation of the Ox Mountains sequence has been suggested.

In the south-western Ox Mountains (Fig. 11) there are a number of thrust slices containing formations typical of the Southern Highland Group of north Mayo.

In north Connemara the Southern Highland Group may be represented by at least 2 km of locally-graded quartzitic grits and semipelites with lenses of serpentinised ultrabasic rocks (Ben Levy Formation) which overlie the dark pelites and marble possibly of the Tayvallich Subgroup. In the east this succession appears to pass over the Connemara antiform and on the south limb may form the greater bulk of metasediments within the migmatite zone. The general facies in Connemara and north Mayo are again comparable. If it is assumed that the limestones of the Tayvallich Subgroup define an approximate time plane, then it follows that in the overlying Southern Highland Group proximal turbidites developed earliest in the south-east (Sperrins, west Tyrone, and south Donegal), then spread north-westwards (Antrim) to Inishowen. However in Inishowen there is evidence of current flow both from the west and north-west and also trending from north-east to south-west. Allowing for sinistral displacement on the Leck Leannan Fault, the Southern Highland Group of north Mayo is brought to the latitude of central Donegal where it could reasonably represent a south-western continuation of the Inishowen succession. Bearing in mind the probability that all these turbiditic rocks are of the same age as some of the Cambrian carbonates of the Durness Limestone to the north-west, it seems likely that the proximal turbidites derived some of their distinctive clasts of metamorphic and plutonic igneous origin from the south-east.

The upper limit of the Southern Highland Group

Where to draw the upper limit of the Southern Highland Group, and hence of the whole Dalradian Supergroup, is uncertain. In Tyrone it appears that the Tyrone Igneous Group has shared in the history of polyphase deformation and greenschist facies metamorphism seen in the Dalradian of the Sperrin Mountains, and so the group is here regarded as the uppermost part of the Dalradian. The Dalradian succession therefore appears to continue up from the Black Schists of Broughderg, though with structural break across a thrust, into a thick succession of basic and minor acid lavas, tuffs, and agglomerates with some rhyolite, but dominantly basic lithic clasts. These volcanic rocks, mostly restricted to the northern side of the Central Inlier (Fig. 11), are intimately associated with deformed shallow intrusions of diorite and quartz porphyry with abundant net veining and hybridisation of basic rocks by the acid ones. Locally these rocks intrude the metamorphic rocks of the Central Inlier, where they clearly post-date the high-grade regional metamorphism and the associated structures. This relationship suggests that the volcanic rocks may have overlapped south-eastwards onto the basement. South-east of the Central Inlier the doler-ites, gabbros, and hybrid granites, which are locally schistose and strongly deformed, are accepted as further examples of the hypabyssal and plutonic equivalents of the volcanic rocks. On Slieve Gallion basic lavas with tuffs are stratigraphically overlain by the lower Caradoc graded graphitic siltstones which pass up into fine-grained basic tuffs and grey cherts at the top of the succession.

Along strike to the south-west of Tyrone, there are very similar Arenig volcanic rocks in the Charlestown inlier of east Mayo, and in the Tourmakeady-Lough Nafooey area of south Mayo and north-west Galway.

The Charlestown Ordovician inlier (Fig. 15) lies 120 km south-west of Tyrone and contains a compar-able succession of volcanic rocks. A ridge of positive magnetic anomalies suggests a subsurface continuity. About 1·3 km of intermediate to acid tuffs, agglomer-ates, and rhyolitic lavas form the Tuffaceous 'Group', which is probably the oldest part of the Charlestown succession. An Arenig graptolite fauna of the *Didymo-graptus hirundo* Zone, belonging to the Pacific faunal province was obtained from black cherty shales and

tuffs near the top of the group. This indicates that the succession is not only similar in facies but also in age to the upper part of the Glensaul Group of the Tour-makeady area. The Felsitic 'Group', containing about 750 m of acid and spilitic lavas and agglomerates, is faulted against the Tuffaceous 'Group' but is thought to be younger than it.

Though it is often assumed that the Ordovician rocks of south Mayo and north-west Galway rest unconformably upon a metamorphic basement of Dalradian rocks, there is no clear evidence to prove it. In fact the Ordovician here is separated from the Dalradian of Connemara by a major pre-Silurian fault system on which a vertical downthrow of at least 9 km has been suggested by J. F. Dewey and others. Because these Ordovician rocks can be cor-related through to the Charlestown inlier and to the Dalradian of the Tyrone Igneous Group, they will be considered here as part of the succession of the ortho-tectonic Caledonides. In Scotland microfossils indi-cate that the Dalradian succession extends into the Ordovician. In south Mayo correlation with the Dalradian is also supported by the presence in the Ordovician of overturned pre-Silurian folds, which can be compared to those in the nearest Dalradian to the north.

The Tremadoc (?) – Llandeilo (?) succession of south Mayo and north-west Galway lies in the Mweelrea-Partry syncline whose limbs are over-stepped by Silurian rocks (Fig. 16). On the south and south-east limb of the syncline the succession is divided into three blocks bounded by faults which probably merge westwards into the single Salrock Thrust (Fig. 17). The oldest rocks exposed in the southern block, recently reviewed by J. B. Archer and P. D. Ryan, form the Lough Nafooey Group, con-taining at least 760 m of basic pillow lavas with minor tuffs, cherts, and keratophyre flows. Cherty argillites near the top of the group contain Pacific faunal province graptolites of the *Didymograptus nitidus* Zone (Locality 1, Fig. 16). A dendroid grapto-lite fauna from a lower horizon (Professor D. Skeving-ton, *pers. comm.*) may indicate a Tremadoc age. In the central fault block the oldest rocks of the Mount Partry Group consist of at least 600 m of extremely coarse-grained conglomerates and cross-stratified arkosic sandstones. Common clasts are of greywacke, schist, quartzite, and granite, and boulders may be up to 1·5 m in diameter. In Glensaul (Loc. 2) and at Tourmakeady (Loc. 3) *Didymograptus nitidus* Zone graptolites of the Pacific faunal province occur in dark pelites above the conglomerates and below at least 300 m of basic and acid tuffs, locally interbedded with rhyolitic breccias and flows, arkosic sandstones, and conglomerates. Though the conglomerates of the Mount Partry Group appear to be of the same age as

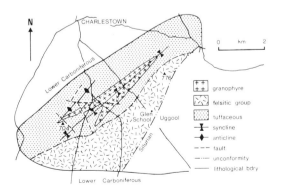

Fig. 15. Ordovician rocks of the Charlestown inlier, County Mayo.

some of the basic lavas of the Lough Nafooey Group, there is neither evidence of interfingering between them nor of derivation of conglomerates from basic flows. The fault between the two blocks may well have had a large horizontal displacement. The Glensaul Group overlies the Mount Partry Group and contains at least 530 m of rhyolitic flows, breccias, and tuffs with local lenses of limestone and limestone breccias in the upper part of the succession. The limestones contain a rich orthid-finkelnburgiid-porambonitacean (late Arenig) brachiopod fauna and a solenopleurid-bathyurid-cheirurid trilobite assemblage of American affinities. In Glensaul (Loc. 5) these faunas occur between two impersistent shale horizons (Locs 4 and 6) containing Pacific faunal province graptolites of the *Isograptus gibberulus* and probably the *Didymograptus hirundo* zones. On the northern limb of the Mweelrea-Party syncline, graptolites no older than the *Didymograptus hirundo* Zone occur near the base of the Derrylea Group (Loc. 11). A *Didymograptus extensus* Zone fauna is recorded from the underlying Sheefry Group (Locs 9 and 10). Therefore the shallow water facies of the Glensaul Group must pass north-wards into a deeper water basinal facies represented by part of the southerly and easterly derived turbidites of the Derrylea Group and the top of the underlying Sheefry Group. Beneath the *extensus* Zone fauna of the Sheefry Group (Fig. 163) lies at least 3·7 km of undated turbiditic sediment with acid tuff bands and conglomerates, showing evidence of derivation from

Fig. 16. Geological map of south Mayo and north-west Galway. Numbers 1-13 refer to Ordovician fossil localities mentioned in the text. B = Bohaun, DRF = Doon Rock Fault, DBF = Derry Bay Fault, MPS = Mweelrea-Partry Syncline, ST = Salrock thrust, T = Tourmakeady, TF = Tourmakeady Fault, A-B = line of section shown in Figure 17.

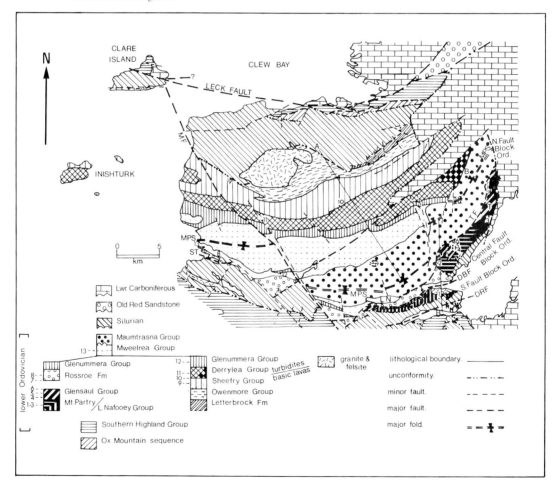

between north-west and east. The base is not seen and the succession could pass down into Cambrian here.

In the northern fault block on the southern limb of the Mweelrea-Partry syncline, the oldest dated rocks are the cherts of Bencraff (Loc. 7) at the base of the Rossroe Formation. Pacific faunal province graptolites here indicate a lower Llanvirn age (*Didymograptus bifidus* Zone). These cherts are overlain by at least 700 m of southerly derived proximal turbidites with channel infills of conglomerates with metamorphic and igneous clasts, local limestone breccias, tuffs, and siltstones. At Rossroe (Loc. 8) a middle Llanvirn graptolite fauna occurs low in this succession. On the north limb of the syncline, the more distal turbidites with local spilitic pillow lavas in the upper part of the Derrylea Group and the lower part of the Glenummera Group are probably the distal equivalents of the Rossroe Formation. East of the Maam Valley faults the Rossroe Formation passes up through 0–70 m of green pelite of the Glenummera

Group into about 360 m of fluviatile arkoses, conglomerates, and agglomerates of the Mweelrea Group, in which five bands of subaerially welded tuffs provide convenient time planes traceable on both limbs of the syncline. In Central Murrisk, on the north limb of the syncline, the Mweelrea Group has less conglomerate and has thickened to at least 2 km. This finer-grained succession includes a probably marine pelitic band. To the west in south-west Murrisk all five tuff bands are thicker and have an unwelded basal facies suggesting deposition in shallow water; there are also three slate bands up to 200 m thick. A shelly fauna from the second slate band about 900 m above the base of the group (Loc. 13) contains an American province brachiopod fauna of late Llanvirn age. The group as a whole shows a progression from a fluviatile environment in the south-east to a shallow marine environment in the north-west. The conglomerates contain extrabasinal clasts up to 1 m in size of quartzite, granite, and schist. Detrital sillimanite has been found in the arkosic sandstones. In eastern Murrisk

Fig. 17. Cross-section of the Ordovician of south Mayo and north-west Galway along line A-B of Figure 16. DRF = Doon Rock Fault. DBF = Derry Bay Fault. TF = Tourmakeady Fault.

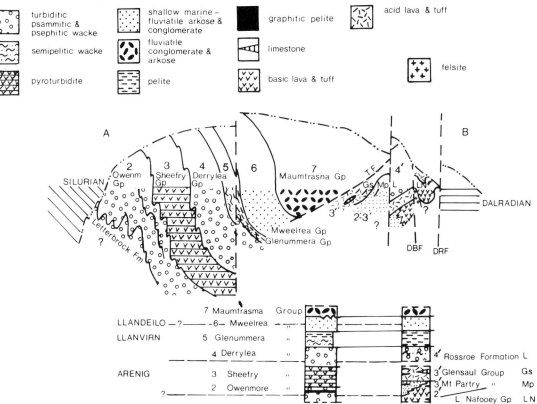

derivation is known to be generally from the south and south-west. The base of the Maumtrasna Group, locally unconformable on the Mweelrea Group, is marked by a sixth band of welded tuff. The overlying 3 km of red and green sandstones and conglomerates contain extrabasinal clasts similar to those in the Mweelrea Group, but these fluviatile sediments were derived from a metamorphic and igneous source lying to the east and south. Above the Llanvirn fauna in the Mweelrea Group lies over 4 km of undated succession probably extending at least into the Llandeilo.

The Ordovician rocks show a consistent palaeogeography, involving eruption of basic and acid magma in a shallow water environment to the south with a deeper water turbidite basin to the north. Influx of metamorphic and igneous detritus from the south and east reached a climax possibly in the Llanvirn and certainly in the Llandeilo, when the basin became largely non-marine.

The Ordovician inliers of Tyrone, Charlestown, and south Mayo – north-west Galway all lie along strike from each other and contain major developments of lower Ordovician basic and acid volcanic rocks suggestive of continental plate margin volcanism of Andean type. In Tyrone the basement to the volcanic pile is of Ox Mountain type continental crust. In south Mayo – north-west Galway the volcanic arc lies on the southern margin of a turbidite trough with a metamorphic and igneous land mass to the south and east. In both this inlier and at Charlestown the faunas show affinity with the Pacific graptolite and American brachiopod-trilobite faunal provinces. At present one can only speculate that these inliers mark a Dalradian volcanic arc, developed along the south-east margin of the Dalradian basin. The north-west margin is seen in the carbonates of the Durness succession in north-west Scotland and Newfoundland.

Structure and metamorphism

Throughout the orthotectonic Caledonides in Ireland there are abundant outcrops with refolded folds or folded lineations or schistosities (Fig. 18) indicating that deformation involved a superposition of several structural phases. Textural relationships between the component metamorphic minerals also indicate that there has been a long history of recrystallisation both during and after structural phases. Before attempting to explain these features it is essential to analyse the three-dimensional form of all structures and to reconstruct their development through time. The conventional method of geometric analysis involves establishing a relative chronology of carefully described structures at individual outcrops, and then

attempting to correlate these regionally using geometric style, attitude, and relationship to recrystallisation as guides. In this way, and by using the outcrop pattern of the stratigraphical succession, the geometry of large-scale structures can be reconstructed. It is now becoming apparent that where such structural and metamorphic 'events' can be calibrated by palaeontological or radiometric time scales, they were formed at different times in different parts and levels of the orogen.

According to Bradbury and co-workers, the regional deformation (D1–D2) of the Dalradian of Perthshire in Scotland was completed before emplacement of the Ben Vuirich granite at 514 +6/–7 m.y. (U/Pb zircon, Rb/Sr W.R.). In north Mayo geological evidence (page 31) suggests that the D1 deformation started in the early Cambrian (c. 550 m.y.) with movement along the basement/cover contact. Deformation and metamorphism appear to have been significantly later in the upper Dalradian to the southeast. In the Ox Mountains the first deformation of the upper Dalradian (Southern Highland Group) took place during emplacement of the Slieve Gamph Igneous Complex at 487 ± 6 m.y. (Rb/Sr W.R.). In Tyrone, correlation of the deformational and metamorphic history of the Tyrone Igneous Group with that of the Dalradian of the Sperrin Mountains requires a mid-Caradoc age (c. 480 m.y.) for these events. The situation is further complicated by the age of 510 ± 10 m.y. (U/Pb zircon) for the post-D1 pre-D2 Cashel Lough Wheelaun intrusion in the upper Dalradian of Connemara, lying effectively farther south. Therefore the convenient episodic method, which will be used to describe structural and metamorphic evolution, may well give a very false impression of episodic orogenic phases. It is much more likely that orogenic deformation was continuous. Rocks may well have been conveyed steadily through sites of continuous deformation and metamorphism during orogeny.

The Leannan Fault of Donegal brings together Dalradian rocks with discordant strikes, as does its probable continuation in Mayo, the Leck Fault (Fig. 11). The Connemara inlier is bounded to the north by the major Doon Rock Fault. The orthotectonic Caledonides are therefore divided by faults into a northwest block (north-west Donegal and north Mayo), a central block (Antrim, Tyrone-Derry-east Donegal and the Ox Mountains inlier) and a Connemara block in the south (Fig. 19).

First structures and metamorphism

North-west Block. In Donegal north-west of the Leannan Fault (Fig. 20) the earliest identified tectonic structure consists of a penetrative fine-grained schistosity, S1, formed by small flakes of muscovite, biotite, chlorite, and graphite. MS1 biotite and oligoclase are locally present indicating low green schist facies metamorphism. Locally S1 is slightly oblique to bedding, forming an intersection lineation and an associated north-west to south-east mineral stretching lineation L1. Usually these early fabrics are only well preserved in hinges of later folds and as curved inclusion trails within later porphyroblasts. There are a number of early dislocations or *slides* defined by

zones of very schistose mylonitic rocks which are subparallel to bedding and folded by second folds. The most important of these, the Horn Head slide, has been mapped regionally and can be shown to cut out stratigraphy progressively on both sides. D. R. Hutton has shown that the bedding usually faces north-west on S1 in this region and that the Horn Head slide is a D2 structure.

Immediately to the south-west of the Main Donegal Granite, the Knockateen slide, of uncertain age,

Fig. 18. F1 isoclines folded by second folds with an associated S2 crenulation cleavage. West coast of Inishowen, County Donegal. *Photograph* by W. E. A. Phillips

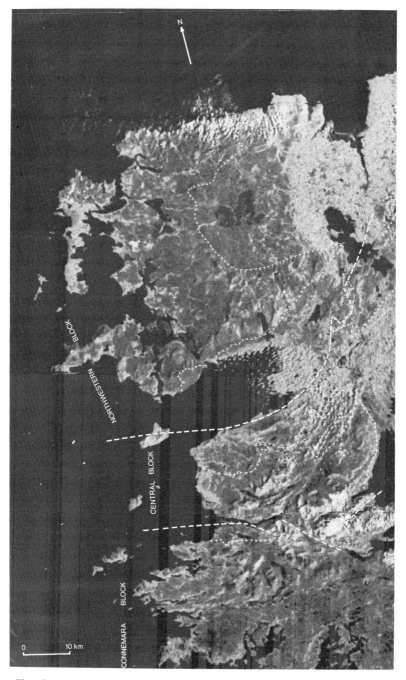

Fig. 19. LANDSAT image of Connemara, west and north Mayo. The boundaries of inliers of the orthotectonic Caledonides are shown by thin broken lines with ticks facing inwards. The thicker broken lines represent the fault boundaries between the northern, central, and Connemara blocks of the orthotectonic Caledonides.

Image supplied by Nigel Press Associates, London

separates the Creeslough succession (Appin Group) on the north-west side from the younger Kilmacrenan succession (Argyll Group). The slide may have brought together separate limbs of a major F1 fold, for F2 folds face up to the north-west on the north-west side, while they face down to the south-east on the other side.

In the north Mayo inlier, (Fig. 22) the earliest Caledonian deformation produced extensive cataclasis (S1a) of the basement gneiss complex during movement along the contact zone with the metasedimentary cover. Pre-Caledonian fabrics have been almost obliterated within a zone up to 1 km thick of semipelitic schist formed from reworked basement with perhaps some cover rocks included. This was followed by widespread minor intrusions of dolerite into basement and cover. These dolerites may well have been feeders to the largely extrusive basic volcanic rocks in the Lough Feeagh Group (Southern Highland Group) near the top of the cover succession. The post-D1 and pre-D2 quartz dolerite intrusions of north-west Donegal may be part of the same suite. Such correlation would mean the D1 deformation had already started at depth in early Cambrian time. This is also implied by the first coarse graded beds in north Mayo, containing gneissic detritus suggesting rapid erosion of recently uplifted basement. Further deformation produced major tectonic slides (D1b) in the cover succession which formed during north-westward thrusting (Fig. 23). The final episode of regional D1 deformation formed a predominantly

flattening fabric (S1c), which is parallel to the axial planes of small- and large-scale F1 folds. On Clare Island in the extreme south of the inlier, D1 structures face to the south and there may well be a D1 symmetry axis between here and the north-west facing structures of the rest of the inlier, though this is obscured by intervening sea and probably by faulting. A D1 symmetry axis on the north side of Clew Bay is also suggested by the major development of basic volcanic rocks in the most southerly derived, uppermost thrust unit of the Lough Feeagh area (Fig. 22). In Scotland comparable basic volcanism developed at the same time in the region of the D1 symmetry axis of the Loch Awe syncline.

This long series of structural events is included within the first period of Caledonian deformation of north Mayo because they were not separated by a static period of metamorphic recrystallisation. Syntectonic recrystallisation (MS1), during the first period of deformation, produced a low greenschist facies assemblage of fine-grained quartz, albite, biotite, muscovite, and locally garnet. This was followed by static recrystallisation (MP1) under low amphibolite facies conditions, with oligoclase, garnet, and kyanite locally developed at deeper levels in the north, and with greenschist facies conditions in the south.

Central Block. South-east of the Leannan Fault, the situation is even more uncertain. In north-eastern Antrim the Dalradian succession is thought to be overturned on the lower limb of a major south-east facing F1 anticline, a continuation of the Tay Nappe

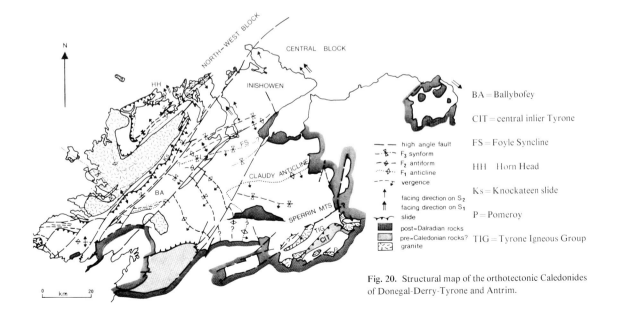

Fig. 20. Structural map of the orthotectonic Caledonides of Donegal-Derry-Tyrone and Antrim.

from Scotland. Minor F1 folds have a low plunge to the north-east or south-west and are associated with a penetrative schistosity (S1 ?) and a strong north-west to south-east mineral stretching lineation (L1 ?). Though detailed subdivision of structural and meta-morphic history has not yet been made here, the main schistosity was associated with growth of muscovite, biotite, and chlorite in pelites and was followed by static growth of albite porphyroblasts.

To the south-west, in the Sperrin Mountains, the Dalradian succession is also overturned and Pitcher and Berger have tentatively suggested that it lies on the lower limb of a major south-east facing *Claudy Anticline.* Though the anticline may be defined by the outcrop of the Crinan Subgroup extending westwards from Dungiven there is as yet no detailed structural

evidence to substantiate its existence, let alone to correlate it with the F1 Tay Nappe. Farther west in the Ballybofey area, major F1 isoclinal folds are refolded by the recumbent F2 Ballybofey antiform. These F1 folds could define the westward continuation of the F1 Claudy Anticline.

In Inishowen, there are numerous F1 folds with wavelengths up to several hundred metres. These folds plunge north-east, they are associated with a pene-trative slaty cleavage (S1), and lie parasitically on the south-east limb of a major north-west facing F1 anti-cline which is truncated by the Leannan Fault. The absence of any major F2 fold in Inishowen makes it improbable that this F1 fold originally faced south-west as suggested by J. C. Roberts. If there is an F1 Claudy Anticline then there is very probably an F1

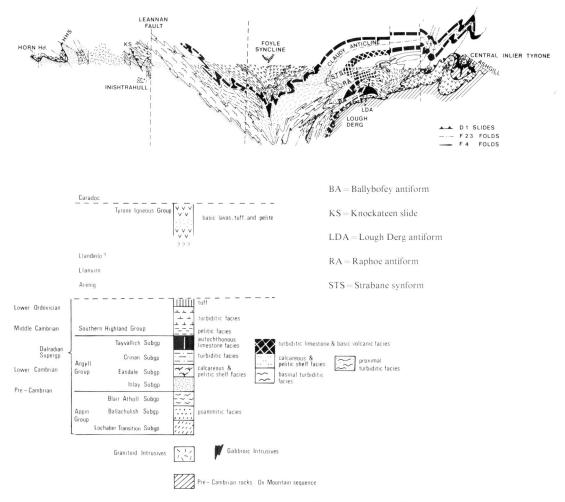

Fig. 21. Structural profile across the orthotectonic Caledonides from north-west Donegal to Pomeroy, central Tyrone.

syncline between it and Inishowen. The synformal outcrop of the Southern Highland Group around the Foyle may well define an F1 Foyle Syncline.

The overturned Dalradian succession of the Sperrin Mountains tectonically overlies the Ordovician Tyrone Igneous Group. Despite the low angle thrust (D1 ?) between these two units, they appear to have shared a similar tectonic and metamorphic history. The earliest deformation of the Tyrone Igneous Group thrust the Pre-Caledonian rocks of the Central Inlier over some of the Ordovician rocks (Fig. 20). These movements were accompanied by local retrogression of the rocks of the inlier, and formation of a penetrative chlorite schistosity in the adjacent Ordovician. Farther west analogous structural situations are seen in south Donegal, the Ox Mountains, and the south Clew Bay-Clare Island areas. In south Donegal, an overturned Dalradian succession, on the southern limb of the F2 Ballybofey antiform, youngs downwards into the older Pre-Caledonian rocks of the Lough Derg inlier. The contact is probably a D1 or D2 Caledonian slide zone. In the Ox Mountains inlier, near Foxford, north of Castlebar, on the south side of Clew Bay and of Clare Island, Southern Highland Group turbidites of the Dalradian tectonically overlie Pre-Caledonian metasediments of the Ox Mountains sequence. The contact is a D1 Caledonian slide zone. Basement rocks have been converted to fine-grained phyllonites, over thicknesses of up to 1 km, by retrogressive low greenschist facies metamorphism and associated mechanical reduction in grain size. Translation was to the south-east and was associated with south-east facing F1 Caledonian isoclinal folds and a penetrative S1 slaty cleavage. This first cleavage often

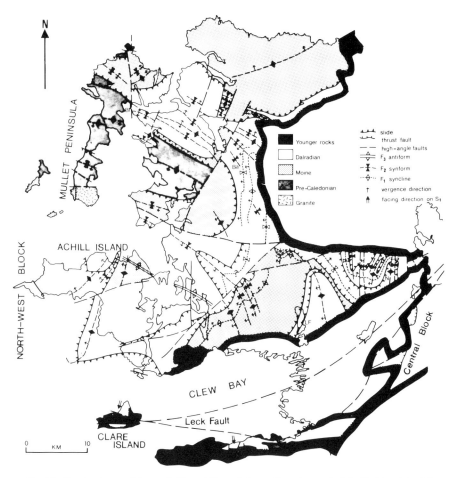

Fig. 22. Structural map of the north Mayo inlier and the south-western end of the Ox Mountains inlier. Bt = Belmullet, Ba = Bangor Erris, LF = Lough Feeagh, N = Nephin.

has a strong sub-horizontal north-east to south-west trending pebble stretching lineation and is therefore an LS fabric; the only recrystallisation was growth of MS1 fine-grained muscovite and chlorite. The Slieve Gamph Igneous Complex was emplaced at 487 ± 6 m.y. (Rb/Sr W.R.) (about Llanvirn-Llandeilo) during this first Caledonian deformation and a strong LS quartz fabric was developed in it during intrusion.

Despite the obvious scarcity of reliable data on the D1 deformation, there is enough evidence to justify the following hypothesis. In north-west Donegal and north Mayo, D1 structures face north-west in conformity with the Islay Anticline of Scotland. An upright F1 synclinal symmetry axis extends from the Loch Awe area of Scotland through the Foyle area and is offset by about 160 km of sinistral displacement on the Leck-Leannan Fault to continue in the Clew Bay area. South-east of this, D1 structures face south-east and are structurally underlain by Pre-Caledonian basement extending from Tyrone through the Lough Derg and Ox Mountains inliers to Clew Bay. Farther south-east lies the Ordovician volcanic area extending from Tyrone through Charlestown to the Lough Nafooey area of south Mayo. In Tyrone these rocks appear to have been deformed with the Dalradian. In Charlestown and south Mayo there is a major angular unconformity below upper Llandovery sediments, and allowance for unfolding of the Silurian reveals earlier overturned folds in the Ordovician which can be compared in style and age with the more intense D1 structures in the nearest Dalradian to the north-west.

Connemara Block. In the Connemara inlier prolonged high grade metamorphism and at least three major folding periods again make recognition of D1 structures difficult. On a small scale, a D1 event is inferred from the presence of a pre-S2 fabric, preserved as inclusion trails in later garnet and plagioclase porphyroblasts. Small folds with an S1 axial planar cleavage may be slump folds. Minor F1 folds have been described by B. E. Leake in disorientated xenoliths and in the marginal hornfels zones of the major post-D1, pre-D2 basic and ultra-basic intrusions. On a larger scale, the facing of folds and the primary stratigraphical distribution within Connemara is due to a complex major isoclinal fold − the Lissoughter Anticline (Fig. 24) − interpreted as F1 by M. E. Badley and as F2 by B. W. D. Yardley. It is not yet clear where this major fold 'roots' nor what its primary attitude was. Leake has shown that an early MS1–MP1 metamorphism of up to garnet grade in pelites is overprinted by the late MP1 hornfels assemblages of the basic-ultrabasic intrusions emplaced at 510 ± 10 m.y. (U/Pb zircon).

Second structures and metamorphism

North-western Block. In north-west Donegal the second deformation produced a shallow dipping regional crenulation cleavage (S2) which is sometimes intensified to a penetrative schistosity. This fabric is parallel to the axial planes of the major north and north-west facing folds in the Creeslough succession. The Errigal Syncline is the largest of these folds. (Fig. 25). South-east of the Knockateen slide, S2 is axial planar to south-east facing major recumbent F2 folds. Deformation was followed by the main peak of metamorphism which reached into the low amphibolite facies in the Glencolumbkille area. Over much of the block there was new growth of chlorite, muscovite

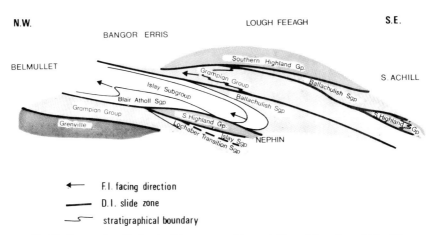

Fig. 23. Structural profile showing D1 structures of the north Mayo, inlier, after unfolding F2 and F3 folds.

and biotite, and segregation of quartz and feldspar. MP2 porphyroblasts of garnet, plagioclase, and minor ilmenite were also formed, and these have often overgrown F2 microfolds. Further deformation caused a flattening of S2 around MP2 porphyroblasts and the development of an S3 crenulation which is nearly parallel to S2. F2 folds were probably tightened by this deformation.

In the north Mayo inlier, the second deformation produced a pervasive S2 schistosity or locally an LS fabric. The schistosity is parallel to the axial planes of most of the major folds, which are therefore of the F2 generation. In the northern part of the Mullet peninsula and in the adjacent part of the mainland, there is an F2 symmetry axis marked by an upright northwest to south-east trending synclinal zone. On either side of this zone, F2 folds are progressively overturned to face and verge away from the axis (Fig. 22). F2 folds are generally of Ramsay's class 3 style, with amplitudes increasing up their axial planes away from the basement. The major swings in strike of S2 shown in Figure 22 have been accounted for by Sanderson in a model of dextral simple shear during D2 along east-west trending steep shear zones. The main shear zone is inferred along the southern margin of the inlier in northern Clew Bay, an earlier one lying to the north in the Belmullet-Bangor Erris region. Syntectonic (MS2) recrystallisation occurred under low amphibolite facies conditions in the basement gneisses and in the lower parts of the cover, with the growth of oligoclase-andesine, garnet, and biotite in pelitic rocks. At higher levels in the south of the inlier, MS2 albite indicates lower grade greenschist facies con-

ditions. Post-tectonic MP2 recrystallisation reached amphibolite facies conditions in the northern part of the area, where andesine, staurolite, and kyanite occur in pelites of the Grampian and Appin groups. At higher structural and stratigraphical levels to the south conditions remained in the greenschist facies with further growth of MP2 albite, biotite, muscovite, and chlorite.

Central Block. In north-east Antrim, the S1 (?) schistosity is cut by a later flat-lying crenulation cleavage (S2 ?), other structures of this episode are yet to be defined. Westwards in the Sperrin Mountains, the recumbent south-east facing Strabane Syncline is a major structure, which by analogy with the Ballybofey antiform may well be an F2 structure. Large north-east to south-west trending folds in the Tyrone Igneous Group are also F2; they have a variably developed S2 axial plane cleavage which dips north-west at 40–50°. In Inishowen, a well-developed S2 crenulation cleavage dips south-east at 30–40°; it is axial planar to abundant minor north-easterly plunging F2 folds which face down to the south-east. The stratigraphical outcrop pattern of south-central Donegal is controlled by the Ballybofey fold complex, the major component of which is the recumbent F2 Ballybofey antiform. The main schistosity of the area is axial planar to this fold and is therefore assigned to S2, though is may also be a composite S2/S3 fabric as in north-west Donegal. There is a strong south-south-easterly plunging quartz rod lineation. A number of other major F2 folds are inferred in the block, but they are as yet unsubstantiated by detailed structural analysis. The second deformation produced

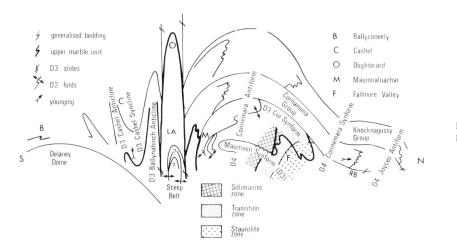

Fig. 24. Structural profile through the Connemara inlier, showing the relationship between structures and metamorphic isograds (modified after Yardley 1976).

upright north-east to south-west trending F2 folds with gently plunging axes in the upper Dalradian rocks of the Ox Mountains inlier, between Foxford and Clare Island. As usual they have a well-developed axial planar crenulation cleavage. Locally a strong nearly horizontal quartz stretching lineation lies on S2.

There has been very little detailed analysis of metamorphism throughout the block. In north-east Antrim the conspicuous inclusion-filled albite porphyroblasts appear to post-date the major cleavages, and therefore probably started to grow during MP2, including S1 and F2 micro-folds. In the Sperrins, biotite and garnet occur in pelites and late porphyroblastic albite is widespread. In the Tyrone Igneous Group, MS2–MP2 chlorite defines the S2 fabric and there is sporadic growth of MP2 albite porphyroblasts. North-west of the Sperrins to Inishowen, there is no detailed information on the chlorite/biotite zone metamorphism. In the north-western part of the block, the MS2-MP2 metamorphic history is rather similar to that of north-west Donegal. North-east of Letterkenny, the S2 fabric in pelites is defined by MS2–MP2 muscovite and chlorite. Sporadic MP2 garnets are augened by an S3 crenulation cleavage. South-west of Letterkenny there is a progressive increase in metamorphic grade

Fig. 25. Errigal Mountain viewed from the north. The Ards Quartzite lying within the F2 Aghla Anticline forms the main peak. Marble and banded quartzites of the Sessiagh Clonmass Formation lie within the F2 Errigal Syncline which is seen on the western slope of the mountain. From the Cambridge University collection of Aerial Photographs.
Photograph by J. K. St Joseph, copyright reserved

leading to the development of coarse biotite-garnet-schists, with sporadic growth of staurolite and kyanite. In the Ox Mountains inlier the metamorphic peak was also reached in MP2 forming small albite porphyroblasts in upper Dalradian pelites and in the D1 phyllonites. There is also growth of some MS2–MP2 chlorite, muscovite, and minor biotite.

Connemara Block. In Connemara the second deformation produced the main penetrative schistosity S2, on which there is both a strong flattening of clasts and also a strong roughly north to south mineral lineation. Emplacement of basic and ultrabasic intrusions and associated quartz andesine migmatites took place before, during, and after these movements. F2 folds are tight to isoclinal, plunging steeply to the north-east or north-west; they have been intensely refolded by later F3 and F4 folds. Yardley has shown that the isograd geometry in central Connemara suggests that F2 folds were upright.

The S2 fabric was coeval with growth of biotite, muscovite, garnet, plagioclase, and hornblende under amphibolite facies conditions. Only near Renvyle and on Inishbofin did conditions remain within the greenschist facies (Fig. 11). The metamorphic peak in western and central Connemara was achieved during MP2 to MS3 with an early growth in pelites of staurolite and locally kyanite, followed by metamorphism up to sillimanite zone conditions. Yardley has shown that in north-central Connemara the late MP2 growth of sillimanite after staurolite, and growth of cordierite and andalusite, can be interpreted in terms of a steepening geothermal gradient and a decrease in confining pressure due to uplift and erosion. A lower pressure higher temperature (Buchan type) metamorphism is here superposed on an earlier MP2 Barrovian metamorphism.

Third and later deformations and metamorphisms

North-west Block. In north-west Donegal the flat-lying S3 crenulation cleavage, subparallel to S2, was probably associated with a general flattening and intensification of the D2 strain, rather than the production of new structures. An S4a crenulation cleavage commonly produces a north-west to south-east trending crenulation lineation on the earlier composite S2/S3 fabric. The relation of S4a to the large-scale open and upright F4b folds is unknown. These folds are co-axial with F2/F3, trending north-east to south-west.

In north Mayo, there is quite a widely developed S3 crenulation cleavage dipping steeply south. F3 folds are mostly small-scale, however a major F3 upright and open antiform plunges gently east from north-east Achill to the adjacent mainland (Fig. 22).

Smaller F3 monoclinal flexural folds are also seen in the Mullet peninsula. In south Achill, S3 swings in strike from east-west to a steeply dipping north-south attitude; this is related to a major gently inclined east-west F4 antiform. There appears to have been widespread retrogression involving chloritisation of biotite during MS3–MP3 in north-west Donegal and north Mayo. This was followed by regional growth (MP4) of randomly orientated porphyroblasts of biotite and some chlorite.

Central Block. Late deformation of uncertain relative age in north-east Antrim formed north-west to south-east trending upright cross-folds. A subsequent phase of albite growth was followed by formation of a gentle north-east to south-west trending upright antiform. Farther west it is only in Inishowen that late structures have been studied in detail. Here there is a strong steeply dipping S3 crenulation cleavage which swings from a north-west to south-east trend in the west to a north-east to south-west trend in the north. Minor F3 folds accompany this S3 fabric. Locally the D4 structures are important; they include chevron folds, monoclines, and kink bands. In the Ox Mountains inlier the fourth structures consist of a flat-lying set of conjugate folds indicating local vertical shortening.

Between south Donegal and Inishowen there was widespread MS3–MP3 retrogression followed by growth of MP4 porphyroblasts of biotite and chlorite.

Connemara Block. In Connemara, unlike the other inliers, formation of major structures and high-grade metamorphism continued long after the second deformation. There is a regional S3 which varies between a crenulation cleavage and a penetrative schistosity. Though there is some flattening on S3, the dominant fabric element of D3 is a lineation parallel to fold axes, defined by elongation of pebbles and of quartz and amphibole. F3 folds are abundant. They strike approximately east-west and have a gentle plunge to east or west, which suggests that F1 and F2 folds were flat-flying before D3. A number of slides were developed during D3. The most important of these is the Renvyle–Bofin slide (Fig. 24), which has been traced round the eastern end of the Connemara Antiform, and may well be of importance on the southern limb of this structure. Both this and other D3 slides often contain small pods of serpentinised ultramafic rock. The conspicuous major folds of the inlier are the east-west trending upright F4 folds, of which the Connemara Antiform is the most important. F3 folds are folded over this structure and face downwards on its northern limb where MP2 isograds (staurolite/sillimanite zone boundary) are also inverted. Unfolding of the antiform indicates that F3 folds were recumbent prior to D4.

During F3 there was continued amphibolite facies

metamorphism (MS3) in southern and eastern Connemara. A later static recrystallisation (MP3 ?) gave rise to a patchy development of andalusite. An S4 crenulation cleavage is sometimes associated with F4 folds. Sporadic retrogressive metamorphism continued during and after D4. The Oughterard Granite, intruded after D4, has yielded a rather poor Rb/Sr isochron age of 510 ± 35 m.y. and a mineral whole rock isochron of 469 ± 7 m.y.

The position of Connemara

The Dalradian succession of Connemara is typical of central parts of the main Dalradian outcrop such as Perthshire in Scotland. However the inlier is south of a zone extending from Tyrone to Clew Bay and south Mayo which shows some evidence of being a south-eastern margin of the Dalradian basin during the Cambrian and the lower Ordovician. A number of solutions to this anomaly can be considered. Firstly, if Connemara has not changed its position relative to the rest of the orthotectonic Caledonides, then the Pre-Caledonian basement of the Ox Mountains-Lough Derg-Tyrone region could be part of a basement horst uplifted within a Dalradian basin in upper Dalradian times, after most of the distinctive Connemara succession had been deposited. The uplift, erosion, and steepened thermal gradient inferred in Connemara for late MP2 times, and the syntectonic calc-alkaline intrusions, could be the deep-seated reflection of Upper Cambrian-lower Ordovician volcanism, now fault-separated in the Lough Nafooey area. The erosion inferred during late MP2 could also be linked to the arrival of southerly derived metamorphic detritus in the Ordovician of south Mayo. Secondly, it is possible to discount the evidence for a south-eastern margin to the Dalradian basin, and regard the Pre-Caledonian rocks of the Ox Mountains as basement thrust high into the Dalradian succession. Thirdly, accepting the south-eastern margin argument, the Connemara Dalradian could have been thrust south over the basin margin, or it could have been moved into position by sinistral displacement on the major pre-Silurian Doon Rock Fault on its northern margin. A sinistral strike-slip solution could also explain the 60° anticlockwise rotation of the palaeomagnetic pole position for the Llanvirn Mweelrea ignimbrites of south Mayo.

BIBLIOGRAPHY

BADLEY, M. E. — 1976 Stratigraphy, structure and metamorphism of Dalradian rocks of the Maumturk Mountains, Connemara, Ireland. *Jl. geol. Soc. Lond.*, **132**, 509–520.

DEWEY, J. F. — 1961 A Note Concerning the Age of the Metamorphism of the Dalradian Rocks of Western Ireland. *Geol. Mag.*, **98**, 399–405.

DEWEY, J. F., McKERROW, W. S., & MOORBATH, S. — 1970 The relationship between isotopic ages, uplift and sedimentation during Ordovician times in western Ireland. *Scott. J. Geol.*, **6**, 133–145.

DOWNIE, C., LISTER, T. R., HARRIS, A. L., & FETTES, D. J. — 1971 A palynological investigation of the Dalradian rocks of Scotland. *Inst. geol. Sci. Rep.* No. 71/9, pp. 29.

HARRIS, A. L. & PITCHER, W. S. — 1975 The Dalradian Supergroup. *In* Harris, A. L. *et al.* (Eds.). A correlation of the Precambrian rocks in the British Isles. *Geol. Soc. Lond. Spec. Rep.*, **6**, 52–75.

HOWARTH, R. J. — 1971 The Portaskaig Tillite succession (Dalradian) of Co. Donegal. *Proc. R. Ir. Acad.*, **71B**, 1–35.

KENNEDY, M. J., PHILLIPS, W. E. A., & NEALE, E. R. W. — 1972 Similarities in the Early Structural Development of the Northwestern Margin of the Newfoundland Appalachians and Irish Caledonides. *Proc. 24th Int. geol. Congr., Montreal*, **3**, 516–531.

KNILL, J. L. — 1963 A sedimentary history of the Dalradian Series. *In* Johnson, M. R. W. and Stewart, F. H. (Eds.). *The British Caledonides*. Oliver and Boyd, Edinburgh, 99–121.

LEAKE, B. E.   1970 The fragmentation of the Connemara basic and ultrabasic
                                      intrusions. *In* Newall, G. and Rast, N. (Eds.). *Mechanisms
                                      of Igneous Intrusion.* Geol. J. Special Issue No. 2, 103–
                                      122.

PANKHURST, R. J.,   1976 Age and structural setting of the Slieve Gamph Igneous
    ANDREWS, J. R.,   Complex, Co. Mayo, Eire. *Jl. geol. Soc. Lond.,* **132,**
    PHILLIPS, W. E. A.,   327–334.
    SANDERS, I. S., &
    TAYLOR, W. E. G.

PHILLIPS, W. E. A.,   1976 A Caledonian plate tectonic model. *Jl. geol. Soc. Lond.,*
    STILLMAN, C. J., &   **132,** 579–609.
    MURPHY, T.

PITCHER, W. S. &   1972 *The Geology of Donegal: A Study of Granite Emplace-
    BERGER, A. R.   ment and Unroofing.* Wiley-Interscience, New York and
                                      London, pp. 435.

ROBERTS, J. C.   1971 The structure of the Dalradian rocks between Dunree Head
                                      and Inch Island, Western Inishowen Co. Donegal. *Proc. R.
                                      Ir. Acad.,* **71B,** 139–153.

YARDLEY, B. W. D.   1976 Deformation and metamorphism of Dalradian rocks and
                                      the evolution of the Connemara cordillera. *Jl. geol. Soc.
                                      Lond.,* **132,** 521–542.

4

CAMBRIAN AND ORDOVICIAN OF THE PARATECTONIC CALEDONIDES

C. H. Holland

One definition of 'paratectonics' takes in 'sedimentary basins deformed within a frame of surrounding massifs', and the term can thus be applied more or less rigorously to the Irish Cambrian and Ordovician rocks south of the Dalradian outcrop (and some associated areas) referred to in the previous chapter. Certainly a distinction between paratectonic and orthotectonic (with alpinotype tectonics) is easier to maintain than the one implied by the terms 'metamorphic' and 'non-metamorphic' Caledonides, which have been used to distinguish these two belts identified in Irish and British Lower Palaeozoic rocks. The rocks of the paratectonic ('non-metamorphic') belt have commonly been subjected to low grade metamorphism; those of the orthotectonic ('metamorphic') belt may in places still provide very fresh indications of their original environment of deposition. It is convenient here to consider the relevant rocks of successive periods of Lower Palaeozoic time separately, beginning with the Cambrian.

Cambrian

In Britain, which includes the type area for the Cambrian System, these rocks (except, that is to say, for the Dalradian Supergroup) are restricted in outcrop. In Ireland the Cambrian of the paratectonic Caledonides is not only similarly restricted but is elusive also in terms of evidence for its stratigraphical age. As shown in Figure 26, outcrops are confined to Howth Head and Ireland's Eye to the north of Dublin Bay, to the Bray Head district to the south of Dublin, and to south-eastern County Wexford. Body macrofossils have scarcely been found in these rocks and the characteristic trace fossil *Oldhamia* has itself been

the subject of biostratigraphical debate – apart from the enigma of its relationships within the classification of living things. Two main forms are known: *Oldhamia radiata*, consisting of ridges radiating from a centre, and *Oldhamia antiqua* with semicircular patterns of radiating ridges which may occur in linear series (Fig. 27). The radiating structures of both species may be seen to penetrate several superimposed sedimentary laminae. Since the first descriptions of it in the middle of the nineteenth century, *Oldhamia* has been ascribed to various animal and plant groups, but is now generally regarded as a trace fossil of radiating burrows. Other records of its species in Europe and North America are of similarly uncertain age, but there are cases of the association of *Oldhamia* with known Cambrian fossils, for example from New York State, Boston, and Norway.

The Howth peninsula to the north of Dublin Bay was an island in early post-glacial time and is still linked to the mainland only by an isthmus of sand and gravel. A small area of Lower Carboniferous dolomitised limestones is present at the landward end of the peninsula and is faulted against the rocks of the Bray Group, ferruginous material being prominent at the contact. These Cambrian rocks are sufficiently similar to those at Bray Head to be given the same lithostratigraphical name. *Oldhamia* is known from Puck's Rocks and from the cliffs north of the Nose of Howth. Other trace fossils are to be found. Of these, T. P. Crimes has recorded *Arenicolites*, *Granularia*, *Planolites*, *Skolithos*, and *Teichichnus* seemingly from beds below those yielding *Oldhamia*. *Oldhamia* is usually associated with relatively deep-water, but proximal, turbidites whereas the lower assemblage indicates shallower water.

Lithologically the most striking feature is provided

by bands and isolated masses of quartzite, relatively resistant to marine erosion and also forming prominent inland ridges and hills. They are characteristically ochreously stained and the so-called 'Howth Stone' is attractively seen in old walls and buildings, though less so in some of the garnishments of modern houses in the Dublin area. The quartzites are repeated by folding but they appear to be stratigraphically numerous. Other sediments are well seen in the cliff sections. They are greenish, red, and grey shales, siltstones, and greywacke sandstones. Bentonitic

clays are common. Sedimentary structures are displayed particularly on the bare rock surfaces washed by the sea. They include parallel lamination, cross-lamination, graded bedding, and flute moulds. Slump structures of various kinds (Figs 28 and 29) are very well seen at many localities, for instance at Kilrock, Hippy Hole, and Sheep Hole. There are slide-conglomerates in which laminated quartzitic clasts set in a silty matrix show primary lamination disturbed by submarine sliding and subsequently cleaved with the matrix. A greywacke facies with much evidence of

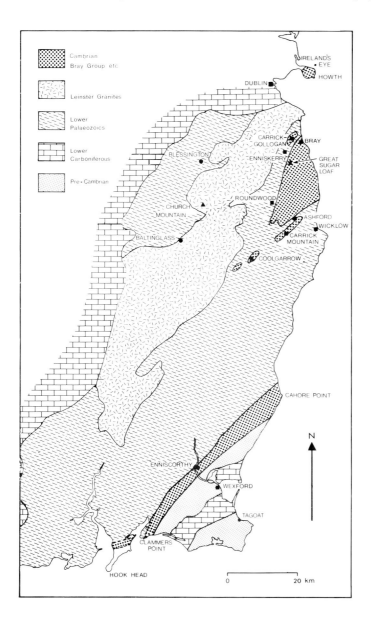

Fig. 26.

Geological sketch-map of south-eastern Ireland to show distribution of Bray Group and related rocks. The small area of Old Red Sandstone in the Hook peninsula is not distinguished from the Lower Carboniferous limestones.

soft sediment deformation and re-sedimentation contrasts with the prominent quartzitic sandstones. In some cases the latter may be simply interbedded with the turbiditic greywackes but in others they are thought to represent exotic blocks which may be as much as 700 m in size. In many cases the precise origin of the quartzites is unclear.

Cleavage is widely developed in the finer sediments and more than one episode is represented in places. The quartzites are well-jointed and there is much faulting, though not necessarily on substantial scale. H. A. van Lunsen and M. D. Max have mapped five formations within the Cambrian rocks of the Howth peninsula and recognise that there is a sequence from sedimentary, through tectono-sedimentary, to true tectonic structures. The effects of slumping on sedimentation and deformation appear to increase as the succession is ascended, slump folding and slumped masses of quartzite in the lower beds giving way to 'chaotic sedimentary breccias' in the higher part of the sequence. All the formational boundaries are thought to involve slumping. The main structure of the area is regarded as a syncline plunging steeply to the east but there is a profusion of smaller scale structures.

Ireland's Eye, the small island about one kilometre from Howth Harbour, has quartzites at its northern and southern ends and finer variegated sediments partly covered at high water in between. The succession has been compared with the lower part of that at Howth. The island must represent part of an isolated anticlinal culmination or be separated from the mainland by faulting. In the latter case its surface profile may approximate to an original post-Carboniferous erosion surface. Micropalaeontology shows promise in elucidating the stratigraphical ages of the Irish Lower Palaeozoic rocks and P. R. R. Gardiner and M. Vanguestaine have already described similar acritarch assemblages from two samples from the succession in Ireland's Eye. Acritarchs are microscopic organic bodies with hollow interiors, generally regarded as the reproductive and/

Fig. 27. *Oldhamia antiqua* Forbes (National Museum of Ireland specimen NMI G2: 1969) Coll. 'Mr. J. R. Joly'. ($\times 4.5$). Part of a specimen figured by Joly (1887). Reproduced from *Cambrian of the British Isles, Norden, and Spitsbergen*, edited by C. H. Holland.

Fig. 28. (above) Large scale disruption (slumping) at Sheep Hole (approximately 2 km west of Baily Lighthouse), Howth with slip apparently from right to left.
    Photograph by M. D. Max

Fig. 29. (below) Pre-main cleavage steeply plunging fold, approximately 0·5 km north of Baily Lighthouse, Howth. Cleavage intersection is parallel to hammer handle.
    Photograph by M. D. Max

or resting stages of planktonic marine algae. By comparison with material from Eastern Europe the assemblages from Ireland's Eye have been said to indicate a Lower to Middle Cambrian age. More recently D. G. Smith has extracted an acritarch assemblage from Howth which, by reference to results from Britain as well as the Baltic area, he shows to be of mid Lower Cambrian age.

Rocks of the Bray Group are also well exposed along the coast at Bray Head and to the south of it and their outcrop extends over a considerable inland area to the south-west. P. M. Brück, T. L. Potter, and C. Downie have recorded poorly preserved acritarchs of late Lower Cambrian or early Middle Cambrian age from the Bray Head Formation (see below) in Rocky Valley, north of the Sugar Loaf mountains.

Oldhamia is commonly found in the thick (more than 4,500 m) succession, particularly in purple and green slates and laminated siltstones at the tops of turbiditic units. Other trace fossils are found of which the worm burrows *Arenicolites* and *Skolithos*, as mentioned already, are probably indicative of relatively shallow water. J. C. Brindley, S. Millan, and E. J. Schiener have suggested that the supposed trace fossils '*Histioderma*' actually represent small sand volcanoes.

The succession at Bray Head consists of predominantly northward dipping and younging green, purple, red, and grey slates and interbedded (often feldspathic) greywacke sandstones and siltstones frequently well-laminated. Massive white to pink quartzites up to at least 100 m in thickness form prominent coastal and inland features, such as the two Sugar

Fig. 30. Great Sugar Loaf viewed northwards from Calary, County Wicklow. Bray Group quartzites of the pre-cleavage Great Sugar Loaf – Little Sugar Loaf syncline here dip generally eastwards. Cleavage in the adjacent greywackes strikes in an east-north-easterly direction.
Bord Failte Photograph

Loaf mountains (Fig. 30). Some of the inland ridges display very well the repeated displacement of the quartzites by cross-faulting (Figs 31 and 32). Sedimentary structures such as graded bedding, cross-lamination, convolute lamination, flute moulds, and less commonly parallel lamination are conspicuously developed and many of the greywackes display some of the charactistic turbiditic intervals which A. H. Bouma and others have widely recognised elsewhere. Those present are regarded largely as indicative of proximal turbidites and the presence of associated quartzites and slump structures is appropriate to this

Fig. 31

View eastwards towards Bray Head from the summit of the Little Sugar Loaf showing the two main quartzite units on Bray Head: the Cross Unit to the left and the Brandy Hole Unit to the right. Faulted offsets of the latter are seen.

Photograph by P. M. Brück

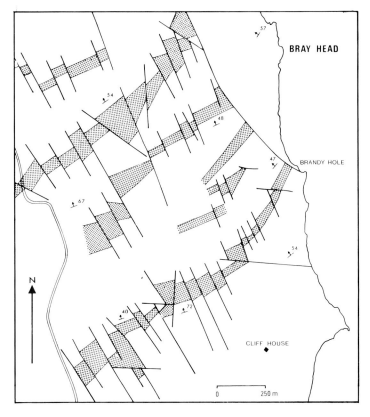

Fig. 32

Faulting in quartzite units at Bray Head. Modified after Brück and Reeves (1976).

view. Sedimentary structures are less easily seen in the quartzites but some of these, as at Howth, are slumped and basal flute moulds are known. Load moulds (and complementary flame structures) are found in the greywacke turbidites as well as at the bases of quartzites.

Brindley, Millan, and Schiener summarised directional evidence available in the area neighbouring Bray Head. P. M. Brück and T. J. Reeves have made additional observations in the whole area of outcrop. Flute moulds are indicative of a north-westerly derivation for the proximal turbidites but there is evidence from ripple drift of more distal material arriving from the north-east. In places, however, a generally northerly origin is indicated. The quartzites, on the other hand, appear to have arrived as slump sheets or grain flows from the south-east or north-west.

Brück and Reeves have recognised a lower Devil's Glen Formation (2,000 m) cropping out anticlinally in the west from south of Enniskerry (Fig. 26), running east of Roundwood towards Ashford. Its greywackes and slates are massive in character and quartzites are very rare.

A narrow strip of country west of this and towards Powerscourt is of the succeeding Bray Head Formation (2,500+ m), as is the majority of the whole Cambrian outcrop from Bray Head, through the Sugar Loaf mountains, Glen of the Downs, and Newtown Mount Kennedy. They suggest that an early pre-cleavage phase which may be largely of sedimentary (slumped) origin accounts for major folds in the area as well as many minor ones. An early cleavage is rare. The main east-north-east cleavage of the area relates to the very numerous tectonic folds of a few metres in scale. Significant plunge on these folds is confined to a southern belt. This cleavage may be seen to cut some of the first phase folds, as in the northerly striking syncline of the Sugar Loaf mountains. A third phase of minor angular folds and kink bands is rarely developed. Apart from the many cross faults cutting the quartzites some of larger extent are found throughout the area, as for instance the Rocky Valley fault extending eastwards for more than 6 km.

Thrusting is important in defining the outcrop of the Bray Group. An isolated mass of these rocks has been thrust to the north at Carrickgollogan, the hill being clear even in the profile of the Dublin mountains seen from the north side of Dublin Bay. A faulted, and possibly thrust, contact has also been suggested at Carrick Mountain in the south (Fig. 26). Two small areas of Bray Group, again possibly in thrust contact with underlying Ribband Group, are found to the south-west of the main outcrop at and near Coolgarrow. The main boundaries of the outcrop of the Bray Group have not proved easy to define. To the north and west again there appears to be a thrust boundary with rocks of the Bray Group overlying the younger rocks of the Ribband Group. To the east of the Leinster Granite, Brück, Potter, and Downie refer to three formations which locally make up the Ribband Group in the area between the granite and the outcrop of the Bray Group. The oldest Maulin Formation, adjacent to the granite, probably extends down into the Cambrian as similar ('Clara Series') rocks in Wexford have yielded acritarchs of this age. A tentative acritarch dating of the third and youngest part of the Ribband Group (the Glencullen River Formation), adjacent in outcrop to the Bray Group and separated from it by a thrust, is of lower Ordovician age.

The southern contact of the Bray Group has been described as faulted, though to the south-west W. E. Tremlett recognised a sequence comprising 'Knockrath Series' (1,300+ m of dark grey and black slates and quartzitic siltstones), Bray 'Series' (purple mudstones followed by grey and green greywackes and massive quartzites more than 300 m in total thickness), and 'Clara Series' (dark slates). The succession here does not (in fact) appear to show any substantial breaks and Downie and Tremlett recorded acritarchs from the Clara Series, which, together with the evidence of associated brachiopods, indicated a Cambrian age. Brück and Reeves refer both Knockrath and Clara Series to the Ribband Group. To the south of Roundwood, County Wicklow, Brindley and Millan have described variolitic (basic) lavas, some with deformed pillow structures, within the 'Knockrath Series'. Just over 5 km to the south-east there are similar rocks at two horizons evidently within the Devil's Glen Formation.

The area formerly recognised as of probable Cambrian rocks in County Wexford has been restricted by the recognition of two groups of Pre-Cambrian age in the area (see page 7). Conversely, it is now necessary to make an extension to include part of the outcrop previously referred to the Ordovician. To the south-west this involves an as yet undetermined proportion of the Duncannon area at the landward end of the Hook peninsula (Fig. 26), where Gardiner and Vanguestaine record Lower to Middle Cambrian acritarchs from two samples. A third sample from the same Booley Bay Formation suggests a Tremadoc to lower Arenig age. The formation comprises some 2,500 m of interbedded grey siltstones and mudstones, with some sandstones and conglomerates. The formation is of distal turbidites and provides an excellent display of sedimentary structures. It is said to be equivalent to the Ribband Group elsewhere.

The inland part of the north-easterly trending strip of outcrop which has been equated with the Bray Group is poorly exposed, so that except for a recent description by P. M. Shannon of the ground between New Ross and Wexford, detailed knowledge is so far confined to the southern and north-eastern coastal strips (Figs 26 and 33). The Cullenstown Formation in southern County Wexford (page 8) can be correlated with the Mona Complex in Anglesey, North Wales. It appears on isotopic evidence to have been metamorphosed about the end of the Pre-Cambrian and the base of the evidently younger Bannow Group above cannot therefore be much older than the base of the Cambrian.

In the south-western coastal area N. B. Dhonau has divided the succession into five formations, of which the oldest, the Cross Lake Formation, is in faulted contact with upper Ordovician (Caradoc) rocks. It consists in its lower part of red and green slates with thin greywackes, mainly fine grained and showing parallel lamination and cross-lamination. These are followed by slump or slide deposits (olistostromes) evidently indicating the proximity of the south-eastern margin of the Wexford-Cumbria Basin

(Fig. 34). Clasts vary from less than 1 cm to 100 m in size and are commonly of white quartzite. There are associated greywackes and shales. The succeeding Kiln Bay Formation is of alternating brown mudstones and thinly bedded greywacke siltstones. Slumping was still significant but the silty greywackes with their cross-lamination, parallel lamination, and grading indicate a somewhat more distal sedimentation. The same trend is seen to continue in the Clammers Point Formation of monotonous green mudstones and greywacke siltstones, commonly cross-laminated. Flute and groove moulds indicate derivation mainly from the north-east. These three formations contain *Oldhamia* and are comparable with the Cahore Group farther north. A sample taken from a disturbed part of the section but seemingly from the Cross Lake Formation has yielded Cambrian acritarchs.

The higher Bannow Island and Bannow Bay formations are lithologically similar to the so-called Ribband Group elsewhere, the age of which is vari-

Fig. 33. Geological maps of the Wexford coast: (A) south Wexford from Ballymadder to Bannow (after Dhonau and Holland 1974); (B) east Wexford from Courtown to Cahore Point (after Crimes and Crossley 1968).

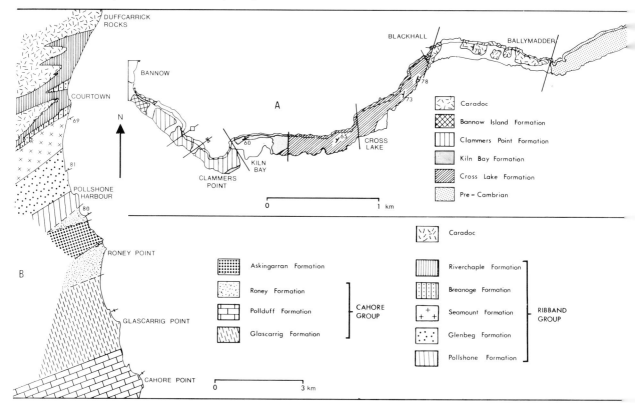

ously Cambrian to lower Ordovician as mentioned above and in what follows.

The north-easterly coastal section was divided by T. P. Crimes and J. D. Crossley into the Cahore Group followed by the Ribband Group. The former comprises three formations: the Glasscarrig Formation (600 m), the Pollduff Formation (more than 750 m), and the Roney Formation (more than 600 m). The second of these contains *Oldhamia* and '*Histioderma*' and the third *Oldhamia* and *Arenicolites*. All three consist dominantly of feldspathic sandstones, siltstones, and red and green shales, with quartzites becoming conspicuous in the third formation. Grading, parallel lamination, cross-lamination, groove moulds, and load structures are present and a proximal origin has been suggested for the coarser sediments. The succeeding Askingarran Formation (not assigned to a group) is of finer-grained sediments with parallel lamination and cross-lamination but rarely with grading. Here again this higher part of

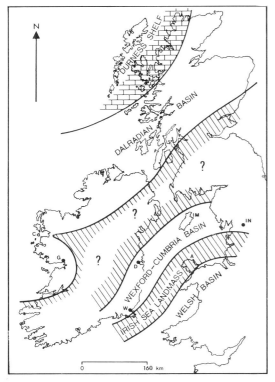

Fig. 34. Cambrian palaeogeography of the British Isles (approximately late Lower Cambrian times).

A = Anglesey
D = Dublin
G = Galway
IM = Isle of Man
IN = Ingleton
W = Wexford.

the succession is regarded as indicative of distal turbidites. The flute and groove moulds in the formation indicate derivation from the west-south-west, but later from the south-south-east.

Though the Askingarran Formation is lithologically different from the Cahore Group below it, there appears to be a gradation between the two over a thickness of a few metres, though within a mechanically disturbed zone. The succeeding Ribband Group appears to follow in regionally northerly younging sequence. These rocks, extending into the lower Ordovician, are considered later in this chapter.

The slumped beds or slide conglomerates in the Cambrian of Wexford indicate proximity to what has long been referred to as the Irish Sea Landmass (Fig. 34). The Welsh Cambrian rocks were deposited in a basin to the south-east of this and the Bray Group and its equivalents were evidently laid down in a corresponding subsiding basin to the north-west. Indications are that this latter Wexford-Cumbria Basin was relatively narrow with active, possibly fault controlled, margins. The Dalradian Basin and its associated carbonate shelf represented by the Durness Group of the North-West Highlands of Scotland (together with their equivalents in Newfoundland) lay farther to the north-west presumably on the other side of a Proto-Atlantic ocean. The Pacific trilobite faunal province represented in the Lower Cambrian of Scotland and Western Newfoundland was distinct from that of the Acado-Baltic Province for which evidence is found in the Welsh Borderland and Eastern Newfoundland alike. As detailed in the previous chapter the Dalradian part of this story is also available to us in Ireland. A tentative Cambrian palaeogeography is attempted in Figure 34. To postulate an ocean in itself wide enough to explain the separation of trilobite faunal provinces is not unreasonable, but additional evidence for a gradually closing Proto-Atlantic must accumulate from other sources.

Lower Ordovician (Tremadoc to Llanvirn)

The possibly Tremadoc, through Arenig and Llanvirn, to possibly Llandeilo rocks of south Mayo and north Galway; the small area or related rocks near Charlestown, at the western end of the Curlew Mountains inlier; and the lower Ordovician volcanic rocks and associated sediments of the Tyrone Igneous Group in the Pomeroy area, still farther north-eastwards, are all best regarded as related to those of North America on the one hand and the Ayrshire area of Scotland on the other — as belonging in fact to a 'Pacific' (or North American), rather than 'Atlantic' (or European) province in terms of their graptolitic and, in places, shelly faunas. As such they have been treated already in the previous chapter of this book. Ordovician successions elsewhere in Ireland generally exhibit a break of more or less magnitude between the lower and upper parts of the system, this representing at least some or all of the Llandeilo Series. These two parts of the Ordovician are therefore treated separately in what follows. The status of the Tremadoc Series remains uncertain until there is international agreement upon a boundary stratotype for the base of the Ordovician. In the type area in Wales historical priority is still (though not entirely unambiguously) being followed, in that the Ordovician is commonly regarded as beginning with the Garth Grit of North Wales as Charles Lapworth designated it, there being usually if not always an unconformity with the Tremadoc below. In other parts of the world such as North America and the Norden countries it has been customary to begin the Ordovician with the Tremadoc Series, the argument resting upon the supposedly Ordovician 'aspect' of Tremadoc trilobites and other fossils. This latter practice is followed (pragmatically) here, though there is very little firm palaeontological evidence for the presence of Tremadoc strata in Ireland*, and the Upper Cambrian (Merioneth Series) is here poorly delimited.

A faulted inlier of red and green mudstones and cherts near Acton, County Armagh provides the oldest fossiliferous rocks so far encountered in Ulster. The red mudstones contain conodonts indicative of the upper Llanvirn or lowest Llandeilo. There being no other indications of lower Ordovician rocks in the northern belt of the Longford–Down massif (the Irish Southern Uplands), we first encounter them in the small poorly exposed inliers of Grangegeeth – Collon and Bellewstown, respectively some 15 km west and 8 km south of Drogheda (Fig. 35). The former is separated from widespread Silurian rocks to the north by a south-westerly trending line of faulting. The Grangegeeth Volcanic Group begins with tuffs and shales which have yielded a graptolite fauna including a species of *Didymograptus*, a diplograptid, and *Pseudoclimacograptus angulatus* aff. *sebyensis*, collectively indicative of the Llanvirn. The shales and tuffs are followed, seemingly directly, by spilitic lavas. The stratigraphy here is under close revision by Dr M. Romano.

In the Bellewstown inlier Ordovician rocks crop out between Duleek and Bellewstown itself. The grey and dark purplish Prioryland Mudstone Formation (760 m), which appears from beneath the unconformable Lower Carboniferous cover near Duleek and dips southwards, has been assigned to the Arenig

because the succeeding Hilltown Formation (445 m) has yielded Llanvirn graptolites of the *Didymograptus bifidus* Zone (species of *Didymograptus*, *Climacograptus scharenbergi*, *Phyllograptus angustiformis*, etc.). However McKee has recorded the presence of acritarchs of Tremadoc age in the Prioryland Formation. These grey mudstones are associated with volcanic rocks mainly in the form of water-laid ashes and fine agglomerates. Some of the latter have been interpreted as laharic mudflows. There are also spilitic lavas, fragments of vesicular spilite being present also in the mudflow deposits. Poorly preserved brachiopods are concentrated in places in the muddy matrix. The Llanvirn volcanic rocks of the Hilltown outcrop are intermediate and acidic in composition.

Farther south lower Ordovician rocks are known in the small inlier of the Chair of Kildare, where the basal olive green siltstones and shales have been presumed to be the source of an old record of *Didymograptus bifidus*. The Caradoc age of the succeeding beds suggests that the gap commonly observed in the Ordovician succession is to be identified here. Otherwise lower Ordovician rocks in Ireland are to be found in the south-east of the country on the northwestern, eastern, and southern flanks of the Leinster Granite and in a small and isolated area in southeastern County Wexford, separated by the Carboniferous rocks of the Wexford Syncline (Fig. 26) from the main area of the Leinster massif to which the other outcrops belong. Until recently separated coastal areas have provided the only detailed age assignments of these rocks, but knowledge has been considerably advanced by P. M. Brück's studies of outcrops in the northern part of the Leinster massif.

North-west of the granite the succession begins with the Butter Mountain Formation of laminated siltstones and slates more than 675 m thick. Some small-scale cross-lamination is helpful in suggesting that the steeply dipping succession youngs westwards. The basal formation is followed by a sequence of greywackes of which the lowest are assigned to the Aghfarrel Formation (570 m) in which shales are associated with brown, green, and grey greywacke siltstones. The greywackes of the succeeding Pollaphuca Formation (1,750 m) are followed by the Slate Quarries Formation in which there is some palynological evidence for an upper Ordovician to lower Silurian age. Brück assigns the first two formations to the Ribband Group to be referred to again later and within the Pollaphuca Formation there is no indication of the usual mid-Ordovician unconformity, though its presence may be difficult to detect in the absence of precise palaeontological evidence.

* Derived Tremadoc acritarchs are known, for instance, in the Lower Carboniferous of the Ballyvergin, County Clare, borehole.

Andesitic (hornblende andesite and porphyritic feldspar andesite) and doleritic igneous rocks, pre-dating the intrusion of the Leinster Granite, occur over a distance of some 40 km along its western margin. Some andesitic lavas and tuffs are associated with intrusive sheets in the northern part of the area, for example at Dowery Hill about 6 km north-east of Blessington (Fig. 26), where pillow lava breccias are seen. A more substantial extrusive development, approximately 900 m thick, forms an oval anticlinal outcrop within that of the Butter Mountain Formation between Baltinglass and Church Mountain, County Wicklow. The recognition by Professor Brück of these lower Ordovician volcanic rocks is an important addition to the record of Ordovician volcanicity in south-eastern Ireland.

To the east, as mentioned already, an Ordovician outcrop is situated between the Leinster Granite and the Bray Group, the latter having been thrust over it. The succession youngs eastwards and the oldest Maulin Formation of grey phyllites, slates, and thin grey quartzites is 900 m thick. The Sleamaine Formation follows with about 650 m of grey laminated siltstones and slates, again with some small-scale cross-lamination. The third and youngest unit is the Glencullen River Formation with buff and grey acid tuffs and acid lavas 500 m in maximum thickness. Palynomorphs here indicate a possibly Arenig age though the assemblage is a poor one and could be older. As noted already (page 47) the Sleamaine and Glencullen River formations are assigned to the Ribband Group.

Work by Crimes and Crossley on the Wexford coast has been mentioned already. Under the mid-Ordovician unconformity five formations are assigned to the Ribband Group and the upper ones are best regarded as Arenig in age rather than possibly Upper Cambrian. There is sedimentological way-up evidence adjacent to inferred contacts of the lower formations and contacts of the two uppermost ones are exposed. The succession (Fig. 33) begins with the Pollshone Formation (100+ m) of dark grey and green mudstones frequently laminated, with bands of light coloured fine siltstone. In the succeeding Glenbeg Formation (150 m) grey green siltstones and greywackes are added to the sequence. The Seamount Formation (600 m) comprises interlaminated grey and black mudstones and grey and white micaceous or feldspathic siltstones and sandstones, extensively bioturbated. There are bands of fine sandstone and siltstone. Dendroid graptolites occur near the top of the succession. In the Breanoge Formation (80 m) interbedded bioturbated mudstones and micaceous siltstones again yield dendroid graptolites. Finally, the Riverchapel Formation (110+ m) is of distinctive, interlaminated red mudstones and siltstones with some green bands. Feldspathic sandstones are common near the top. Dendroid graptolites are present together with a lower Arenig species of *Clonograptus* and didymograptids.

Modern work is also available for the Duncannon area at the landward end of the Hook peninsula, County Waterford, where P. R. R. Gardiner's Booley Bay Formation of siltstones and shales is also assigned to the Ribband Group. The base is not exposed but some 2,500 m are present. Where visible, the contact with the overlying Caradoc volcanic rocks is faulted. One sparse sample of palynological material has given an age of Tremadoc to early Arenig. Evidence that the formation may range upwards from Middle Cambrian has already been mentioned (page 47).

At Tramore the coastal exposure to the west of the beach includes an estimated thickness of 1,300 m of Tramore Shales, whose contact with the Tramore Limestone may well be tectonic and whose assignment to an age preceding the widely recognised mid-Ordovician unconformity appears to be uncertain.

Finally, reference must be made to south-east Wexford where the so-called Tagoat Beds, exposed near Rosslare Harbour and unconformable upon the Pre-Cambrian rocks of the Rosslare Complex, have yielded not only extensiform didymograptids of Arenig age but also a shelly fauna of trilobites and brachiopods which is comparable to the Arenig shelly faunas of Anglesey, North Wales. These shelly faunas can be related to opposite sides of the Irish Sea Landmass (Fig. 36).

Much more remains to be understood about local details of the lower Ordovician rocks around the southern part of the Leinster Granite and doubtless additional faunal finds will contribute to an increasingly accurate picture. Thus P. J. Brenchley, J. C. Harper, and D. Skevington in their description of the Tagoat faunas also included reference to the Arenig graptolite fauna from Kiltrea near Enniscorthy, thus adding to the older record of a likely Llanvirn graptolite fauna from the same district, and again indicating that the Ribband Group as a whole may encompass at least lower Arenig to Llanvirn strata.

It is appropriate finally to take up the broader palaeogeographical picture again, at the level of the Llanvirn. Professor Skevington has shown that from south to north within the Atlantic Province as evidenced in Britain and Ireland pendent didymograptids decreased in importance relatively to biserial graptolites, with an accompanying slight increase in taxonomic diversity. The large number of pendent forms in the type Llanvirn of South Wales is well known. The relative change in proportions of the graptolite fauna is seen already in North Wales. In the eastern Irish areas of County Meath, as in the English Lake

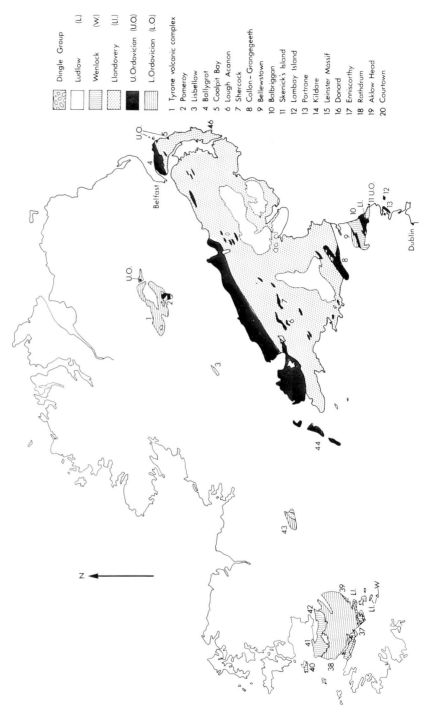

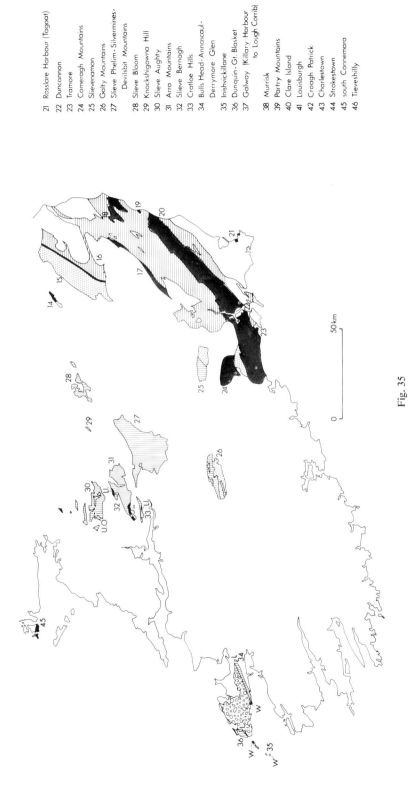

21 Rosslare Harbour (Tagoat)
22 Duncannon
23 Tramore
24 Comeragh Mountains
25 Slievenamon
26 Galty Mountains
27 Slieve Phelim-Silvermines-
   Devilsbit Mountains
28 Slieve Bloom
29 Knockshigowna Hill
30 Slieve Aughty
31 Arra Mountains
32 Slieve Bernagh
33 Cratloe Hills
34 Bulls Head-Annascaul-
   Derrymore Glen
35 Inishvickillane
36 Dunquin-Gt. Blasket
37 Galway (Killary Harbour
   to Lough Corrib)
38 Murrisk
39 Partry Mountains
40 Clare Island
41 Louisburgh
42 Croagh Patrick
43 Charlestown
44 Strokestown
45 south Connemara
46 Trevershilly

Fig. 35

Ordovician and Silurian rocks of Ireland (modified draft by Gayle Thompson from prototype compiled by Dr J. Parkin).

District, pendent forms have become subordinate to other elements of the Llanvirn graptolite fauna. However the sharper change comes between the faunas of Meath and those to be found in north-western Ireland which have been referred to in the previous chapter. This change in the Llanvirn graptolites may, as Skevington has suggested, relate to climatic variation from one Ordovician latitudinal belt to another. The substantial separation required between what are now Mayo and Meath can again be explained by the original presence of a Proto-Atlantic ocean between the two (Fig. 36), though the graptolitic evidence alone does not of course demand this particular explanation of separation. Indeed *Didymograptus bifidus* itself is present in the Arenig rocks of Texas and evidently reached the European side of the Proto-Atlantic in early Llanvirn times.

Upper Ordovician (Llandeilo to Ashgill)

The evidence for a fairly widespread mid-Ordovician break in sedimentation in Ireland has already been referred to and the presence of Llandeilo as distinct from Caradoc rocks is, in any case, to some extent a matter of definition. Thus in his introduction to the Geological Society of London's correlation of Ordovician rocks in the British Isles, Alwyn Williams suggests that the range of the *Nemagraptus gracilis* Zone, long considered as confined to the lower part of the Caradoc Series, must, on the basis of associated shelly macrofaunal, microfaunal, and graptolitic evidence from Wales be extended downwards to approximately the top of the lower Llandeilo. The

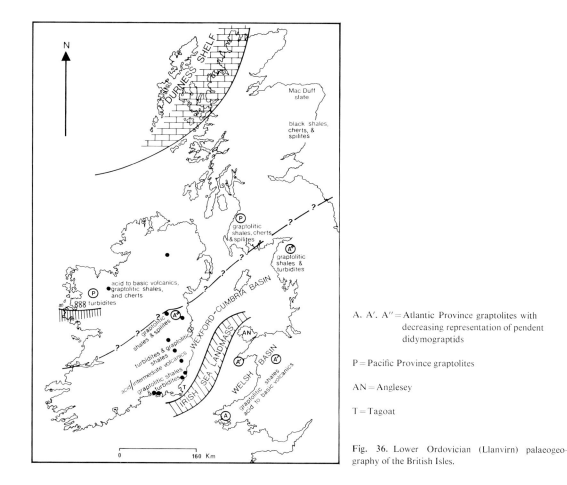

A. A'. A'' = Atlantic Province graptolites with decreasing representation of pendent didymograptids

P = Pacific Province graptolites

AN = Anglesey

T = Tagoat

Fig. 36. Lower Ordovician (Llanvirn) palaeogeography of the British Isles.

upper boundary of the zone is put into the lowest, Costonian Stage of the Caradoc. Ordovician chronostratigraphical and biostratigraphical divisions are listed for reference in Table 6. It has been generally recognised that by this later part of the Ordovician Period, possibly related to the gradual closing of the Proto-Atlantic ocean by subduction, faunas both graptolitic and shelly had become more uniform.

Beginning in the north again and moving successively southwards, we first see these later Ordovician rocks of the paratectonic belt in a small area around Pomeroy (Fig. 35). They are folded and ill-exposed. Along Caledonoid strike south-westwards, evidence in south Mayo is tantalisingly lacking.

At Pomeroy the Bardahessiagh Formation (160 m)

Table 6.

Ordovician (excluding Tremadoc) chronostratigraphical and biostratigraphical divisions.

SERIES	BIOZONES		STAGES
Ashgill	anceps		Hirnantian
			Rawtheyan
			Cautleyan
	complanatus		Pusgillian
Caradoc	linearis		Onnian
	clingani		Actonian
			Marshbrookian
			Longvillian
	wilsoni		Soudleyan
	peltifer		Harnagian
			Costonian
Llandeilo	gracilis		
	teretiusculus		
Llanvirn	murchisoni		stages not yet defined
	bifidus		
Arenig	hirundo		
	extensus	gibberulus	
		nitidus	
		deflexus	
		approximatus	

of sandstones and conglomerates probably rests unconformably (the break here being within the Caradoc) upon the Tyrone Igneous Group. In the past the formation has yielded a rich shelly shelf fauna, closely comparable with that of the Girvan area of Scotland and including orthid and strophomenid brachiopods; harpid, lichid, and other trilobites; and gastropods. W. I. Mitchell has recently revised the Ordovician brachiopod faunas of Pomeroy and dates this part of the succession as Caradoc. The succeeding Killey Bridge Formation (65-160 m) of calcareous mudstones and siltstones has shelly fossils (trinucleid trilobites, etc.) assigned to the lower part of the Cautleyan Stage of the Ashgill Series. *Dicellograptus anceps* and other graptolites are present. Finally the evidently disconformable Tirnaskea Formation (33 m) of calcareous siltstones and mudstones with the trilobite *Dalmanitina* represents the highest Hirnantian Stage of the Ordovician, to be discussed later. It also yields some graptolites. It is followed conformably by graptolitic Silurian rocks of the *Akidograptus acuminatus* Zone. The shelly fossils of the Pomeroy inlier have been well known since the time of Portlock's memoir on the district and figure in many palaeontological articles and in museum collections. Finds by the early collectors included rich assemblages of coiled gastropods.

The upper Ordovician rocks in County Down are very similar to their counterparts in Galloway, Scotland, from which they are separated by less than ten kilometres of the North Channel. The northern strip of the Longford–Down massif, which is marked largely as Ordovician in general geological maps of Ireland, is some 10 km wide but extends southwestward for over 150 km. Particularly between Lisburn and Portadown it is more or less hidden by Permian or Mesozoic, or by Tertiary basaltic rocks. It consists largely of greywackes of turbidite facies. At the western end of Helen's Bay Beach, less than 5 km west of Bangor, E. N. Sharpe has described an inverted succession, dipping south, which has spilitic pillow lavas (Fig. 41) succeeded by agglomerates with pebbles of spilite in blue green and purple tuffs. These are followed by black graptolitic shales, black cherts, and greywackes. The shales which crop out at Ballygrot immediately to the north of the pillow lavas contain graptolites of the *Nemagraptus gracilis* Zone. J. H. Morris has now recognised (with graptolitic evidence) a continuation of the upper Ordovician greywacke belt in the separated inlier near Strokestown where possibly 2,500 to 3,000 m of poorly exposed greywackes are succeeded by mafic volcanic rocks associated with more greywackes, cherts, and siltstones. To the south, siltstone turbidites with interbedded jasper horizons are present between these two parts of the succession, but they lense out northwards.

He has geophysical evidence for continuation of the volcanics south-westwards under the Lower Carboniferous cover.

A glimpse of possibly correlative rocks is seen over 100 km south-westwards along strike in the form of two small outcrops of the so-called South Connemara

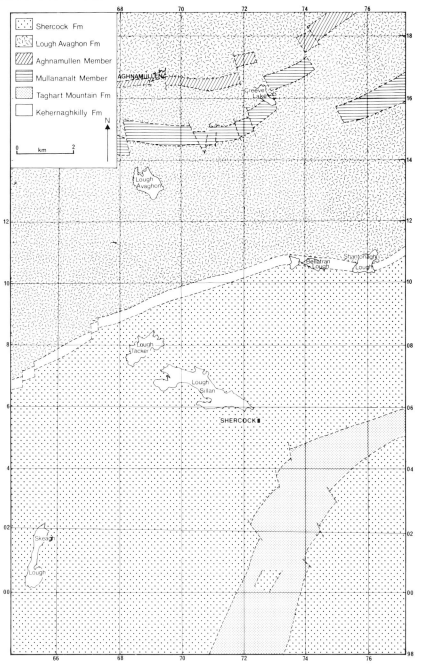

Fig. 37. Geological map of the Shercock-Aghnamullen district, Counties Cavan and Monaghan (simplified from O'Connor 1975).

Group seen in inverted sequence south of the Galway granite on the north side of Galway Bay. The sequence is very thick, perhaps as much as 12,000 m, younging northwards. Pillow lavas and tuffs are prominent particularly in the lower part of the succession. There are amphibolites, quartzites, cherts, slates, greywackes, and conglomerates, and good evidence of slumping. There is, however, no palaeontological evidence of age and the sequence may possibly be lower Ordovician.

Most of the relatively large roughly triangular area of the Longford–Down massif is of Silurian rocks, probably mostly inverted. Narrow strips of Ordovician of generally Caledonoid trend are present and are becoming increasingly well known.

At Coalpit Bay on the east coast of County Down a faulted inlier of Ordovician shales has yielded graptolites of the Caradoc *Climacograptus wilsoni* and *C. peltifer* zones and possibly younger indicators of Ashgill age up to and including the highest, *Dicellograptus anceps* Zone of the Ordovician. The total succession of mudstones and black shales is only 75 m thick, though parts of the sequence are cut out by faulting.

The fourth edition of the one-inch Belfast Sheet of the Geological Survey of Northern Ireland shows several fault-bounded strips of higher Ordovician

rocks within the more widely developed Llandovery outcrop south of Belfast and Lisburn. Fine to medium, grey greywackes are subordinate to more or less silty mudstones and shales. Graptolites are present in places. For instance at Yate's Corner, a little outside the Belfast Sheet, J. Pollock and H. E. Wilson have recognised the *Nemagraptus gracilis* Zone as well as the higher *Dicranograptus clingani* and *Pleurograptus linearis* zones. The upper Ashgillian *Dicellograptus anceps* Zone has been recorded from a trench in the Killaney inlier.

Detailed mapping in the Shercock–Aghnamullen district of Counties Cavan and Monaghan (Fig. 37) by E. A. O'Connor established the presence of an Ordovician unit some 100 m thick, the Kehernaghkilly Formation, of pale green and grey silty shales becoming more micaceous and flaggy upwards and followed by black flaggy lutites with a middle Caradoc graptolitic fauna. Climacograptids and dicranograptids are well represented and the succession spans the *peltifer*, *wilsoni*, and *clingani* zones. Silurian greywackes to the north-west and south-east are probably separated from the Ordovician by faulting. The Ordovician outcrop can be extended north-eastwards along a narrow belt of lakeland country probably related to these relatively fine-grained sediments. Black shales are certainly present near Lough

Fig. 38. Distribution of belts of black shales across the Lower Palaeozoic outcrop of the Longford-Down massif. Major areas of granitic rocks and Lower Carboniferous within the massif are indicated by ornamentation (after O'Connor 1975).

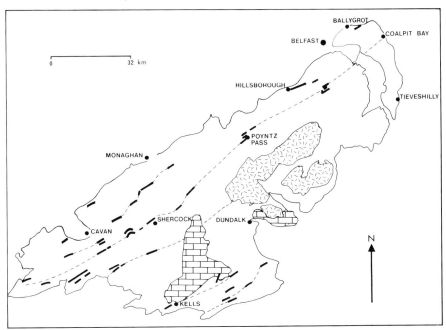

Egish. There are various such linear belts of black Ordovician lutites in the Longford–Down massif (Fig. 38) which may usually be bounded by strike faults. This has already been seen to be the case at Coalpit Bay and south of Belfast. In the small Loch Acanon district to the south-west of Shercock there is conformity between black Ordovician graptolitic shales and greywackes apparently Llandovery in age.

The upper Ordovician graptolitic shale facies of the Central Belt of the Southern Uplands of Scotland and its continuation in the Irish Longford–Down massif is seen again to the south-west in south Galway and Clare, where various small inliers are known in association with the more extensive Silurian developments of the Slieve Aughty and Slieve Bernagh inliers. In Slieve Aughty (Fig. 39) various small areas of Ordovician rocks are seen within the Upper Old Red Sandstone outcrop between Loughrea and Gort. The

exposure is poor but stream sections have allowed G. T. Emo to recognise nine individual Ordovician inliers. The largest of these, the Toberelatan–Kilchreest inlier, extends for nearly 5 km north-eastwards. It is an anticlinal structure with a core of black and grey cherts above which are grey and black graptolitic shales, succeeded by grey and green bioturbated mudstones, siltstones, and fine greenish grey sandstones. More than 800 metres of the Toberelatan Formation are seen. The *Nemagraptus gracilis* Zone has been recognised. Relationships with the more extensive Silurian inlier to the south are unknown but are most likely to involve faulting. Farther south, near Lough Graney, the Caher Hill Formation of basic tuffs and agglomerates, basaltic and trachytic lavas, and grey cherts and shales is faulted against the Silurian. Graptolites of the *peltifer* or top *gracilis* Zone are present in the shales.

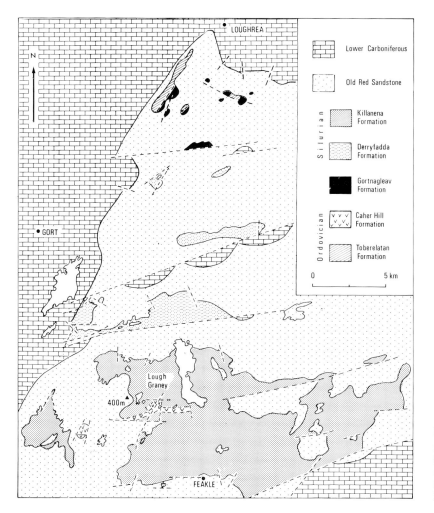

Fig. 39

Lower Palaeozoic rocks of Slieve Aughty, Counties Clare and Galway. Information kindly supplied by G. T. Emo.

In the Slieve Bernagh inlier the Ordovician forms the core of the Broadford Mountains anticlinal structure. Here J. A. Weir has described a lowest division of unfossiliferous, grey, greywacke sandstones and mudstones (about 75 m), faulted against the Caradoc Belvoir Group which comprises some 340 m of brownish, pink, and grey cherts; 75 m of 'Nemagraptus gracilis Beds'; and 90 m of mottled siltstones. Climacograptids occur in some of the cherts but a much richer graptolite fauna is found in the succeeding strata. The fauna is similar to that of the Glenkiln Shales in the Southern Uplands of Scotland though the zones of *Nemagraptus gracilis* and *Climacograptus peltifer* cannot be separately distinguished. The succeeding Ballyvorgal Group of brownish mudstones and shales is about 180 m thick. Near the base a shelly band yields trilobites, brachiopods, and echinoderm fragments. The trilobite fauna can be compared most closely with a lower Ashgill fauna at Girvan, Scotland. Harper's recognition of *Dicellograptus complanatus* a little below the shell bed confirms this assignment.

Similarly, a dark graptolitic shale facies with its implications of restricted circulation and with associated dark cherts has been recognised more recently by R. B. Rickards and J. B. Archer in a very small inlier near Tomgraney, County Clare, on the northern flank of the Slieve Bernagh syncline, where it is faulted against Silurian rocks and partly covered unconformably by Upper Old Red Sandstone (Fig. 40). The list of graptolites from here differs considerably from that of the Broadford Mountains and it has been argued that they are likely to be of *peltifer* rather than *gracilis* Zone age. It appears that all these Ordo-

vician occurrences in west central Ireland are brought up by strike faulting and subsequently revealed in the Hercynian, generally anticlinal, structures which affect Old Red Sandstone and Lower Palaeozoic rocks alike.

The Lower Ordovician rocks of the small and poorly exposed inliers of Grangegeeth–Collon and Bellewstown on the south-eastern margin of the Longford–Down massif have already been referred to. Above the spilitic lavas of the Grangegeeth Volcanic Group are some 100 to 610 m, thickening northwards, of rocks variously referred to as 'autobreccias' and 'brecciated keratophyres', also said to include conglomeratic developments and to be followed by feldspathic sandstones. They are prominent in the topography and have been quarried. It has been suggested that the conglomerates, overlying as they do beds of Llanvirn age, may relate to the mid-Ordovician break noted elsewhere. There is thought to be a continuous succession into fossiliferous tuffaceous sandstones and brown and grey shales above. The shales are well exposed in the Brickworks Quarry nearly 2 km south of Grangegeeth where a rich fauna is dominated by trilobites – *Deacybele, Decordinaspis* (a trinucleid described from here), *Opsimasaphus, Platylichas, Sphaerexochus, Sphaerocoryphe, Tretaspis*, etc. There are also brachiopods, bryozoa, molluscs, and echinoderms and a graptolite fauna including species of *Climacograptus, Dicellograptus, Dicranograptus, Laziograptus, Orthograptus*, and *Pseudoclimacograptus*. The trilobites are related to those of the Balaclatchie fauna of Ayrshire and the graptolites are indicative of the *Climacograptus peltifer* Zone. Somewhat older shelly fossils from the

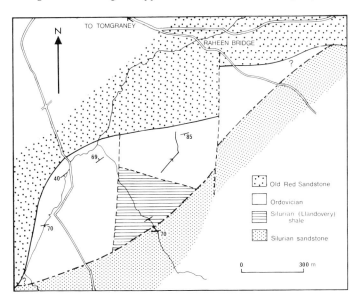

Fig. 40

Ordovician and Llandovery rocks near Tomgraney, County Clare (modified after Rickards and Archer 1969).

formation relate to those of the Tramore Limestone, referred to later.

In the neighbourhood of Mellifont Abbey an area of brown weathering shales contains a shelly and graptolitic fauna possibly of the same age as the 'Upper Tuffs and Shales' just referred to. Some 3 km east of Grangegeeth is a small area of black shales and chert bands. An assemblage of species of *Climacograptus*, *Dicellograptus*, and *Orthograptus* indicates the Zone of *Dicranograptus clingani*. Another assemblage indicates the *Pleurograptus linearis* Zone and, though relationships are not clear, the black shales are evidently partly at least of Ashgill age and significantly younger than the beds previously referred to. Finally the so-called 'Oriel Brook Mudstones' exposed in a stream a little north of Mellifont Abbey are again of uncertain relationships. Grey, greenish weathering mudstones have yielded trilobites and brachiopods and nearby possibly faulted black shales yield graptolites of the *linearis* Zone. The shelly fauna of the mudstones is evidently of a younger Ashgill age, corresponding to that of the Upper Whitehouse Beds of Girvan.

The Llanvirn, Hilltown Formation, of Bellewstown (page 50), is followed by calcareous shales and limestones of the Bellewstown Limestone Formation, only 6 m thick, which again yield shelly fossils akin to those of the Tramore Limestone; conodont evidence, too, giving no indication that the succession rises above the Llandeilo. The succeeding shales, mudstones, and calcareous ash of the Carnes Formation (305 m) have Harnagian (Caradoc) trilobites and brachiopods below and graptolites of the *Diplograptus multidens* Zone above. Farther east at Balbriggan thick andesites, pillow lavas, and tuffs follow upon mudstones with probably Longvillian shelly fossils. Above is a faulted graptolitic black shale sequence of Ashgill age, referred to again in the next chapter.

The advent of mixed successions with upper Ordovician shelly as well as graptolitic fauna and with associated evidence of volcanicity remains farther south in the small inliers of Portrane and Kildare where respectively fossiliferous limestones are relatively well known (Fig. 35).

At Portrane about 18 km north of Dublin a small inlier of Lower Palaeozoic rocks is exposed, particularly on the coast, at the eastern extremity of the Lower Carboniferous outcrop of the Dublin Basin. Conglomerates of Old Red Sandstone facies but Lower Carboniferous age lie above the much faulted and folded Lower Palaeozoic sequence. The elements of the situation were made clear by Gardiner and Reynolds, who about the turn of the century provided accounts of the stratigraphy of various Irish Lower Palaeozoic areas. At the north-western corner of the inlier the Old Red Sandstone conglomerate dips away north-westwards. From under it appear south-easterly dipping andesitic lavas, with higher associated volcanic rocks and some intrusive porphyritic rock, all of which are referred to in a later chapter. Laharic breccias are particularly striking with their angular and rounded clasts of ash and limestone. Calcareous tuffs from this part of the succession yield upper Ordovician brachiopods. A thin band of graptolitic shale is present. From the northern Martello Tower southwards along the rocky shore and cliffs the Portrane Limestone is exposed, in faulted contact with adjacent rocks. The limestone is of particular interest as its rich brachiopod, coral, bryozoan, and ostracode fauna is silicified and thus can be extracted sometimes in a state of good preservation by acid solution of blocks of the limestone. It is for this reason that the fossil corals are conspicuously seen weathered out by the sea, though in fact silicification of these forms is incomplete. The brachiopod fauna includes inarticulates as well as abundant orthids, dalmanellids, and other articulate forms. The age of the fauna is high Cautleyan — that is mid-Ashgill. There are thinly bedded limestones both below and above a massive member, the former showing conspicuous folding.

On the nearby island of Lambay volcanic rocks are beautifully displayed and there is graptolitic evidence that the main episode of volcanicity was completed by middle Caradoc times. There is clear evidence of slumping involving both volcanic and calcareous material.

Evidence for the presence of rocks of Llanvirn age in the small inlier of the Chair of Kildare has already been referred to. The narrow ridge of higher ground, broken by faulting, is a conspicuous element in the topography to the traveller south from Dublin. It appears to lie along the anticlinal structure first seen at Lambay and there is some geophysical indication of continuity. Andesitic flows are again present with ashy sediments below and above. There is a Caradoc shelly fauna of Soudleyan age below and a Longvillian (the next stage) one above, the latter in light greyish-olive siltstones, the brachiopod assemblage very similar to one from calcareous ashes of Longvillian age from the Bala district of North Wales. The succeeding Kildare Limestone forms the Chair Hill itself. Since the time of M'Coy's well-known work on Irish Palaeozoic fossils it has been known as a rich source. The fauna strongly resembles that of the Keisley Limestone of the North of England. Of the varied trilobite assemblage described from the limestone by W. T. Dean only one form, appropriately named *Cyphoniscus socialis*, occurs at all commonly as whole exoskeletons. Perhaps as he puts it 'this may well reflect the mode of life of the species with the small, gregarious trilobites inhabiting cavities in the reef, out of reach of currents and perhaps predators which would otherwise have disseminated their remains.' The reef limestone of the Chair of Kildare is an unbedded grey and pink rock. Towards the top are interbedded lenses of grey mudstone containing a rich shelly fauna including the brachiopods *Cliftonia*, *Cryptothyrella*, *Plectothyrella*, *Dalmanella*, *Hirnantia*, and *Eostropheodonta* (in that order of abundance). Fragments of trilobites include a record of *Dalmanitina*. Collectively this is now very well known as the 'Hirnantia' fauna in which the trilobite *Dalmanitina* is found together with a characteristic assemblage of brachiopods. The top Hirnantian Stage of the Ashgill is named, as is the nominal brachiopod, from the Hirnant Valley in the Bala district of North Wales. The fauna has been widely recognised in Europe from Ireland and the North of England through Wales to Bohemia and Poland. It occurs also in Sweden and elsewhere in the world. In Kazakhstan a similar *Dalmanitella mucronata* assemblage is reported as occurring with basal Silurian graptolites. Precise relationships and consequent definition of the Ordovician–Silurian boundary arc under international discussion. The *Hirnantia* fauna is probably in fact somewhat diachronous in occurrence.

There remain the upper Ordovician rocks of the Leinster massif, the largest area of Ordovician rocks in Ireland, details of which are not yet fully known. Palaeontological information from the area northwest of the Leinster Granite is slight. As already mentioned (page 50) the so-called Slate Quarries Formation has provided some palynological evidence for an upper Ordovician to lower Silurian age. Brück has also described three higher formations, also of greywackes: the Glen Ding Formation, Tipperkevin Formation, and Carrighill Formation (Fig. 44), which are referred to in the next chapter.

In the ground to the east and south of the Leinster Granite, as mentioned before, upper Ordovician rocks appear to follow unconformably upon the Ribband Group. The Ordovician here is well known for its volcanic rocks, making a striking, if discontinuous, belt across the geological map of Ireland from Wicklow to the Waterford coast. They are commonly calc-alkaline in character and show an evolving range of compositions from basic to acid. It is the nature of this volcanicity in upper Ordovician times which provides the substantial contrast with rocks presumably related to an oceanic environment on what was the other side of the Proto-Atlantic ocean and suggests the presence of a volcanic arc related to the then south-eastern continental margin. These palaeogeographical aspects are better appreciated after consideration of the volcanic rocks themselves. The picture is consistent with that gained from the Scottish and English evidence.

Returning to the upper Ordovician stratigraphy of the area south and east of the Leinster Granite, near Rathdrum, County Wicklow (Fig. 35), black graptolitic shales of the *peltifer* Zone are exposed in the railway cutting. Above them are tuffs and then pale

Fig. 41. Ordovician pillow lavas, Horse Rock, Helen's Bay, County Down.
Photograph by G. B. Curry

mudstones yielding a substantial shelly fauna at the old fossil locality of Slieveroe more recently excavated by J. C. Harper. Trilobites here include trinucleids, calymenids, lichids, and phacopids and the trinucleid species *Broeggerolithus* cf. *nicholsoni* is regarded as indicative of the lower Longvillian Stage of the Caradoc. Brachiopods are also well represented by orthids and strophomenids.

Farther southwards, intensely folded, cleaved, and faulted Ordovician rocks are exposed on the coast north of Courtown (Fig. 33). The prominent cleavage is axial planar to both major and minor folds and plunge is unusually variable. West and north of Courtown a tectonically deformed unconformity repeated by folding separates the upper Ordovician from the thick Ribband Group, referred to earlier, the top formation of which is the Riverchapel. Farther north, between Clones Strand and Kilmichael Point, much disturbed and partly concealed rocks of the Ribband Group are separated by exposure gap from the Arklow Head volcanics.

The upper Ordovician sequence begins with the Courtown Formation (50 m) of calcareous siltstones and sandstones with thin nodular silty limestones, formerly quarried at Courtown itself. There is a thin basal conglomerate. Various brachiopod genera are present including *Dalmanella*, *Dolerorthis*, *Glyptorthis*, *Hesperorthis*, *Howellites*, *Nicolella*, *Platystrophia*, *Porambonites*, and *Sowerbyella*. Poorly preserved trilobites of various groups are also present. The stratigraphically useful *Eirelithus* cf. *thersites* is recorded. There are common bryozoa and gastropods. The succeeding Ballinatray Formation (30 m) is of black graptolitic shales with *Nemagraptus gracilis* and species of *Amplexograptus*, *Climacograptus*, *Cryptograptus*, *Dicellograptus*, *Dicranograptus*, *Didymograptus*, *Orthograptus*, and *Pseudoclimacograptus* which did not allow D. Skevington to specify the *gracilis* as distinct from the *peltifer* Zone. The Ballymoney Formation (100–200 m) is largely of intermediate and acid tuffs, evidently both subaerial and submarine in origin. A rich shelly fauna likely to be Harnagian to Soudleyan in age includes many brachiopod genera as well as trilobites such as *Atractopyge*, *Broeggerolithus*, and *Trinodus*. The youngest Gorey Rhyolite Formation, several hundred metres in thickness, forms south-westerly trending inland ridges.

Farther south-westwards again, at Enniscorthy, reviewed with these other upper Ordovician localities by P. J. Brenchley, J. C. Harper, I. Mitchell, and M. Romano, the purple and brown slates of the lower Ordovician are again succeeded unconformably by a mixed succession with Caradoc brachiopod and trilobite assemblages, graptolitic shales, and volcanics. In south-west Wexford the Duncannon Volcanic Formation (320 m) is in mechanical contact with the lower Ordovician or older rocks of the Booley Bay Formation mentioned above (page 51). Intermediate and acid lavas and pyroclastic rocks are associated with graptolite shales of the lower Caradoc. The succeeding Arthurstown Formation (400 m) of siltstones and mudstones gives way to the mud-dominant Ballyhack Formation (400 m). Graptolites of the *clingani* Zone occur here. The Duncannon Group as a whole is completed by the Campile Volcanic Formation (1,000+ m), largely of rhyolites.

Lastly, the Ordovician succession near Tramore on the Waterford coast includes thick volcanics to be described in Chapter 6. Associated are fossiliferous calcareous sediments. In faulted contact with the Tramore Shales, already mentioned as of uncertain age, is the well known Tramore Limestone. These dark blue arenaceous and argillaceous nodular limestones thin northwards from some 80 m until only a 3 m calcareous siltstone is present. The limestones yield a rich brachiopod fauna of Baltic aspect. Trilobites represented here include *Cybele*, *Eirelithus thersites*, *Encrinuroides*, *Flexicalymene*, *Isotelus*, *Remopleurides*, and *Trinodus*.

The succeeding Lower Tramore Volcanic Formation is from 250 to 2,000 m thick, mainly of rhyolites and andesites. A basal shale member yields *Nemagraptus gracilis* and *Diplograptus multidens* occurs in other shales associated with the volcanics. A thick development of rhyolites of the Upper Tramore Volcanic Formation completes the succession.

W. I. Mitchell, H. Carlisle, N. Hiller, and R. Addison have recently emphasised the growing impression of a consistent upper Ordovician biostratigraphy in the belt from Courtown to Tramore. Mrs Carlisle considers the Tramore Limestone and its equivalents (at Courtown and Bellewstown) to have a Llandeilo rather than Caradoc fauna and the presence of *Nemagraptus gracilis* above it is now consistent with this picture. Higher faunas range through the Costonian, Harnagian, and Soudleyan stages.

BIBLIOGRAPHY

BRENCHLEY, P. J., HARPER, J. C., MITCHELL, W. I., & ROMANO, M. 1977 A re-appraisal of some Ordovician successions in Eastern Ireland. *Proc. R. Ir. Acad.*, **77B**, 65–85.

BRENCHLEY, P. J., HARPER, J. C., & SKEVINGTON, D. 1967 Lower Ordovician shelly and graptolitic faunas from south-eastern Ireland. *Proc. R. Ir. Acad.*, **65B**, 385–390.

BRENCHLEY, P. J. & TREAGUS, J. E. 1970 The stratigraphy and structure of the Ordovician rocks between Courtown and Kilmichael Point, Co. Wexford. *Proc. R. Ir. Acad.*, **69B**, 83–102.

BRÜCK, P. M. 1975 A map and outline description of the Lower Palaeozoic rocks of S. W. Wicklow and S. Kildare (One-inch sheets 128 and 129). *Geol Surv. Ir. Rep. Ser.*, 75/2, pp. 6.

BRÜCK, P. M., POTTER, T. L., & DOWNIE, C. 1974 The Lower Palaeozoic stratigraphy of the northern part of the Leinster massif. *Proc. R. Ir. Acad.*, **74B**, 75–84.

BRÜCK, P. M. & REEVES, T. J. 1976 Stratigraphy, sedimentology and structure of the Bray Group in County Wicklow and south County Dublin. *Proc. R. Ir. Acad.*, **76B**, 53–77.

COWIE, J. W., RUSHTON, A. W. A., & STUBBLEFIELD, C. J. 1972 A correlation of Cambrian rocks in the British Isles. *Geol. Soc. Lond. Spec. Rep.*, 2, pp. 42.

CRIMES, T. P. 1976 Trace fossils from the Bray Group (Cambrian) at Howth, Co. Dublin. *Geol. Surv. Ir. Bull.*, 2, 53–67.

CRIMES, T. P. & CROSSLEY, J. D. 1968 The stratigraphy, sedimentology, ichnology and structure of the Lower Palaeozoic rocks of part of north-eastern Co. Wexford. *Proc. R. Ir. Acad.*, **67B**, 185–215.

DEAN, W. T. 1971 The trilobites of the Chair of Kildare Limestone (Upper Ordovician) of eastern Ireland. *Palaeontogr. Soc. (Monogr.) Part 1*, 1–60.

HOLLAND, C. H. (Ed.) 1974 *Cambrian of the British Isles, Norden, and Spitsbergen.* John Wiley & Sons, London, pp. 300.

MITCHELL, W. I. 1977 The Ordovician brachiopoda from Pomeroy, Co. Tyrone. *Palaeontogr. Soc. (Monogr.)*, pp. 138.

SANDERS, I. S. & MORRIS, J. H. 1978 Evidence for Caledonian subduction from greywacke detritus in the Longford–Down inlier. *J. Earth Sci. R. Dubl. Soc.*, 1, 53–62.

SHANNON, P. M. 1978 The stratigraphy and sedimentology of the Lower Palaeozoic rocks of south-east Co. Wexford. *Proc. R. Ir. Acad.*, **78B**, 249–267.

SKEVINGTON, D. 1974 Controls influencing the composition and distribution of Ordovician graptolite faunal provinces. *In* Rickards, R. B., Jackson, D. E., and Hughes, C. P. (Eds.). Graptolite studies in honour of O. M. B. Bulman. *Spec. Pap. Palaeont.*, 13, 59–73.

VAN LUNSEN, H. A. & MAX, M. D. 1975 The geology of Howth and Ireland's Eye, Co. Dublin. *Geol. J.*, 10, 35–58.

WILLIAMS, A., STRACHAN, I., BASSETT, D. A., DEAN, W. T., INGHAM, J. K., WRIGHT, A. D., & WHITTINGTON, H. B. 1972 A correlation of Ordovician rocks in the British Isles. *Geol. Soc. Lond. Spec. Rep.*, 3, pp. 74.

WRIGHT, A. D.   1963 The fauna of the Portrane Limestone. 1. The inarticulate
                          brachiopods. *Bull. Br. Mus. nat. Hist. (Geol.)*, **8**, 223–254.
WRIGHT, A. D.   1968 A westward extension of the upper Ashgillian *Hirnantia*
                          fauna. *Lethaia*, **1**, 352–367.

5

SILURIAN

C. H. Holland

When J. C. Harper summarised knowledge of the Lower Palaeozoic rocks of Ireland in 1948, relatively little was known of its Silurian strata. At the time of writing of the Geological Society of London's Silurian correlation paper to be published in 1971, additions had been relatively few, though of some significance particularly in the north-west where research workers from Imperial College London, the University of Oxford, and Trinity College Dublin had been active in investigation and publication. Since then much has been achieved, though the finally satisfying synthesis remains somewhat elusive.

Taking a western area first, there are two tracts of Silurian in Mayo and Galway (Fig. 16), separated by the wider extent of the Ordovician outcrop referred to in Chapter 3. To the north there is a belt from Clare Island (Fig. 35), through the Louisburgh area of the south coast of Clew Bay, and thence through the splendid quartzite peaks of the Croagh Patrick range. To the south a discontinuous strip runs south of Killary Harbour and on towards Lough Mask and Lough Corrib. The structure of the area is referred to in Chapter 7.

The Telychian, uppermost stage of the Llandovery (Table 7), is well represented in the south by a clastic succession up to 600 m thick, which rests on an irregular surface of Ordovician rocks or of Connemara Schists. D. J. W. Piper has brought together a rationalisation of the stratigraphical nomenclature (built up by various workers over many years) and relationships, as shown in Figure 42. The basal Lough Mask Formation (0–170 m) begins with variable breccias and conglomerates, but is typically of massive and cross-stratified red sandstones, with interbedded thin siltstones and mudstones and some cobble conglomerates. It is probably a braided fluviatile deposit. Keratophyre is present in the lower part of the formation in the east. The Kilbride Formation

(up to 340 m), is of green and grey sandstones, quartzites with vertical burrows (*Skolithos*), and some microconglomerates and siltstones. There are brachiopod faunas including *Eocoelia curtisi* of C5 (middle Telychian) age in the lower part of the Kilbride Formation (the Annelid Grit of earlier nomenclature) as a nearshore marine environment becomes represented, and its upper part (Finny School Beds) shows a deeper water *Clorinda* community. The overlying Tonalee Formation (up to 75 m) is largely of mudstones with the bright purple and red colouration which is widely indicative of the *Monoclimacis crenulata* Zone, the top graptolite zone of the Llandovery. A. M. Ziegler and W. S. McKerrow have suggested that such colouration might have arisen from oxidised soils in the absence of plant cover, and, in conditions of transgression, might be preserved in marine sediment offshore and in deeper seas in the absence of the biological reworking which would characterise near-shore regimes. Some thin green feldspathic tuffs are also present.

The overlying Gowlaun Formation (30–370 m) of the eastern part of the belt is believed to be diachronous so that it forms the lateral equivalent of the Llandovery sequence in the west. It probably ranges up into the Wenlock. The formation is characterised by a mudstone facies with lenticular conglomerates and coarse or medium, grey green, massive sandstones. Thinner bedded, graded sandstones are common higher in the succession. The beds are poorly fossiliferous though a *crenulata* Zone fauna is recorded by R. B. Rickards from an exposure in Kilbride. Piper has interpreted this unit as the deposits of a slope area and submarine fans between a shallow continental shelf and deeper basins in which turbidites accumulated.

The Llandovery is not well represented in the northern belt (its thickness is only 6 m in the Croagh

Patrick range), but in the Wenlock a more comprehensive picture emerges involving evidence from both Silurian tracts. In the north, around Louisburgh (Fig. 35) a basal banded formation (over 230 m) of laminated red siltstones with bands of green and pink sandstone represents intertidal conditions. Small-scale cross-stratification, convolute bedding, extensive burrowing, and polygonal desiccation cracks are commonly seen. Carbonate concretions are abundant. Elongate lenses of sandstone with their erosional bases reflect tidal creeks in which locally ash fall tuffs are preserved. A succeeding green or buff sandstone formation (400 m) shows much evidence of channels. Above this, a red or green laminated siltstone formation (100–290 m) shows ubiquitous small-scale ripple-drift cross-stratification and there are many burrows,

together with convolutions and desiccation cracks. It appears to represent a return to intertidal conditions. The sedimentary structures, as is the case with the metamorphic clasts of the earlier formation, are indicative of a northerly origin. The succession is closed with a thick (more than 530 m) formation of pink or green pebbly arkoses and arkosic sandstones, seen for example at Roonah Quay where channels are well displayed. The channel deposits show large-scale cross-stratification and some slumping. These poorly sorted sandstones with their abundant channels and presence of calcrete concretions indicate a fluviatile environment, perhaps in braided conditions. Sedimentary structures again suggest a northerly origin.

A very similar succession is seen in the north-western part of Clare Island, though here an older

SERIES	BIOZONES		STAGES
Ludlow			Ludfordian
	bohemicus		
	leintwardinensis		
	tumescens	incipiens	Gorstian
	scanicus		
	nilssoni		
Wenlock	ludensis		Homerian
	lundgreni		
	ellesae		Sheinwoodian
	linnarssoni		
	rigidus		
	riccartonensis		
	murchisoni		
	centrifugus		
Llandovery	crenulata		Telychian
	griestoniensis		
	crispus		
	turriculatus		Fronian
	sedgwickii		
	convolutus		Idwian
	gregarius		
	cyphus		Rhuddanian
	vesiculosus ≃ atavus		
	acuminatus		
	persculptus		

Table 7.

Silurian (Llandovery to Ludlow only) chronostratigraphical and biostratigraphical divisions. The Gorstian Stage comprises the former Eltonian and Bringewoodian; the Ludfordian Stage comprises the former Leintwardinian and Whitcliffian.

formation (18–30 m) can be recognised below the banded formation referred to above and following unconformably upon the metamorphic basement. A sheet-like basal conglomerate is locally developed below the cream coloured sandstones which form the bulk of the formation. W. E. A. Phillips has drawn up a most detailed picture of palaeogeographical conditions in the region, with a northerly source area of metamorphic rocks like those of the Deer Park Complex being also the site of the contemporaneous volcanoes marginal to the Silurian trough. Bipolar (herringbone) cross-stratification, orientation of oscillation ripple marks, and other features are used to reconstruct a shoreline trending somewhat south of west, across which the flood and ebb tides of the time moved respectively north-westwards and south-eastwards. The evidence of the actual source area itself is believed to be lost as a result of movement along the Leck fault which provides the northern boundary of the Silurian outcrop in Clare Island.

Farther eastwards, the variable quartzites of the Croagh Patrick range are thought to represent sand infillings of a submarine canyon which originally carried material to the south.

In the southern Lower Palaeozoic tract of North Galway the Wenlock succession is well exposed to the south of Killary Harbour where it is dominated by the Lettergesh Formation (about 1,520 m) representing the maximum extent of marine transgression in the area. Poorly sorted and often graded sandstones are associated with conglomerates, breccias, and silty mudstones. Angular grains of quartz, feldspar, and rock fragments (including jasper) are set in a fine matrix which has been chloritised. The rocks can be described as arkosic greywackes and their common grading, sharp bases to sandstone beds, and lateral continuity of individual beds all suggest a turbiditic origin. Rickards and Smyth have recognised both *Cyrtograptus murchisoni* and *Monograptus riccartonensis* zones from the Clonbur area between Lough Mask and Lough Corrib. A younger graptolite

fauna of middle Wenlock age including *Monoclimacis flumendosae* and *Monograptus flemingii* was collected from a locality near Owenduff Bridge in the lower part of the formation.

The succeeding Glencraff Formation (65 m) is similar but of finer grain size. The Lough Muck Formation (200–280 m) reflects a return to shallower water conditions and M. G. Laird and W. S. McKerrow have detailed the good evidence of a passage through continental rise and slope conditions into shallow marine shelf conditions as the formation is ascended. The succession is well displayed north of Lough Muck and on the southern slopes of Knockraff. Mudstones and siltstones are associated with sandstones, arkosic in composition but better sorted than those of the earlier part of the succession. Low in the formation a shelly fauna is recorded from Knockraff which includes brachiopods and gastropods as main components associated with bryozoans, corals, crinoids, and trilobites. The shells have been transported but are certainly dominated by the species *Eocoelia sulcata*. Higher in the formation the middle Wenlock graptolite *Monoclimacis flumendosae* is again present and there are other shelly assemblages. The siltstones show a succession from chaotic slump deposits, giving way to rotational slumps and then to abundant cross-bedded sandstones with common marine benthonic organisms. The succession is closed by the Salrock Formation (some 815 m) dominantly of red mudstones and siltstones. The beds are well exposed around Killary Bay Little. To the east greenish beds are more common. The direction of derivation is from the west or north-west. *Lingula* and poorly preserved gastropods are the lingering marine or quasi-marine fauna.

Along strike to the north-east of the area so far considered, the three small outcrops of Silurian rocks at Charlestown, Lisbellaw, and Pomeroy (Fig. 35) have been known for a long time and serve to illustrate the variable character of the basin margin in Llandovery times. At Charlestown the situation is

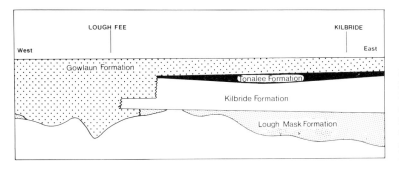

Fig. 42. Diagrammatic vertical section to show the relationship between Llandovery and lowest Wenlock lithostratigraphical units of north Galway (after Piper 1967). Piper (1972) has subsequently treated the Gowlaun as a member of the succeeding Lettergesh Formation.

similar to that in Mayo with brachiopod faunas of C4 age and some coral limestone. At Lisbellaw slide-conglomerates with clasts from the Dalradian and from the Tyrone Igneous Group are sandwiched within graptolitic shales of the *Monograptus gregarius* Zone. At Pomeroy is an entirely graptolitic mudstone and siltstone sequence faulted against the Ordovician but spanning much of the lower, all of the middle, and the basal part of the upper Llandovery.

The most extensive tract of Silurian rocks in Ireland is that of the Longford–Down massif, referred to already in respect of its Ordovician rocks. The richly graptolitic sections in places along the north-east coast have long been known. Charles Lapworth, reflecting on the close comparison between the Coalpit Bay succession and that in the Southern Uplands of Scotland, wrote that 'The Coalpit Bay Division of the County Down Silurians has yielded all the Graptolites of the Birkhill Shales [Rhuddanian, Idwian, and part of the Fronian], with the exception of one special group, viz., that of the *Rastrites maximus* zone [equivalent to the lower part of the *Monograptus turriculatus* Zone], which lies at the very summit of the Moffat series.' These graptolitic shales pass upwards into massive greywackes (Fig. 43). Northwards, beyond a fault gap, older greywackes are latterly equivalent to them. At Tieveshilly, where (Fig. 35) the youngest graptolitic beds of this part of Ireland are thought to be present, *Monograptus riccartonensis*, a lower Wenlock (Sheinwoodian) zonal index, is commonly present. Much of the Ards peninsula forming the eastern extremity of the Longford–Down massif is of greywackes occurring in various fault blocks.

A recent detailed investigation by E. A. O'Connor of the Shercock–Aghnamullen district (Fig. 37), Counties Cavan and Monaghan, is probably representative of the central part of the massif. Here, as elsewhere within it, drift cover is substantial and in places drumlins dot the landscape. The local succession is as follows:

Silurian	Shercock Formation (*c.* 3,000 m)	Lough Avaghan Formation (*c.* 2,800 m)
	Taghart Mountain Formation (500–1,700 m)	
Ordovician	Kehernaghkilly Formation (*c.* 100 m)	

The fault-bounded strip of Ordovician black graptolitic shales has already been mentioned. The Taghart Mountain Formation is of quartz mudstones with convolute bedding and sole markings, alternating with bands also at least several centimetres thick of soft silty shales. The beds mostly young north-westwards, though the dip is generally to the south-east. In the Shercock Formation flaggy to massive greywackes are interbedded with black shales and greenish or greyish silty shales. Many of the greywackes are graded and sole markings are common. Plentiful graptolites in scattered localities indicate that the Rhuddanian and Idwian stages of the lower Llandovery are represented from the *Cystograptus vesiculosus* Zone to the *Monograptus gregarius* Zone. As in the older formation, the beds tend to young north-westwards and dip south-eastwards. There are two outcrops of which the south-eastern is faulted against the Taghart Mountain Formation. In the north-western outcrop, however, the inverted Shercock Formation appears to continue the north-westerly younging seen in the probably older Taghart Mountain Formation.

The Lough Avaghan Formation is lithologically similar to the Shercock Formation, though generally somewhat coarser in grain size. Quartz pebble greywackes are more common. Palaeontological evidence is sparse, an approximately zonal level of diagnosis being achieved only for the *Monograptus cyphus* Zone represented in the lower beds of the formation.

Proximal and distal turbidites are present in the Silurian succession. A northerly source is indicated, probably from the Tyrone Igneous Group. All the finer beds are prominently cleaved and the beds face downwards as well as upwards on the cleavage. Thus pre-cleavage folding and perhaps thrust slicing are involved, as are cross-folds following upon the main phase of folding and its associated cleavage. It is possible that sedimentary (slump) tectonics may be involved. Elsewhere in the Longford–Down massif certain thick structureless quartzites appear to be grain flow deposits and there are certainly slide-conglomerates and slump structures.

In general the appearance of massive greywackes in the Irish Lower Palaeozoic successions appears to become younger southwards. Thus they are already present in the Ordovician of the northern strip of the Longford–Down massif. In the area near Lough Acanon there appears to be continuity of Ordovician to Silurian graptolitic shales with greywackes present only in the lower part of the Llandovery as is the case in the Shercock-Aghnamullen district some 8 km to the east.

Projecting the strike of the Lower Palaeozoic rocks of the Longford–Down massif south-westwards, we meet the inliers of Slieve Aughty and those centred upon Slieve Bernagh. These are the north-westerly members of a scattering of Lower Palaeozoic inliers in south-central Ireland. Surrounded by Old Red Sandstone rocks of strong topographical expression,

Fig. 43. (above) Sole markings—loaded flute moulds—on inverted Silurian greywacke, near Galloways Burn, Donaghadee, County Down.

Photograph, Geological Survey of Northern Ireland

Fig. 44. (below) Carrighill Formation (Silurian), north bank of River Liffey, west of Kilcullen, County Kildare. Graded greywackes with S1 of cleaved tops steeper than bedding.

Photograph by P. M. Brück

they contrast strongly with the surrounding country floored by the Lower Carboniferous.

In the Slieve Aughty inlier the regional strike of the pre-Old Red Sandstone rocks is seen to have swung to a more westerly direction. The inlier is crossed by a series of strike faults (Fig. 39), some at least of which were re-activated in post-Carboniferous times. G. T. Emo has defined three formations of Silurian, or partly Silurian, age. The Gortnagleav Formation (more than 650 m) is of unfossiliferous greenish or mottled mudstones, siltstones, and greywacke sandstones with some thin lavas, faulted against the Ordovician in the north of the area. The much thicker (more than 2,500 m) Derryfadda Formation is of coarser, green, proximal turbidites interbedded with siltstones and mudstones. The beds young northwards but dip to the south and are crossed by a number of strike faults. One locality has yielded graptolites of the *Monoclimacis griestoniensis* Zone. Emo and Smith have obtained confirmatory palynological evidence.

A wide area of the southern part of the inlier is occupied by the Killanena Formation (more than 3,000 m) of rocks thinner bedded and finer grained than those below, though grey-greenish greywackes again alternate with laminated and cross-laminated fine sandstones, siltstones, and mudstones. Again the beds young northwards, dip to the south, and are affected by strike faults. Both distal and proximal turbidites are present and slump structures are common. This formation contains more material suitable for palynological investigation. Miospores and acritarchs both indicate a mid-Silurian (upper Llandovery to lower Wenlock) age. One assemblage is of Tremadoc to Arenig aspect and appears to represent that reworking of early Ordovician acritarchs which is so widespread in the British Isles. There are some coarse turbiditic sandstones near the top of the Gortnagleav Formation which may represent a prelude to those found in the Derryfadda Formation. The Killanena Formation is evidently partly at least equivalent in age to the latter.

The inlier of Slieve Bernagh, the Broadford Mountains, and the Arra Mountains is cut by the southern end of Lough Derg and the River Shannon in an area of outstanding natural beauty. The presence of Llandovery black shales, the first such beds to become known in the southern half of Ireland, was established by R. B. Rickards and J. Archer in the small area already referred to in terms of its Ordovician rocks (Fig. 40). The *Akidograptus acuminatus*, *C. vesiculosus*, and *M. turriculatus* zones are present. Dr A. M. Flegg has identified mottled siltstones and shales of *Monograptus crispus* Zone age elsewhere in Slieve Bernagh. The first turbidites in the inlier appeared during *crispus* Zone times and continued until the late Wenlock. Their arrival was thus roughly contemporaneous with that of the turbidites of Slieve Aughty but later than that recorded in the Longford–Down massif. These higher beds comprise conglomerates, greywacke sandstones, siltstones, banded mudstones, and slates (as at Killaloe). Dr A. J. Weir, who provided the first substantial account of the geology of these areas, has more recently recognised the upper Wenlock (Homerian) age of an allochthonous assemblage including brachiopods, molluscs, and trilobites in a thin conglomerate found in the Arra Mountains. *Meristina obtusa* is present. Enteletaceids are the dominant brachiopods though rhynchonellids are also prominent. There is very little additional evidence of shelly fossils within this thick, predominantly basinal, succession (over 8,000 m in Slieve Bernagh and the Broadford Mountains).

The remaining Silurian rocks of Ireland lie to the south-east of a Navan–Nenagh line (and its continuation), whose significance continues to be debated. These outcrops can be considered in turn in three groups: those of Leinster, the south-central area, and the Dingle peninsula in the south-west.

The graptolitic Silurian rocks of Balbriggan are well exposed in coastal section described by R. B. Rickards, V. Burns, and J. Archer (Figs. 35 and 45). Minor faulting eliminates the *Glyptograptus persculptus* Zone at the base of the succession. Interrupted only by further minor faults the succession continues to the *M. turriculatus* Zone. Above this greywackes are largely present for the remainder of the Llandovery. Graptolitic mudstones of Wenlock age continue into the *M. riccartonensis* Zone. There are then associated greywackes, the graptolitic evidence persisting into the *Cyrtograptus lundgreni* Zone. A development of banded bluish mudstones in the *C. murchisoni* Zone recalls the Brathay Flag lithology and indeed the whole Silurian sequence at Balbriggan is directly comparable with that in the English Lake District. The completeness of the Balbriggan graptolitic succession is probably diminished only by the effects of minor faulting and the graptolitic biostratigraphical record is certainly the best available in Ireland. Inland exposures are much poorer but Miss V. Burns continues to accumulate graptolitic evidence from this unpromising ground. Some 50 Silurian graptolite species are now known from the inlier. Above the graptolitic sequence of the Balbriggan Formation (greater than 560 m), which is also taken to include a thin development of black shales of the Ordovician *Dicellograptus anceps* Zone, are largely unfossiliferous greywacke sandstones of the Skerries Formation (more than 350 m), which have yielded fragmentary graptolites and must be of high Wenlock age and possibly younger.

At Portrane, between Balbriggan and Dublin, a small area of greywacke sandstones, siltstones, and mudstones, regarded as in thrust contact with the Ordovician, has been assigned to the Silurian only upon lithological comparison. In the Kildare inlier, along strike to the south-west, black shales, olive and red mudstones, and coarser greenish beds similar to those at Portrane can all be dated as Silurian, D. C. Palmer and L. M. Magee having discovered graptolitic evidence of the *M. gregarius* Zone in the black shales.

The older Lower Palaeozoic formations west of the Leinster Granite have already been referred to together with the possibly middle Ordovician to lower Silurian age of the fourth of these, the Slate Quarries Formation (40 m). There follow in upward sequence the Glen Ding (430 m), Tipperkevin (110 m), and Carrighill (760 m) formations. All are of grey, pale greenish, or brownish greywackes with associated slates and with slaty tops (Fig. 44). The lithology is suggestive of a Silurian age and Brück and Downie have recorded diagnostic assemblages of chitinozoa indicating a Silurian age for the Glen Ding Formation and a specifically Llandovery age for the succeeding Tipperkevin Formation, one of their samples coming from within 4 m of the top of the latter. Crinoid ossicles and rare bryozoan and brachiopod fragments occur in the two highest formations.

The greywackes become generally finer upwards. In the Glen Ding Formation their matrix is largely of sericite and chlorite. In the Tipperkevin Formation it is largely illite, whereas the Carrighill Formation has an unusual carbonate matrix mainly of iron-rich dolomite. This overprints some chlorite and sericite, which can themselves be seen to corrode grains showing recrystallisation post-dating stresses related to the formation of the regional (S1) cleavage. Graded bedding, convolute bedding, flute moulds and other characteristic sedimentary structures are commonly present. The increasingly varied sequences of Bouma intervals present in individual graded units as the succession is ascended contribute to evidence that proximal turbidites gave way in time to those of more distal origin. Derivation was from the eastern quadrant throughout.

The smallest of the Silurian inliers of south-central Ireland is that of Knockshigowna Hill (Fig. 35) where these rocks form a ridge less than 3 km² in extent. It lies within the horseshoe of Lower Palaeozoic inliers of Slieve Aughty, Slieve Bernagh, Slieve Phelim, and Slieve Bloom. The succession described by B. M. Prendergast comprises 500 m of greywackes, flaggy siltstones, and shales followed in the axis of a syncline by some 150 m of conglomerates. Shales associated with the greywackes yield *M. riccartonensis* and *Monoclimacis vomerinus* indicative of a lower Wenlock (Sheinwoodian) age. The conglomerate contains clasts of quartz, jasper, and chert from 1 to 10 cm in size. In sandy pockets within it an upper Wenlock (Homerian) shelly fauna is found, dominated by

Fig. 45. Geological map of the Balbriggan inlier (after Rickards, Burns, and Archer 1973).

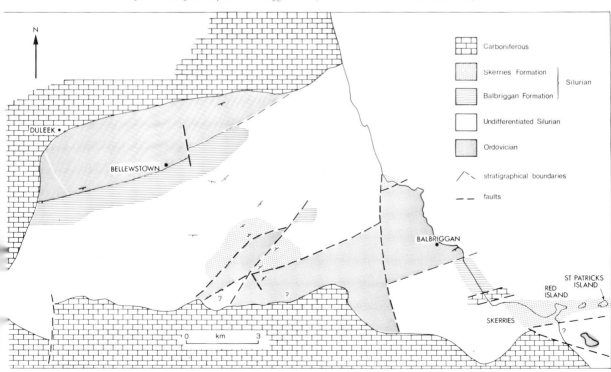

brachiopods but with bivalves, gastropods, trilobites, and other forms. The brachiopods include *Eoplectodonta duvalii*, *Isorthis clivosa*, *Leptaena depressa*, and *Meristina obtusa*. The assemblage appears to have been derived from a low intertidal to subtidal environment, though its state of preservation is not indicative of prolonged transportation.

The complex pattern of inliers of Silurian rocks appearing within the high, rolling, and much wooded Old Red Sandstone country of the Slieve Bloom mountains is still under investigation, but J. Feehan has already shown that the facies is the familiar one of greywackes of various grades and siltstones. Sole markings are not commonly seen but there are indications of a north-easterly derivation. A graptolite fauna discovered by W. P. Loughlin from the upper part of the succession is of *M. riccartonensis* Zone age. Palynological samples from the relatively isolated outcrop along the Capard ridge in the north-east of the Slieve Bloom area are dominated by abundant well-preserved Wenlock spores.

The relatively large area of Lower Palaeozoic rocks forming the generally elevated country of the Slieve Phelim–Devilsbit inlier are very largely confined to the late Wenlock *C. lundgreni* Zone, though this is probably more than 1,000 m thick. In the south R. J. P. Doran has given detailed description of the repetitive sequence of greywackes, laminated siltstones, and mudstones, assigning the whole to a single Hollyford Formation. The rocks are in places stained red to a depth at least 240 m below the unconformable Upper Old Red Sandstone. Graptolites are found at many localities in the coarser, brown weathering, 'biscuity' laminae of the laminated siltstones. *Pristiograptus dubius*, *Monograptus flemingii*, *P. pseudodubius*, *Cyrtograptus lundgreni*, *C. hamatus*, and *Paraplectograptus eiseli* are recorded, those listed first being the most common. A quiet water regime was evidently interrupted sporadically by distal turbidity currents forming the graded beds now seen as greywackes. The dominant flow was southwards, though farther north in the inlier there are indications of an easterly or north-easterly derivation. D. C. Palmer has shown that the supposedly Ludlow rocks of the north-eastern corner of the inlier (the Devilsbit Mountain district) are in fact of *Pristiograptus ludensis* Zone age, the first indication of this highest Wenlock graptolite zone in Ireland. *P. ludensis* is associated with *Monograptus auctus*. Apart from graptolites and orthoconic nautiloids other fossils are relatively rare throughout the whole inlier. R. N. Cope analysed those present, recognising that the greywackes carry derived faunas of thick-shelled brachiopods and crinoids, certain micaceous siltstones show a terrestrially derived association of plant fragments and a phyllocarid, whereas possibly benthonic thin-shelled brachiopods, small bivalves, and crinoids occur in the more common laminated siltstones.

In the remaining three inliers of the Galty Mountains, Slievenamon, and the Comeraghs the successions are now known to include rocks older than Wenlock. In the Galty Mountains area (Fig. 46) thickly bedded, grey and greenish-grey greywackes, siltstones, and mudstones of the Inchacomb Formation (550–650 m) are followed by dark grey to black siltier greywackes and shales of the Ballygeana Formation (1,275 m). The former consists of two members, the older of which forms the core of an anticline crossing the area from west to east. The middle of the lower member has purple mudstones and siltstones interbedded with the normal grey and greenish beds. The upper member contains a high proportion of calcareous siltstones and mudstones, interbedded with dark green to grey mudstones, micaceous silty sandstones, and minor greywackes.

The dark grey to black shales of the Ballygeana Formation yield graptolite faunas, the lowest record being that of a single diplograptid (associated with trilobite fragments) of presumed Llandovery age at a level of 188 m above the base of the formation. In higher beds A. A. Jackson recognised three successive graptolite assemblages. The first typified by the presence of *Cyrtograptus centrifugus*, *Monograptus priodon*, *Monoclimacis vomerinus*, and *Pristiograptus* suggests the occurrence of the *centrifugus* Zone. The second yields *Monograptus riccartonensis*, *M. firmus*, *M. firmus sedberghensis*, *M. priodon*, and *Plectograptus* of the *riccartonensis* Zone. The third fauna is of *Monograptus flexilis flexilis*, *Monoclimacis flumendosae*, *Monograptus flemingii*, *Pristiograptus dubius*, *P. menaghini*, and *Cyrtograptus*, the assemblage indicating the *Cyrtograptus linnarssoni* Zone.

The Silurian rocks here form a relatively subdued topography compared with the magnificent range of the Galty Mountains of Upper Old Red Sandstone and the lesser hills of the same rocks to the south and west. The best exposures of the Silurian are in streams draining the Galty Mountains, though the relatively poorly exposed lower lying areas have useful old roadstone quarries. The nature of the exposures together with the effects of cleavage and of bedding plane slip have tended to obscure evidence of sole markings. The modal development of each formation is a 'middle absent' Bouma sequence though within each there is an upward change in relative proportions, 'top absent' sequences giving way to 'bottom absent' sequences as the formation is ascended. The turbidites are neither clearly distal nor clearly proximal in character. Some conglomeratic beds are present in the area within certain graded units or as channel infillings. Rhyolites and orthoquartzites are conspicuous amongst the clasts.

Details of the roughly rectangular area of Lower Palaeozoic rocks of the Ninemilehouse Tableland within its rim of higher Old Red Sandstone ground were unknown until J. R. J. Colthurst established the pattern of north-easterly strike (Fig. 47), the sequence younging north-westwards except for the effects of folds of relatively small amplitude. The succession comprises:

(4) South Lodge Formation (possibly more than 3,400 m)
(3) Rathclarish Formation (340 m)
(2) Ahenny Formation (about 3,000 m)
(1) Carricktriss Formation (more than 800 m)

The first formation is poorly exposed in the southeast. Much is of a volcano-clastic origin, though there are convoluted siltstones and black shales. There is faulted contact with the Ahenny Formation though this has bands of tuff in its basal part. Grey banded slates and blue black slates are characteristic of the Ahenny Formation and are well seen in old slate quarries. About the middle of the succession is a characteristic Brownstown Member (230 m) of graded and imbricate conglomerates with clasts of varied composition up to 2 cm in length in a muddy matrix. The overlying Rathclarish Formation is of well developed, graded, grey greywackes, siltstones, and mudstones typically turbiditic in character. The South Lodge Formation forms a little more than half of the inlier and is characterised by greenish greywackes and slates. Most of the greywackes have a calcareous matrix and weather easily to a brownish material. These beds are seen in road cuttings along the Callan to Clonmel (T6) road. As in the Galty Mountains area, sole markings are not easily seen. The upper three formations are best interpreted as turbidites, those of the Ahenny Formation being distal in character, the remainder proximal. J. R. J. Colthurst and D. G. Smith have made effective use of micropalaeontology in the biostratigraphy of this succession, in which the only available macrofaunal evidence is of a few unidentifiable graptolites from the South Lodge Formation. Acritarchs, chitinozoa, scolecodonts, and spores have been recovered variously from the samples, though they are usually rare.

The Carricktriss Formation (Ribband Group) contains Upper Cambrian (Merioneth Series) and Tremadoc-Arenig acritarchs. The latter may possibly be reworked. The two middle formations certainly contain early Ordovician assemblages in which reworking is involved. Silurian (probably upper Llandovery) acritarchs have been obtained from near the base of the Ahenny Formation and the Rathclarish Formation also contains trilete spores indicative of the Silurian. The South Lodge Formation is shown to

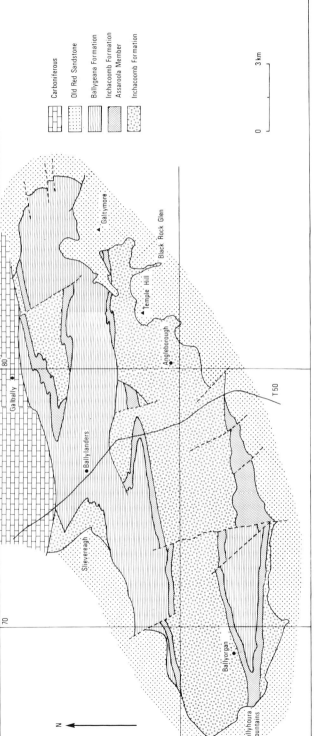

Fig. 46. Geological map of the Galty Mountains inlier. Information kindly supplied by Audrey A. Jackson.

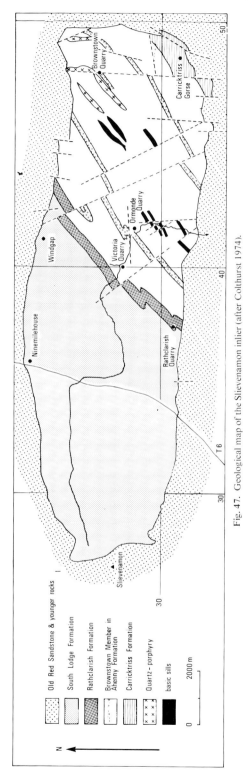

Fig. 47. Geological map of the Slievenamon inlier (after Colthurst 1974).

South Lodge Formation

Rathclarish Formation

Brownstown Member in Ahenny Formation

Carricktriss Formation

Quartz - porphyry

basic sills

Old Red Sandstone & younger rocks

2000 m

0

N

be Wenlock by the presence high in the sequence of abundant trilete spores, almost entirely of one type. The samples lack the diversity of Ludlow assemblages. These Silurian rocks of the Slievenamon inlier have been referred to collectively as the Kilcullen Group, which, as indicated, must be separated from the local Ribband Group by a substantial stratigraphical break.

The Lower Palaeozoic rocks of the Comeragh Mountains area are separated from the Slievenamon inlier by the narrow Lower Carboniferous and Old Red Sandstone tract of the Suir valley. The succession has been investigated by S. R. Penney, who sees possibilities of close lithological comparison with the Slievenamon succession, particularly in the case of the Ballyhest Member, equivalent to the Brownstown Member of Slievenamon and well developed in the north. The Comeraghs appear to have been closer to the source of the submarine fans represented by these members. There are east-north-east to west-south-west folds across the area and strike faulting is probably significant. The Silurian Ballindysert Formation here follows directly upon the Ribband Group and yet bears close lithological comparison with the Ahenny Formation of Slievenamon. Biostratigraphical evidence from the Ballindysert Formation comes largely from Llandovery acritarchs occurring with reworked Ordovician forms, though there is also a single record of an *Orthograptus*, indicative simply of an age older than upper Llandovery.

Attempting to recognise general relationships in all the Silurian inliers of south-central Ireland, Harper and Brenchley distinguish between the north-western inliers of Slieve Aughty and Slieve Bernagh–Arra Mountains and those of the Cratloe Hills, Slieve Phelim, Knockshigowna, and Slieve Bloom. Shelly faunas (though certainly rare) are present along with graptolites in the latter groups, whereas the north-western inliers tend to be devoid of macrofossils. The carrying of a shelly fauna into the Arra Mountains succession has already been mentioned. A north-westerly facing palaeoslope is thus postulated, its line perhaps related to the Navan-Nenagh line already mentioned. Weir has subsequently written of a Limerick–Tipperary shelf in contrast to the Silurian basin of Slieve Aughty and Slieve Bernagh.

There remains for consideration the Dingle penin-sula, County Kerry, an area relatively remote from the Lower Palaeozoic inliers so far discussed and one in various ways unique in Irish Silurian geology. Fossiliferous Silurian rocks of the Dunquin Group are present in the Dunquin inlier at the western extremity of the peninsula and in the long narrow strip of the Annascaul inlier (Fig. 48). The beautiful mountain Caherconree lies at the eastern end of this inlier and from its summit, capped with Upper Old Red

Sandstone, the Annascaul inlier is seen as a topographical trough within the higher ground made by the Upper Old Red Sandstone to the south and Dingle Group to the north. On the north-eastern side of the mountain, Derrymore Glen cuts deeply through the Old Red Sandstone to provide another small inlier of Silurian rocks. At its western end the Annascaul inlier reaches the sea in the bay to the west of Minard Head and there is a small disconnected inlier to the north of Bull's Head. Finally, fossiliferous Silurian rocks are seen again in Inishvickillane, the most remote of the Blasket Islands. The Dingle peninsula provides the only proved Ludlow strata in Ireland and its Wenlock succession is characterised by rich assemblages of shelly fossils and a splendid display of volcanic rocks. The fossiliferous Silurian rocks of the Dunquin inlier pass up into a thick purplish fluviatile sequence, the Dingle Group, probably ranging from middle Ludlow through part, if not all, of the Přídolí, and thus providing the only record in Ireland of rocks of post-Ludlow, pre-Devonian age. They are considered along with the remainder of the Old Red Sandstone in Chapter 8 of this book.

The formations of Wenlock and Ludlow rocks now recognised in the various inliers of the Dingle peninsula together with their lithologies and thicknesses are indicated in Figure 49. The succession in the Dunquin inlier is very well displayed in almost continuous coastal sections (Fig. 50). Its arrangement in an overfold (Fig. 71) with a faulted middle limb has long been known through the Geological Survey memoir by Jukes and Du Noyer and through the detailed stratigraphical study by Gardiner and Reynolds published in 1902. All the shelly faunas here are indicative of a relatively shallow water, sometimes bioturbated, sometimes storm washed, shelf environment. They are dominated by brachiopods, corals, and crinoids.

The Ferriters Cove Formation is confined to the area around the bay of that name and is characteristically of greenish and yellowish siltstones with a rich shelly fauna particularly of broken fragments. Brachiopods are conspicuous as are bryozoa, corals, gastropods, and trilobites. Layers of broken and disturbed tabulate corals are common in places. The upper Wenlock brachiopod fauna includes *Amphistrophia funiculata*, *Atrypa reticularis*, *Dolerorthis rustica*, *Hedeina crispa*, *Hesperorthis davidsoni*, *Leptaena depressa*, *Holcospirifer bigugosus*, *Meristina obtusa*, *Resserella canalis*, *Rhynchotreta cuneata*, *Sphaerirhynchia wilsoni*, and *Strophonella euglypha*.

The Clogher Head Formation shows the main volcanic development in the area comprising flow-banded and other rhyolites, ignimbrites, and pyroclastics. These are seen, repeated by the folding, at three places in the cliff sections. They form substantial cliffs at the seaward end of Clogher Head and to the south of it. The typical rhyolitic crags extend inland to Minnaunmore Rock seen to the east of the Dunquin to Ballyferriter road. Farther east they are cut off at a north-south fault. There are some good examples of volcanic mudflows. Some of the tuffs are graded and may show shelly fossils such as gastropods. Associated, more or less calcareous, siltstones yield a rich shelly fauna with elements similar to those of the Ferriters Cove Formation. The seemingly endemic brachiopod *Holcospirifer bigugosus* is conspicuous on some bedding planes.

The Mill Cove Formation is not fossiliferous but its red colouration in contrast to the greyish, greenish, or yellowish rocks above and below is a striking element in the cliff sections. The Drom Point Formation above shows some changes in emphasis in its Wenlock brachiopod fauna. *Meristina obtusa* is still present. *Atrypa reticularis* and *Sphaerirhynchia wilsoni* are particularly common, *Rhynchotreta cuneata* is no longer found. Obviously differences in original community structure are involved and the shells in this formation tend to be concentrated in lenses. Its most remarkable characteristic is the profusion of the trace fossil *Chondrites* on many bedding planes. The coastal sections go no higher than the Drom Point Formation, but a small faulted area of fossiliferous Silurian beds at the northern end of the Great Blasket Island shows the same beds passing upwards into a level with rich banks of the pentamerid *Rhipidium hybridicum*, a species also evidently endemic to the area. Fortunately the same banks can be identified in the less well exposed inland area of the mainland along the Dunquin River.

Above here the succession can be traced into the thick calcareous siltstones and silty limestones of the succeeding Croaghmarhin Formation which form the conspicuous conical hill of that name. They appear to span the uppermost Wenlock and the lower and middle parts of the Ludlow. The facies remains similar across the Wenlock–Ludlow boundary and the fauna, with its sheets of tabulate corals preserved as branching and broken, hollow, yellow coated, moulds and its brachiopod assemblage, reflects this. There are changes such as the disappearance of *Dicoelosia biloba* as the succession is ascended. The highest part of the formation is of more evenly bedded, less calcareous, siltstones in which the shelly fauna appears to be identical with that of the lower Leintwardine Beds of the Welsh Borderland. Present are *Dayia navicula*, 'Camarotoechia' nucula, *Shagamella ludloviensis*, *Chonetoidea grayi*, *Howellella* cf. *elegans*, *Isorthis orbicularis*, *Protochonetes ludloviensis*, *Shaleria ornatella*, and *Sphaerirhynchia wilsoni*. Pteronitellid bivalves and crinoid ossicles are

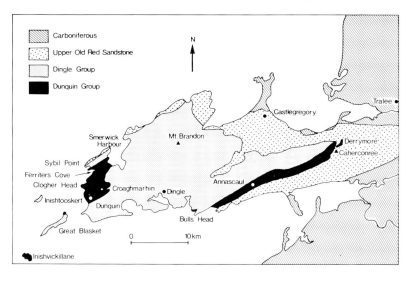

Fig. 48

Geological map of the Dingle Peninsula. County Kerry.

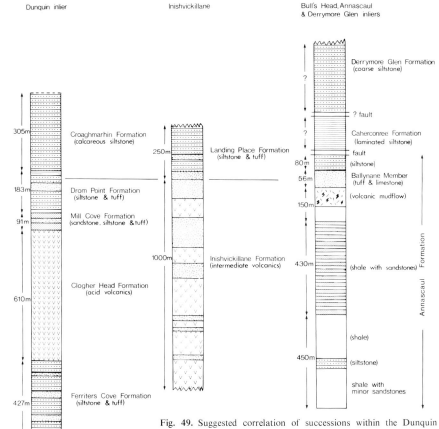

Fig. 49. Suggested correlation of successions within the Dunquin Group (Silurian) of the Dingle Peninsula and Blasket Islands (modified from Parkin 1976).

also common. Recent finds of graptolites in these beds tend to suggest a Ludlow age older than that of the Leintwardine Beds. The succession passes upwards into the Dingle Group as mentioned in Chapter 8.

J. Parkin has described the geology of Inishvickillane. The Inishvickillane Formation is of intermediate lavas and tuffs and the Landing Place Formation includes fossiliferous grey siltstones with tuff bands. Shelly faunas from its lower part can be correlated with those of the upper part of the Drom Point Formation. As in the Dunquin inlier, an Hercynian cleavage postdating the main folding is sporadically developed.

About 60 years ago John Joly (1857–1933), Professor of Geology and Mineralogy at Trinity College Dublin, observed lavas similar to those of Inishvickillane making the Foze Rocks some 5 km from the island outwards into the Atlantic, and hence the most westerly occurrence of Silurian rocks in Europe. He travelled, hazardously it would now seem,

Fig. 50. View from Clogher Head north-eastwards across the northern part of the Dunquin inlier. In the distance (back right) the higher slopes of Mount Brandon (Dingle Group) are in cloud. Along the Atlantic coast (back left) the serrated ridge marks the narrow strip of Upper Old Red Sandstone which dips steeply seawards and rests unconformably upon the Dingle Group. The latter occupies the slope between Smerick Harbour (the long inlet in the background) and Ferriter's Cove. Crossing a fault to the south-east the Dunquin Group is reached. Within it the splendidly exposed ascending succession of the Ferriters Cove, Mill Cove, Clogher Head, and Drom Point formations is clearly seen in the low cliffs. Bedding planes of the Drom Point Formation are seen dipping towards the sea in Trabane Clogher, the bay in the centre right with the road running towards it. The photograph is taken from the outcrop of the mainly volcanic Clogher Head Formation. The beds here on the headland are inverted and exposure of purple Mill Cove Formation and greyish Drom Point Formation are encountered if the north face of the headland is descended towards the sea. Reference should be made to Figures 48 and 71.

Bord Failte Photograph

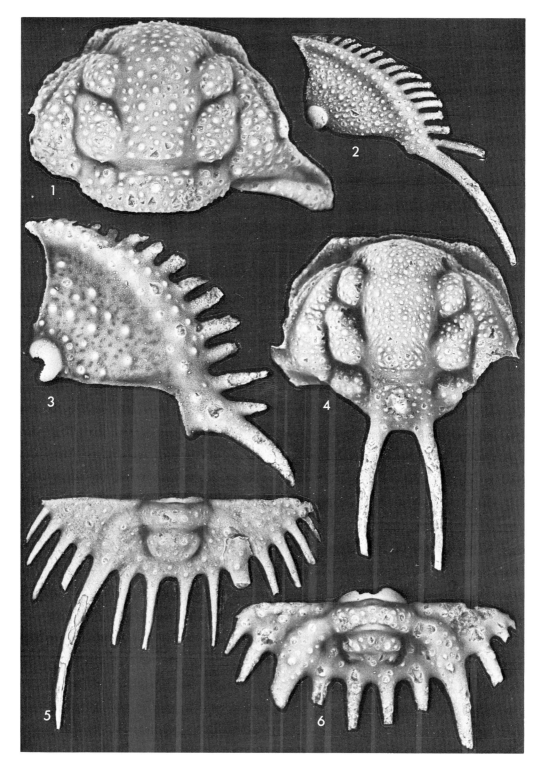

in an open four-oared boat with two companions and three local boatmen. During his geological investigations one of his companions remained aboard, evidently to ensure the continued loyalty of the crew. It is fair to add that they had come through fog, guided only by a pocket compass, their approach heralded by the weird cries of seals at first unseen.

The Annascaul Formation occupies the Bulls Head inlier and the Annascaul inlier from Minard Bay eastwards to the lower slopes of Caherconree. Its upper Wenlock (Homerian) fauna is mostly confined to a member found in the Bulls Head inlier, at Ballynane in the centre of the Annascaul strip, and on the slopes of Caherconree. The brachiopods here include: *Amphistrophia funiculata*, *Atrypa reticularis*, *Dicoelosia biloba*, *Eoplectodonta duvalii*, *Leangella segmentum*, *Leptaena depressa*, *L. holcrofti*, *Meristina obtusa*, and *Resserella canalis*. The fauna varies from place to place. Crinoid ossicles and bryozoa are common. The fossils are characteristically preserved as randomly orientated moulds in volcanic tuff.

Thin bands and nodular masses of limestone from the Ballynane Member on the flanks of Caherconree have yielded to D. J. Siveter an abundant and excellently preserved trilobite fauna (Fig. 51) comprising proetids, otarionids, cheirurids, calymenids, phacopids, odontopleurids, lichids, dalmanitids, and encrinurids. The odontopleurids comprise the dominant element of the fauna. One locality also yielded a *sagitta* Zone condont fauna.

The Caherconree Formation is seen in steam sections and crags on the mountain side where it is affected by minor faults and by plunging folds of small amplitude. The rocks are laminated siltstones present also in Derrymore Glen. The graptolite fauna present here includes *Saetograptus varians*, *S.* cf. *chaemira semispinosus*, *Cucullograptus scanicus*, and *Pristiograptus dubius*. There are also orthoconic nautiloids, cardiolid bivalves, and other rare shelly fossils. The graptolites are indicative of the *C. scanicus*

Zone of the Ludlow and these siltstones are faulted against the Wenlock. The succeeding Derrymore Formation is seen only in Derrymore Glen and displays a shelly fauna. The trilobite *Calymene puellaris* found here is characteristic of the upper Leintwardine Beds in various British areas. There are appropriate ostracodes and a brachiopod assemblage including '*Camarotoechia*' *nucula*, *Chonetes minimus*, *Dayia navicula*, *Howellella elegans*, *Isorthis orbicularis*, *Leptostrophia filosa*, *Protochonetes ludloviensis*, *Salopina lunata*, and *Sphaerirhynchia wilsoni*.

J. Parkin has drawn together a local palaeogeographical picture with the volcanic centres of the Blasket Islands and Clogher Head giving way to turbiditic sandstones with lava clasts and volcanic mud flows in the equivalent rocks of Annascaul. A palaeoslope dipping approximately east-north-eastwards is thus suggested and would also account for the development of a graptolitic facies in the region of Caherconree in *C. scanicus* Zone times.

In summary, Llandovery rocks are well represented in Ireland. Indications of the variable history and character of the north-western shore of the marine trough are seen in Galway, at Charlestown, and at Lisbellaw. The Llandovery turbidites described by Brück in Leinster were derived from a Silurian 'Irish Sea Landmass' to the east. Elsewhere the Llandovery record is of turbidite formations of greywackes and siltstones, associated with shales or slates representing the background sedimentation of the basin. Llandovery graptolite faunas are well seen in the Longford–Down massif, in the Balbriggan inlier, and in places in Slieve Bernagh. Other areas of Llandovery rocks such as those of Slieve Aughty and Leinster are strikingly lacking in macrofossils. On the whole the advent of greywackes into the basin came later in more southerly areas.

The Wenlock is much the best represented of the Silurian series in Ireland. The suggested palaeogeography given in Figure 52 can be related to the very varied evidence detailed elsewhere in this Chapter. Assuming that the closure, or elimination, of the Proto-Atlantic was to continue into Ludlow times, and that the Irish Silurian rocks have subsequently been involved in both Caledonian and Hercynian earth movements, one can only state that the Wenlock seaway shown on the map must originally have been of much greater extent. The Wenlock evidence does not itself demand that the Proto-Atlantic was eliminated by the coming together of plates, though it is not inconsistent with such a process. Positive evidence from Ordovician volcanic rocks is given in Chapter 6 of this book. There appears to be no substantial evidence for a Proto-Atlantic suture during the Wenlock as demonstrable in Irish rocks. The presence of Bohemian elements in British and Irish

Fig. 51 (facing)

Trilobites from the Ballynane Member, Annascaul Formation (upper Wenlock, Homerian) of Caherconree, Dingle Peninsula (Parkin 1976, Locality 36). Figs. 1, 3, and 6. Cranidium, free check, and pygidium of *Primaspis* sp. Figs. 2, 4, and 5. Free check, cranidium, and pygidium of *Odontopleura ovata* Emmrich 1839. Magnifications as follows: Figs 1, 6 × 7·7, Fig. 3 × 9·5, Fig. 2 × 6·0, Fig. 4 × 5·5, Fig. 5 × 4·9. Bulk limestone samples collected by C. R. Harris, J. Parkin, and D. J. Siviter. Trilobites prepared and photographed by D. J. Siviter.

Silurian rocks requires a marine connection south-eastwards into what is now Central Europe.

Marine Ludlow rocks are so far known in Ireland only from the Dingle peninsula. By upper Ludlow (Whitcliffe Beds) times the record is confined to the fluviatile sediments of the Dingle Group, though in mainland Britain marine sediments are found in Wales, the Welsh Borderland, and northern England.

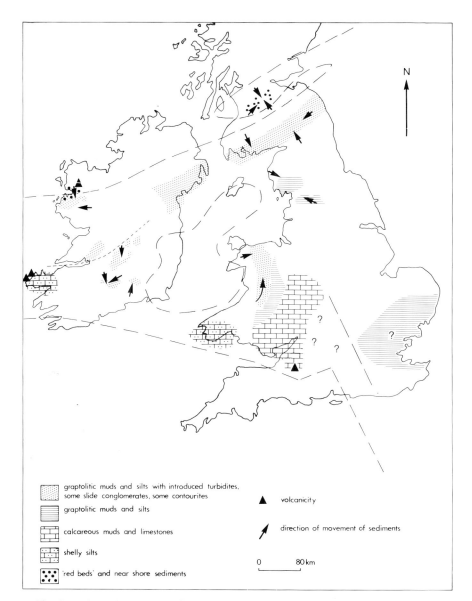

Fig. 52. Wenlock palaeogeography of the British Isles. North arrow and scale relate to present geography.

BIBLIOGRAPHY

BASSETT, M. G., 1976 The affinities of two endemic Silurian brachiopods from
  COCKS, L. R. M., &   the Dingle Peninsula, Ireland. *Palaeontology*, 19, 615–
  HOLLAND, C. H.   625.

BRÜCK, P. M. 1972 Stratigraphy and sedimentology of the Lower Palaeozoic
                    greywacke formations in Counties Kildare and west
                    Wicklow. *Proc. R. Ir. Acad.*, 72B, 25–53.

BRÜCK, P. M. & 1974 Silurian microfossils from west of the Leinster Granite.
  DOWNIE, C.   *Jl. geol. Soc. Lond.*, 130, 383–386.

COCKS, L. R. M., 1971 A correlation of Silurian rocks in the British Isles. *Geol.*
  HOLLAND, C. H.,   *Soc. Lond. Spec. Rep.*, 1, pp. 34 [also published as *Jl. geol.*
  RICKARDS, R. B., &   *Soc. Lond.*, 127, (1971), 103–136].
  STRACHAN, I.

COLTHURST, J. R. J. & 1977 Palaeontological evidence for the age of the Lower Palae-
  SMITH, D. G.   ozoic rocks of the Slievenamon inlier, County Tipperary.
                             Proc. R. Ir. Acad., 77B, 143–158.

EMO, G. T. & SMITH, D. G. 1978 Palynological evidence for the age of the Lower Palaeo-
                                 zoic rocks of Slieve Aughty, Counties Clare and Galway.
                                 Proc. R. Ir. Acad., 78B, 283–293.

HARPER, J. C. & 1972 Some points of interest concerning the Silurian inliers of
  BRENCHLEY, P. J.   southwest central Ireland in their geosynclinal context: *a*
                         statement. Jl. geol. Soc. Lond., 128, 257–262.

HOLLAND, C. H. & 1979 The Silurian rocks of the Capard Inlier Co. Laois. *Proc.*
  SMITH, D. G.   *R. Ir. Acad.*, 79B, 99–110.

JACKSON, A. A. 1978 Stratigraphy, sedimentology, and palaeontology of the
                      Silurian rocks of the Galty Mountain area. *Proc. R. Ir.*
                      Acad., 78B, 93–114.

LAIRD, M. G. & 1970 The Wenlock sediments of north-west Galway, Ireland.
  McKERROW, W. S.   *Geol. Mag.*, 107, 297–317.

O'CONNOR, E. A. 1975 Lower Palaeozoic rocks of the Shercock-Aghnamullen
                       district, Counties Cavan and Monaghan. *Proc. R. Ir.*
                       Acad., 75B, 499–530.

PARKIN, J. 1976 Silurian rocks of the Bull's Head, Annascaul and Derry-
                  more Glen inliers, Co. Kerry. *Proc. R. Ir. Acad.*, 76B,
                  577–606.

PHILLIPS, W. E. A. 1974 The stratigraphy, sedimentary environments and palaeo-
                          geography of the Silurian strata of Clare Island, Co.
                          Mayo, Ireland. *Jl. geol. Soc. Lond.*, 130, 19–41.

PIPER, D. J. W. 1972 Sedimentary environments and palaeogeography of the
                       late Llandovery and earliest Wenlock of North Conne-
                       mara, Ireland. *Jl. geol. Soc. Lond.*, 128, 33–51.

RICKARDS, R. B., 1973 The Silurian sequence at Balbriggan, Co. Dublin. *Proc. R.*
  BURNS, V., & ARCHER, J.   *Ir. Acad.*, 73B, 303–316.

SMITH, D. G. 1979 New evidence for the age of the Ahenny Formation. Slieve-
                    namon inlier, County Tipperary. *J. Earth Sci. R. Dubl.*
                    Soc., 2, 61–63.

WEIR, J. A. 1975 Palaeogeographical implications of two Silurian shelly
                   faunas from the Arra Mountains and Cratloe Hills, Ire-
                   land. *Palaeontology*, 18, 343–350.

6

CALEDONIAN IGNEOUS ACTIVITY

C. J. Stillman

As has been seen in earlier chapters, the Caledonian orogen developed during the closure of the Proto-Atlantic ocean. A certain type of igneous activity is characteristically associated with the margins of ocean basins during the period of closure, when the oceanic crust is being consumed by subduction beneath the continental forelands. The igneous rocks are known as the Orogenic Volcanic Series, the principal components of which are basalts, andesites, dacites, and rhyolites, which are commonly erupted from volcanoes making up island arc systems. In the early stages of these volcanoes the eruptions are submarine, but later, when the volcanic edifice has raised itself above sea level, the eruptions are subaerial and characteristically a large proportion of erupted material is pyroclastic. Recent studies have shown that there is a petrographic zoning across modern volcanic arcs, from the ocean basin to the continental margin; the outermost volcanics are tholeiitic whilst the main part of the arc is calc-alkaline, becoming more alkaline with distance away from the trough, over the continental crust. The situation can best be explained by reference to a diagram (Fig. 53). The zonal system changes with time, as the early eruptives are dominantly tholeiitic basalts and the late ones calc-alkaline andesites and rhyolites.

As well as eruptive volcanism, certain types of intrusion are quite common during the period of subduction and trough sedimentation. Here basic and ultrabasic intrusions, closely related to the submarine eruptions of basalt, are frequently found at shallow depth, often emplaced in the ocean floor sediments or the submarine lavas themselves. They are sometimes seen as dykes which may be feeders to the submarine lavas above.

This type of volcanism comes to an end when the subduction of oceanic crust ceases — perhaps, as in the case of the Caledonian orogen, when the two sides of the ocean collide and fold mountain belts are developed. This represents the climax of the orogenic cycle and it is here that the characteristic granitic plutons of the fold mountain belts are emplaced. Such orogenic granites have a complex history and are intimately related to the metamorphism and the history of uplift of the orogen.

The Caledonian orogen in Ireland comprises two parts which closed over different periods of time. The orthotectonic belt of the north-west involved the deposition of Dalradian sediments and their subsequent high grade metamorphism and complex deformation in late Cambrian to middle Ordovician times. Some eruptive volcanism took place during the infilling of the basin, together with significant basic and ultrabasic intrusions, as is seen in Connemara and along its south-eastern margin on the south Mayo-Tyrone volcanic line; but the most noteworthy activity was the emplacement of the granitic plutons of Donegal and Connemara. The time of emplacement of these plutons is of great interest as they are for the most part post-tectonic with respect to the main Dalradian deformation, though the Donegal Main Granite poses something of a problem to this interpretation.

The paratectonic belt of the south and east closed later at the end of the Silurian with much less metamorphism and complexity of deformation and the junction between the plates is here referred to as the 'Caledonian suture'. South of the suture extensive volcanic arcs developed in upper Ordovican times. The arcs apparently bordered the south-eastern margin of the Proto-Atlantic ocean, and considerable geochemical variation' is seen, ranging from the 'Andean' continental margin of the andesite-rhyolite association in Waterford and Wexford, to tholeiitic and calc-alkaline basalts erupted to form oceanic islands far from land in the upper Ordovician basinal sediments in north County Dublin and Meath. North of the suture contemporaneous volcanicity is also seen in scattered localities in the north and west of the Longford-Down massif and perhaps in south Connemara, though little is known of geochemical zonation.

Volcanic eruptions in the orthotectonic Caledonides

Eruptive volcanism in the Dalradian sedimentary basin

In the orthotectonic Caledonides considerable difficulty arises in the recognition of eruptive volcanics because of the degree of metamorphism and deformation. Many green beds, epidiorites, and amphibolites are recorded but in the absence of clear evidence of intrusive contacts, or of definite eruptive fabrics such as pillows, or of sedimentary structures, it is often difficult to recognise the true origin of these rocks. However sufficient evidence is now available to indicate some of the general features of Dalradian volcanism.

During Dalradian sedimentation, volcanic activity was of a relatively minor nature. It appears to have been essentially basic in character, though of course it is possible that the much greater difficulty of recognising acid volcanics in a metamorphosed sequence may have prejudiced this assessment.

Basic pillow lavas are known from Strabane – the Strabane Pillow Lavas and the Altigarvan Pillow Lavas – and from the Sperrin Mountains, both in County Derry. Similar pillow lavas have been recognised in north-west Mayo, north of Clew Bay in the Lahardaun Basic Volcanic Group. They are usually hornblende-epidote-albite rocks with concentric rings of vesicles defining the pillows, and are commonly found in association with green schists which have sometimes a recognisable sedimentary character but in part may represent basic tuff, possibly subaqueously reworked.

Green schists containing abundant hornblende, epidote, and albite are known from many areas, including the Inishowen Peninsula, County Derry; Torr Head, in north-east Antrim; County Donegal; and the Ox Mountains in County Sligo and north-west Mayo. In all these areas there is little doubt now that much of the schist is tuffaceous; sometimes sedimentary structures are recognised but the detritus itself is either pyroclastic or derived from volcanic debris. Epidiorites and amphibolites are also widely known and many of these are clearly metamorphosed basic intrusions, and in some cases, as in the Sperrin Mountains, they have closely related eruptive equivalents.

Recent work in Galway and Mayo suggests that where acceptable correlations of Dalradian successions have been carried out, the basic eruptive volcanicity is largely restricted to a well defined situation in which the volcanics are submarine, and are associated with the deposition of coarse psammitic and psephitic sediments. The pattern of sedimentation indicates a sudden change in topography and the implication, drawn elsewhere in the volume, is that the change was caused by major faulting; the basic volcanism may well be related to this faulting. Though the volcanics are typically basic pillow lavas and tuffs deposited on the bed of a sea, the situation is not that of a developing oceanic crust; the volcanics overlie a thick prism of continental margin sediments, and it is likely that they are lenses representing local volcanic centres of broadly Cambrian age (Southern Highlands Group). It is interesting to note that abundant amphibolite dykes and sills, which can be dated as pre-Dalradian F1, are found lower in the succession, in the Moine and lower part of the Dalradian in north Mayo, but die out upwards, to be replaced by the dominantly extrusive volcanics described below. It is

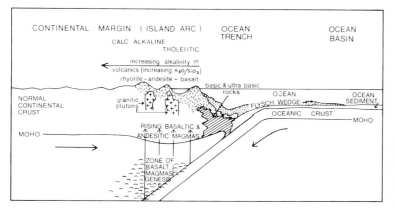

Fig. 53
Diagrammatic section to show magma generation and volcanicity at a subducted oceanic plate boundary with a continental plate (after Sutton 1971 and Ringwood 1974).

possible that the intrusive amphibolites may represent a feeder system to the eruptives.

The south Mayo–Tyrone volcanic line

From south Mayo to County Tyrone there are a number of occurrences of volcanic rocks ranging in age from Tremadoc to Caradoc. In this region it is often difficult to distinguish the volcanicity and sedimentation of the Dalradian basin from that of the paratectonic region to the south-east. An association of basic and acid volcanicity is characteristic and perhaps implies proximity to continental crust, between the two basins. The sialic basement may have been brought up in fault blocks, as suggested by the older Pre-Cambrian horst of the Ox Mountains. In Murrisk, County Mayo (Fig. 54), Cambro-Ordovician shallow water volcanics occur in the southern margin of a south Mayo trough which deepens northwards and contains a faunal province quite different from that of the paratectonic basin to the south. The im-

plication is that the Cambro-Ordovician volcanicity of south Mayo and north-west County Galway was related to a geanticlinal zone with shore line in north Connemara and an Arenig deep water trough to the north. In the Curlew Mountains to the north-east, volcanicity is Arenig in age, and in the Pomeroy area of County Tyrone volcanics lithologically very similar to those of south Mayo – in particular to the Arenig rocks of Tourmakeady and Lough Nafooey – are pre-Caradoc. However here they may represent the uppermost part of the Dalradian succession (see Chapter 3) and thus be truly orthotectonic.

In the Murrisk region west of Lough Mask there is a most extensive and significant development of volcanics. On the Kilbride peninsula great thicknesses of spilites with pillow structures occur and similar spilites are found at Lough Nafooey, where they are associated with tuffs and cherts which include notable quantities of jasper. A substantial development of acid sheets and a mixture of acid and basic lithic clasts in some agglomerates invites comparison with

Table 8. Summary of Irish Caledonian igneous activity.

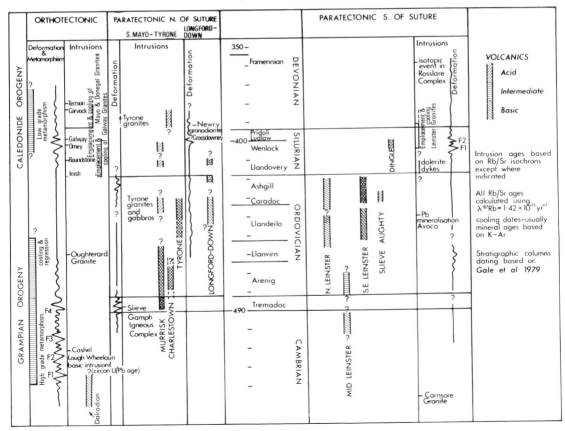

the Tyrone Igneous Group. These rocks are now believed to be Tremadoc to Arenig in age, and succeeding Llanvirn marine sediments show an upward transition to shallow water and subaerial sediments together with welded tuffs. Northward, beyond Killary

Harbour, the volcanic sequence passes laterally into pyroturbidite deep-water sequences (turbidite-like mass-flow hyaloclastic units). On the southern limb of the Mweelrea syncline there is a break in the succession followed by unfossiliferous subaerial and fluvia-

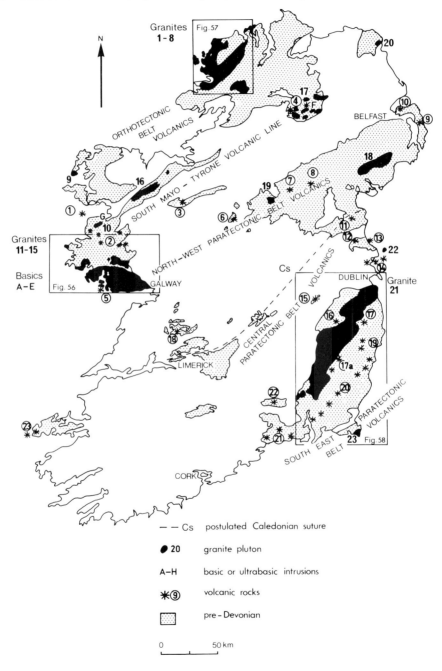

--- Cs   postulated Caledonian suture

● 20   granite pluton

A–H   basic or ultrabasic intrusions

✳⑨   volcanic rocks

▢   pre – Devonian

0   50 km

tile arkoses of Llanvirn/Llandeilo age. A pattern, which is repeated in Tyrone, emerges of basic and acid eruptives mainly submarine, joined later by predominantly acid volcanics some, at least, of which are subaerial, associated with many minor intrusions often emplaced in the earlier submarine pile.

Some 48 km to the north-east in the Curlew Mountains south of Charlestown (Fig. 54), Arenig pyroclastics comprising basic and intermediate tuffs and agglomerates are associated with spilitic lavas. These volcanics are cut by later more acid intrusives, commonly dacites and feldspar porphyries. Similar acid intrusives, together with granite and aplites, are found as boulders in the Llandovery (Idwian) Lisbellaw Conglomerate of County Fermanagh and it is possible that they have been derived from a continuation of the Tyrone Igneous Group.

A most noteworthy succession of pre-Caradoc age is seen in the Pomeroy area of County Tyrone (Fig. 11), closely adjacent to the crystalline foreland. The volcanics of the Tyrone Igneous Group consist of a spilite-andesite-rhyolite suite of lavas, agglomerates, and tuffs with some chert and black shales. The spilites are pillowed, and in addition to the hornblende andesites some soda trachytes are found. The thin, vesicular pillow lava flows are interbedded with crystal-rich, lithic, shardy, and occasionally pumiceous tuffs which were deposited, and sometimes reworked, in a subaqueous environment. These bedded volcanics were then intruded by localised vents which produced agglomerates and breccias, and more widely by quartz porphyries and quartz-feldspar porphyries, which commonly appear to be shallow intrusives often violently autobrecciated on emplacement, and in some instances to be almost synchronous with the tuffaceous eruptives. There are also some flow-banded rhyolites. This whole volcanic sequence is intruded by a suite of granites.

The Ordovician outburst of volcanism along this line was succeeded by a long period of quiescence. In Galway and Mayo there appears to have been a period of uplift and non-deposition from Llandeilo

Fig. 54. (facing) Location of Irish Caledonian intrusions and Lower Palaeozoic volcanic rocks.

CALEDONIAN GRANITIC PLUTONS

1-8	Donegal granites	18	Newry Granodiorite
9	Blacksod Granite	19	Crossdowney Granite
10	Corvock Granite	20	Cushendun Microgranite
11-15	Galway granites	21	Leinster granites
16	Slieve Gamph Igneous Complex	22	Rockabill Granite
17	Tyrone Igneous Complex granites	23	Carnsore Granite

CALEDONIAN BASIC AND ULTRABASIC INTRUSIONS

A-E	Connemara basic and ultrabasic plutons
F	Tyrone Igneous Complex basic plutons
G	Clew Bay and Ox Mountains late or post-orogenic basic and ultrabasic bodies
H	Leinster dolerite dyke swarm

LOWER PALAEOZOIC VOLCANICS: ORTHOTECTONIC CALEDONIDES

volcanics in the Dalradian Basin
individual localities not shown

the South-Mayo-Tyrone volcanic line

1	Clare Island	3	Curlew Mountains
2	Murrisk-Tourmakeady-Lough Nafooey	4	Pomeroy

ORDOVICIAN-SILURIAN VOLCANICS: PARATECTONIC CALEDONIDES

volcanic rocks north of the postulated Caledonian suture

5	Gorumna, South Connemara	8	Lough Avaghon
6	Strokestown	9	Ards Peninsula
7	Lough Acanon	10	Ballygrot

volcanic rocks south of the postulated Caledonian suture
central paratectonic belt volcanics

11	Grangegeeth	15	Grange Hill, Hill of Allen, Kildare
12	Bellewstown	16	Donard, Baltinglass
13	Balbriggan	17	Roundwood, Devils Glen
14	Lambay, Portrane, Donabate	17a	Aughavannagh, Borris
		18	Slieve Aughty

south-eastern paratectonic belt volcanics

19	Wicklow	22	Slievenamon
20	Arklow to Waterford Harbour	23	Dingle, Inishvickillane
21	south-east County Waterford		

to upper Llandovery times, and when sedimentation recommenced, volcanism was much less intense. The base of the upper Llandovery in north-west Galway is marked by a presumed subaerial albite trachyte lava followed by fluviatile sediments. The sedimentary conditions pass through shelf to basinal deposition and in the Wenlock several tuffaceous horizons appear. These are all submarine acid tuffs, ranging from under a metre to five metres in thickness and in some instances can be traced for several kilometres. Acid pumice tuffs and ignimbrites are also recorded from the Wenlock of Clare Island (Fig. 54); these subaerial and water laid tuffs are concentrated near the north-western margin of the Silurian basin and were followed by minor porphyry intrusions on the Mayo mainland and by basic sills farther to the south. These may have been feeders to Devonian volcanics.

Whilst in general the sedimentation and associated volcanism within both orthotectonic and paratectonic Caledonides came to an end prior to the end-Silurian Caledonian movements, some igneous activity is recorded from the Lower Old Red Sandstone of that region which is considered to be an extension of the Midland Valley of Scotland, where the Caledonian movements continued into at least Middle Old Red Sandstone times. In the Curlew Mountains a lower series of andesites and an upper series of similar lavas together with acid pyroclastics are strongly affected by pre-Carboniferous movements. Similar volcanic activity took place in the large area of Old Red Sandstone in Tyrone and Fermanagh, where, in the Fintona region, it is provisionally dated as Lower Old Red Sandstone. In north-east Antrim, at Cushendall, tuffs and dacitic lavas are associated with conglomerates of Lower Old Red Sandstone age. From the nature of the associated sediments, this Old Red Sandstone volcanicity is essentially continental, though the tuffs and agglomerates give evidence of aqueous reworking. Like the Ordovician Tyrone volcanics these eruptives are also associated with granitic intrusions.

Volcanicity associated with the paratectonic Caledonides

The paratectonic Caledonides are transected by the postulated Caledonian suture and the majority of observed volcanic rocks are found south of this line, on the south-eastern (European) plate. The central part of the paratectonic belt lies immediately south of the suture and there appears to be a significant difference between the volcanic rocks of this region and those farther to the south-east. The former appear to have erupted some distance from the edges of the

continent, whilst the latter show many of the features of a continental margin 'Andean' volcanic province.

Paratectonic belt: volcanicity north of the Caledonian suture

It seems possible that the volcanics found in the north-western part of the paratectonic belt may have erupted near to a basin margin, in a trough receiving sediment from a nearby land mass, to the north. The eruptive rocks of the Strokestown inlier (Fig. 54) and those in the northern part of the Ards Peninsula at Ballygrot belong to an upper Ordovician greywacke sequence. At Strokestown low Caradoc (*N. gracilis* Zone) greywackes pass up through cherts, sandstones, and pelites to basic pillow lavas and tuffs. At Ballygrot a similar association of pillow lavas (Fig. 41) with metadolerites, minor cherts, and shales, is followed by tuffaceous agglomerates, graptolitic shales (with *N. gracilis*), cherts, and greyackes. Gravity and magnetic anomalies suggest that the Strokestown volcanics may be linked to the Gorumna volcanics (Fig. 54) which occur in the South Connemara Group. These are again spilitic pillow lavas and acid tuffs, which follow a greywacke sequence, the age of which is still uncertain.

Along this belt, volcanicity continued into the Silurian. Upper Ashgill submarine andesitic lavas and tuffs are found east of Cavan at Lough Acanon, whilst a little farther to the north-east, lower Llandovery agglomerates and tuffs of basalt and pyroxene andesite have been recorded in the Lough Avaghon Formation north of Shercock (Fig. 37). Grey ash bands of similar age are also known in the Birkhill Black Mudstones of the Ards Peninsula.

Paratectonic belt: volcanicity south of the Caledonian suture

Volcanic rocks of the central paratectonic belt. In the central part of the paratectonic belt there is much less continuity of outcrop, and the volcanics are found only in isolated inliers of Lower Palaeozoic rocks in northern Leinster. They differ from the volcanics north of the postulated suture in that the associated sediments are essentially non-terrigenous and acid rocks are very rare over most of the region. At Portrane, Donabate, and Lambay Island, County Dublin and in Kildare at Grange Hill and the Hill of Allen argillaceous sediments and limestones are associated with basalts and andesites, often pillow lavas or pillow lava breccias, with very few acid rocks. The same situation is seen in Counties Louth and Meath at Grangegeeth, Bellewstown, and Balbriggan (Fig. 54). The volcanicity starts in the Llanvirn at Bellewstown and Grangegeeth and in the

Caradoc elsewhere (Lambay, Portrane, Kildare, Balbriggan). It reaches its peak in the Caradoc and is substantially reduced by Ashgill times. Common lava types are basalts, some having conspicuous plagioclase or pyroxene phenocrysts, and andesites. Intrusives are of the same type, the most distinctive being the Lambay Porphyry first described by Von Lasaux in 1878, which consists of pale green andesine phenocrysts commonly 1 to 5 mm in length in a dense green matrix of feldspar and chlorite. The compositional range is limited to basalt and andesite, though in the slightly earlier eruptives of Grangegeeth and Bellewstown there are also some acid representatives.

The volcanics were erupted onto the sea bed in an area where largely non-terrigenous intra-basinal mudstones and local limestones were being deposited. Considerable thicknesses of lavas and shallow intrusives (1,500 m and more) built up shield volcanoes to sea level and even formed islands, but there is only very local evidence of subaerial deposition in, for example, the spatter deposits and subaerial lavas of Lambay, and relatively little erosion and re-deposition of the volcanoes. An implication is that subsidence almost kept pace with the volcanic build up and there is ample evidence of crustal instability in the slump bedding and breccias of Lambay, Portrane, and Balbriggan, which have been ascribed to seismic activity. Tuffs are relatively scarce throughout much of the sequence but increase in abundance towards the tops of the piles where they are commonly reworked, with lithic and crystal tuffs and hyaloclastites winnowed from pillow lava breccias. Pumice is rare. Slumping of pillow lava breccias and agglomerates produced submarine lahars which grade up into limestone slump-breccias with occasional volcanic clasts and ashy matrix. That some of the abundant porphyritic intrusions were contemporaneous is shown by the presence of blocks of porphyry together with other lava types in the polygenetic slump breccias.

Approaching the south-eastern part of the belt, a somewhat older volcanic episode is found preserved in outcrops flanking the Leinster Granite. Here there is evidence of late Cambrian to lower Ordovician activity, apparently coeval with the south Mayo eruptions on the other side of the suture. East of the Leinster Granite the Bray and Ribband Group sediments contain deep-water variolitic pillow lavas and associated dolerites. Farther south a narrow belt of volcanic rocks has been recorded in County Carlow, running from Aughavannagh to Borris (Fig. 54), in which andesitic lavas are followed by acid tuffs to a total thickness of some 400 m. Across the Leinster Granite, andesitic and doleritic igneous rocks within the Ribband Group flank the western margin of the batholith for some 30 km from the Tallaght Hills southwards to Baltinglass (Fig. 26). Petrographically

some of the lava types, for instance the pyroxene-phyric and feldspar-phyric andesites, are similar to the later Caradoc lavas of Lambay and Kildare; others, such as the hornblende andesites and variolitic types, are rather different. Acid pyroclastics have also been recorded in the region. Minor intrusions are abundant and include dolerite sheets and dykes, which are prominent in the Tallaght Hills; these may be somewhat younger than the extrusives, though still predating the emplacement of the granite batholith (see page 98). There are also appinites which are related in some way to the granite plutonism (page 100).

Elsewhere some volcanics have been recorded in the isolated Lower Palaeozoic inliers, as for instance the basic tuffs and agglomerates with basaltic and trachytic lavas found in upper Ordovician strata in Slieve Aughty (Fig. 39). Throughout the central area volcanic activity seems to have passed its peak by Ashgill times.

Volcanicity in the south-eastern paratectonic belt. The belt of Ordovician rocks extending for 140 km from Wicklow to the Waterford coast contains the greatest development of Caradoc volcanicity in Ireland, and the southern coast line exposes a succession of volcanics and intrusions which Sir Archibald Geike described as '....perhaps the most wonderful series of volcanic vents within the British Islands'.

From Wicklow to Waterford Harbour (Fig. 54) the igneous rocks occur in long narrow bodies with a north-east to south-west trend; a form largely imparted by strong Caledonian folding but also by the sub-vertical dyke-like form of many intrusions. Southwest of Waterford Harbour the pattern changes and the outcrops of volcanic rocks spread out over a large oval area some 360 km^2 in extent, in which the lithological distribution is controlled by faulting rather than folding. Some of the faults appear to have been active during and immediately after the period of volcanicity, as well as during the subsequent orogenies.

Throughout this region there was little volcanicity in Arenig times, only a few tuff bands are found in the sediments of the Ribband Group, which is seen in close proximity to the south-eastern crystalline foreland of the Rosslare Complex. The Llanvirn is not represented, possibly due to post-Arenig massive block faulting. Close to the foreland at Duncannon in County Wexford, deposition recommenced with Caradoc acid subaerial volcanicity, followed by the development of a sedimentary basin and transition to marine sediments with associated andesite-dacite volcanicity, which, however, quite soon reverts to mainly acid eruptions.

Farther from the margin of the trough, post-Arenig deposition apparently started earlier, in Llandeilo times, with marine sediments associated with major

andesite-basalt volcanicity as seen at Bonmahon, in County Waterford. Eruption began with the outpouring of relatively gas-poor andesite lava into the submarine basin; this chilled and disintegrated in the sea water and, with the pyroclastic products of occasionally more violent eruptions, built up two or more extensive shield volcanoes. Unstable accumulations led to the sloughing off of pyroturbidites, probably triggered off by seismic shocks associated with volcanic eruptions. Injected at shallow depth into the tuffs were abundant sills of andesite which pillowed and sometimes sagged into their partly lithified floors, or broke through the underlying tuffs in load casts. Large intrusions of pyroxene diorite with chemistry very similar to that of the andesites are also found and these probably represent high-level stocks crystallising from the same magma.

The initial activity was followed by a pause marked by the deposition of the Tramore Limestone, now believed to be Llandeilo in age; then by renewed deepening of the basin in early Caradoc times, with the incursion of turbidites. Further crustal instability, shown by the occurrence of seismites and slumping, presaged a new phase of volcanic activity that started with a voluminous eruption of acid vitric ashes which reached their place of deposition as mass-flows, and the further injection of andesite sheets. Rhyolites erupted explosively from a number of relatively small scattered vents, some of which built their cones above sea-level. Ash-fall deposits, such as those at Dunhill Castle, show sorting of the ash column in air and the production of accretionary lapilli; impact structures are seen below ballistic bombs which are the precursors of repeated ash showers and there is aqueous re-sorting of the tops of fall units. In contrast to the andesites, the rhyolite eruptions were highly gas-charged and some ignimbrites have been recorded. The scale of the rhyolite volcanoes was much smaller than that of the andesites, as can be seen at Arklow Head, near the northern end of the volcanic belt, where a small cinder cone, some 40 to 50 m high and only a few hundred metres across was built up above water level, to be then blanketed in somewhat more extensive vitric and crystal tuffs. The fringes of this volcano were below water and the tuffs pass laterally into bedded tuffaceous 'grits'.

At a later stage the rhyolite produced many sills (Fig. 55) and a deep-seated dyke swarm which extends from south-west of Waterford city, north-

eastwards into Wexford. This swarm was locally responsible for intense alkali metasomatism.

Cutting through the rhyolites are a number of tholeiitic dolerites and some more alkaline intrusions. South of Waterford the latter tend to be syenitic; elsewhere more basic intrusions such as essexites are seen. One of the best examples of these intrusions is the nepheline-normative pyroxene diorite which intrudes the rhyolite pyroclastics at Arklow Head.

The main phase of volcanicity ended in Ashgill to Llandovery times, though a few eruptive and andesitic volcanics and intrusions of rhyolite and dacite are known to occur in possible Silurian rocks north-west of Waterford in the Slievenamon inlier (Fig. 47). Further study of these rocks may well throw light on the relationship of the acid volcanics with the Leinster Granite magma.

Far to the west are Silurian volcanics which, on the evidence of geophysical data, may represent an extension of south-eastern volcanicity. In the Dingle Peninsula, County Kerry, sedimentary conditions indicate transition from shelf to basin in Wenlock times, and here the Clogher Head volcanics, subaerial in part, perhaps indicate the build up of volcanic islands. Ignimbrites and flow-banded rhyolites are well displayed, together with acid tuffs and agglomerates. On Inishvickillane volcanicity of the same age but rather different character is seen. Here lava flows, breccias, agglomerates and tuffs are andesitic, mainly tholeiitic in chemistry. These volcanic rocks represent the last known eruptive activity in the south-eastern part of the paratectonic belt.

Intrusive activity associated with the Caledonian deformation

Early basic intrusions

Metadolerites. Prior to the late Cambrian-Ordovician orogeny in the orthotectonic Caledonides great quantities of tholeiitic magma were injected into lower Dalradian and Moinian rocks in the form of quartz dolerite sills. This magma may perhaps be parental to the eruptive basic volcanicity in the upper Dalradian.

The sills have been subjected to the Dalradian regional metamorphism and converted to amphibolites or the 'epidiorites' of the old Geological Survey maps. They are generally concordant or broadly transgressive; many are continuous over long distances, others have a more lenticular form. They range from about one to a hundred metres in thickness and in northern Donegal, where they are most abundant, they comprise up to 20 per cent of the total Dalradian succession. In the central parts of the

Fig. 55 (facing)

Columnar jointing in a rhyolite sheet, exposed along the coast east of Stage Cove, Bonmahon, County Waterford. The columns shown in the foreground are about 2 metres high.

Photograph by C. J. Stillman

thicker sills original ophitic texture is retained with primary pyroxenes and plagioclase, whilst the margins are converted to hornblende-feldspar schists. The smaller bodies are often broken up into lenses and boudins of amphibolite, sometimes garnet bearing.

Basic and ultrabasic plutons. In the Dalradian belt, complex orogenic deformation and metamorphism followed the injection of the dolerites, and a series of basic to ultrabasic plutons was emplaced syntectonically. Crystal differentiation resulted in layering and the ultrabasics are regarded as crystal accumulates. Many such intrusions are known in Connemara (Fig. 56), where they are dispersed on either side of the Connemara antiform yet have very similar setting, petrology, and mineralogy. They were injected after the Dalradian F1 deformation and sillimanite grade metamorphism, but synchronously with the F2 phase by which they were disrupted, folded, and metamorphosed. Later differentiates of the magma gave rise to an extensive series of migmatitic gneisses and agmatites by mixture of quartz diorite gneiss with both the country rock metasediments and the already solid basic and ultrabasic rock. The migmatisation took place from F2 to F3 times, with accompanying metamorphism.

The largest of the plutons is the *Errismore-Roundstone-Gowla* intrusion which covers more than

50 km^2 and is a complex of layered gabbro with both ultramafic (peridotite, allivalite) and leucocratic (anorthosite, leucogabbro) derivatives. The Errismore and Gowla parts of the intrusion are largely metamorphosed to foliated hornblende-plagioclase rock but the central Roundstone part retains its igneous nature. To the north of Gowla is the *Cashel-Lough Wheelaun* intrusion, a concordant, troughlike body almost 8 km long, cut into two by faulting. Its primary composition ranges from peridotite and pyroxenite to olivine gabbro and norite. It shows primary igneous lamination as well as subsequent metamorphic foliation developed during contemporaneous folding, which affected both the pluton and its envelope of high grade schists. It has been dated at 510 ± m.y. (Zircon U/Pb age). Later it was affected by the regional migmatisation.

On the northern flank of the antiform are the *Doughruagh* and *Currywangaun* gabbroic bodies, which resemble the Cashel body, and the *Dawros* peridotite which is almost feldspar-free and composed of alternating bands of dunite and pyroxenite. Other small ultrabasic bodies are seen on *Crump Island* north of the Renvyle Peninsula and in the *Cannaver Islands* in Lough Corrib. The present form of all these bodies is due to deformation and fragmentation, with folding and disruption of the igneous layers

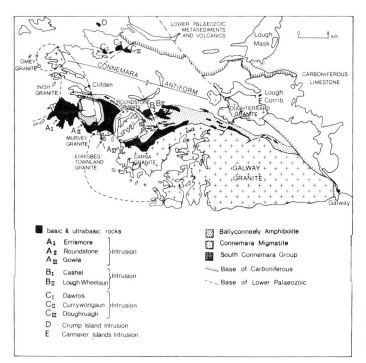

Fig. 56

The Galway granites and basic and ultrabasic bodies (after Leggo, Compston, and Leake 1966; and Leake 1970).

during Dalradian high grade metamorphism and F2 and F3 folding.

Dolerite dykes of similar age are seen on Illion Mountain in the core of the antiform.

In Tyrone (Fig. 54), a layered basic plutonic complex is found immediately south of the Central Inlier high-grade metasediments of possible Pre-Cambrian age, and in close proximity to the Ordovician volcanics. This basic sequence consists of dolerite and gabbro with rhythmic banding of felsic and mafic layers intruded by massive dolerite and gabbro. Part of this intrusion has been foliated and metamorphosed to amphibolite schist by an apparently Dalradian deformation, and a correspondence with the Connemara basic plutons has been suggested by some authors.

Late basic intrusions

During the end-Silurian to early Devonian phase of Caledonian orogeny large numbers of uniform tholeiitic dolerites injected the Lower Palaeozoic sediments in south-eastern Ireland. These intrusions are virtually absent from the rest of the Irish Caledonides, but form a belt which is known to extend across the Irish Sea to Wales, where an example from Anglesea has been dated at 410 m.y. The dolerites constitute a swarm of many hundreds of small sheet intrusions of tensional origin that centres on the Tallaght hills south-west of Dublin city. In the central part of the swarm the basic rock – a uniform, somewhat porphyritic, ophitic augite-labradorite rock – may predominate over the country rock. A characteristic feature is the late-stage alteration: uralitisation and saussuritisation of the dolerite and adinole formation in the wall rocks. Dykes in the swarm trend in general east-north-east to west-south-west, but there is a spread from this to a north-west to south-east orientation.

Outlying members of the swarm extend over an area of several hundred square kilometres from Howth, north of Dublin, along the east flank of the granite pluton to Wicklow; examples occurring as far south as Waterford. The uniformity of the dolerite and the common presence of gabbro xenoliths may perhaps suggest derivation from a large body of basic magma.

The dolerites are to be distinguished from somewhat older hornblende diorites and occasional pyroxene diorites which form a group of sheet intrusions in the Caradoc volcanic belt running from Wicklow to Waterford. Some of these intrude and chill against the tuffs and lavas yet appear chemically to belong to the same Caradoc calc-alkaline volcanic suite as the extrusives.

Late Caledonian granite plutons

The most widespread and characteristic intrusions are the late Caledonian granites which are found in both the orthotectonic and paratectonic Caledonides on both sides of the 'suture' (See Fig. 54) and have many characteristics which equate them with the 'Newer Granite' plutons of Scotland. A considerable body of literature is available for the granites of Donegal, Connemara and Leinster, summaries of which have been provided by J. C. Brindley in 1969 and B. E. Leake in 1978. These and the other selected references listed at the end of this book will augment the necessarily brief introduction given here.

The granites show a variety of mechanisms of emplacement, most of which can be recognised in Donegal where a number of plutons of widely differing forms are found in a relatively small area. Though displaying cross-cutting relationships which enable a sequence to be established, their ages are so similar that radiometric dating cannot separate them. One group, characterised by hornblende diorite and granodiorite, develop elaborate reaction contacts and exhibit to some degree a ghost stratigraphy of the host rocks. These plutons are now thought to have been emplaced by stoping, though previously some authors ascribed them to granitisation with a complementary basic front. They are high energy bodies with protracted cooling and evolution, their cooling histories ending with a phase of static metamorphism. Other granites have generally circular outlines, parts of which are steep-walled ring fractures of cauldrons. Such permissive intrusions involved no major displacement of surrounding rocks but were emplaced by a combination of block subsidence and piecemeal fragmentation of the country rock. They apparently cooled quickly, and produced aureoles which were limited both in extent and time. Yet a third group, emplaced during deformation, have schistose aureoles which provided mobile envelopes to the developing intrusive bodies and in some cases reveal a complex interplay of regional orogenic and localised intrusion stresses. Around these granites the metamorphic history of the aureole is complicated and spans a considerable period of time.

When considering this range of styles, it is perhaps helpful to bear in mind that the mechanism of emplacement of any body of magma is dependent on the resolution of stresses produced by a combination of magmatic, hydrostatic, and regional pressures acting on rocks of varied physical properties. Since the Caledonian granitic plutons cooled, crystallised, and rose during the late-Caledonide regional deformation and metamorphism, their style of emplacement would be strongly influenced by their position relative to regional or local stress fields. For instance granite emplaced in the vicinity of intense horizontal strike-slip deformation might develop a strong foliation parallel to the regional fabric, whilst a pluton arriving in a stress-shadow region at the same time might be emplaced passively by stoping or cauldron subsidence and be quite unfoliated.

Petrographically the Caledonian granites show a general progression from quartz diorite through granodiorite to adamellite. At a relatively late stage in the cooling, potash feldspar porphyroblasts developed in some cases. Aplitic granite developed subsequently, sometimes as a pervasive modification of the pluton, sometimes as satellite intrusions; greissenisation also occurred at this stage, dominantly in roof areas. Indeed for some plutons, notably the Leinster granite, much petrographic variability can be ascribed to the water-rock interactions produced by hydrothermal circulations set up by the mass of hot granite rising into cool, water-bearing metasediments. The late-orogenic plutons, again for instance the Leinster granite, are accompanied by suites of re-

lated porphyry intrusions of clearly magmatic parentage, emplaced late in the plutonic history. They are associated often with lamprophyres; some of those most closely related to particular plutons are appinitic and apparently result from a complex interplay of granitic and basic magmatism, metasomatism, and disruptive intrusion, and some belong to widespread swarms whose genesis is a function of the regional plutonism.

The Donegal granites. These have been the subject of very extensive field and laboratory studies, the results of which have been collated in the *Geology of Donegal* by W. S. Pitcher and A. R. Berger, to which the reader is referred for detailed information. Eight granite plutons are found (Fig. 57). Their relative ages are not completely known because they are not all in juxtaposition. Though some radiometric ages are available, individual dates do not always agree with the relative ages of plutons as determined in the field: this is not surprising in view of the complex cooling

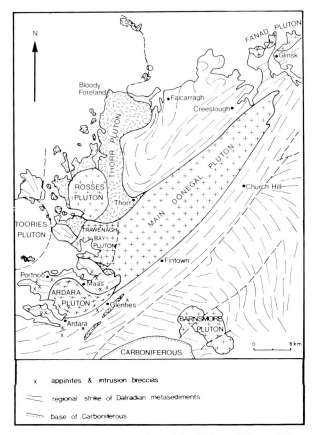

Fig. 57. The Donegal granite plutons (after Pitcher and Berger 1972).

history. The Thorr Pluton is older than the Rosses and is probably also older than the Ardara, since the Thorr aureole is cut by an appinitic complex thought to predate the Ardara. Dykes of the Rosses swarm cut the northern margin of the Ardara aureole. The Main Donegal Granite intrudes both Thorr and Ardara plutons and the Trewenagh Pluton is thought to be somewhat later than the Main Granite. This gives the sequence: Thorr, (Toories), Ardara, Rosses, Main Granite, Trewenagh. There is no way of assessing the relative ages of the isolated Fanad and Barnesmore plutons.

A Rb–Sr isochron published some years ago connecting points for the Rosses ring granites and the Trawenagh Bay Pluton suggests that there is no significant difference in their date of emplacement, which was given as $(487 \pm 5$ m.y.)*. K–Ar mineral dates available for most of the plutons probably record the final cooling of the complex and perhaps of the region as a whole: they range from 404 ± 8 m.y. to 372 ± 6 m.y. If these dates are accepted the complex as a whole was emplaced then cooled over a long period of 70 to 100 m.y. Nevertheless the emplacements of the granitic plutons and their associates are not separated by great time intervals and all form part of one magmatic episode. Their emplacement was later than the peak of the regional Dalradian deformation and metamorphism, and recent as yet unpublished isochrons for the Rosses, Ardara, and Donegal Main Granite all suggest that the early date is seriously in error, and that the emplacement may well have been much closer to the K–Ar cooling dates. Some of them were unlikely to have been emplaced under any great thickness of cover, as for example the cauldron subsidence of Barnesmore and the Rosses, and all are probably high level intrusions.

The Thorr, Fanad, and Trawenagh plutons were emplaced by stoping. The Thorr consists of a transgressive granite with a roof zone migmatitic quartz diorite in which can be traced a pronounced ghost stratigraphy. Abundant evidence of contemporaneous movement in the envelope and of reaction with the country rock suggest that the emplacement process was active stoping. At Fanad similar relations are seen but contemporaneous movement in the envelope was much weaker and reaction with country rock less severe; the stoping here is largely passive. Both plutons are surrounded by broad static aureoles superimposed on the regional metamorphic assemblages. Thus clearly there was a considerable temperature difference by the final stages of emplacement, the regional metamorphism having long since cooled; but only at Thorr is there much metasomatism from the granite, presumably indicating a more volatile

rich magma. The Trawenagh Bay Pluton was emplaced, at least partly, by piecemeal stoping in an entirely static environment and the contact effects are very slight.

Permissive emplacement is shown by the Rosses and Barnesmore plutons. Both are centred complexes in which a roughly concentric pattern of closely related granites has resulted from repeated cauldron subsidence of large dome-shaped or cylindrical blocks of the roof. Predictably the contact effects are slight.

The Ardara Pluton illustrates the process of forceful emplacement. It was intruded diapirically by successive pulses of magma which caused radial distension of the wall rocks. An early foliated monzodiorite mantle surrounds a structureless granodiorite core. The accompanying aureole in its complexity provides evidence of recurrent interaction of crystallisation and deformation; metasomatism is restricted to a narrow inner zone. The Toories Pluton, seen only in offshore islands, appears to be similar to the Ardara pluton in having a circular outline, a deformed envelope, and a strong marginal foliation.

The Donegal Main Granite is more complicated. Its salient features are a concordant outline, an intense internal fabric throughout marked by a strong mineral alignment, a banding, a preferred orientation of inclusions, and a severely deformed envelope in which kyanite, staurolite, and garnet schists of regional metamorphic aspect are found together with contact metamorphic minerals such as cordierite, andalusite, and fibrolite. The Main Granite apparently postdates the static magmatic intrusion of Thorr, the high level diapir of Ardara, and even the permissive ring complex of the Rosses, none of which is affected by the main regional metamorphism. The characteristics appear to result from strong deformation of the granite at the present crustal level, i.e. with its envelope, during the later stages of consolidation. Most of the original features produced during emplacement have thus been obliterated yet it is still apparent that the granite came into place by wedging into its country rocks.

Pitcher and Berger suggest that in broad outline the history of pluton and envelope may be interpreted in two ways: according to one view, if the 487 m.y. isochron is accepted, at some time subsequent to the local Dalradian D4 deformation – i.e. late in the early Caledonian or Dalradian orogenic period – a plexus of coalescing granitic sheets wedged into the country rock with a flattening deformation of the envelope. High temperature metamorphic minerals such as kyanite, staurolite, garnet, and plagioclase were developed in the envelope with subsequent recrystallisation of the granite and further injection of micro-

* All Rb/Sr ages quoted in this chapter have been calculated using a decay constant $^{87}Rb = 1.42 \times 10^{-11}$ yr^{-1}

granite and pegmatite dykes. Then followed a deformation which may have been the end-Silurian to early Devonian main Caledonian folding that deformed envelope and granite alike, with low-grade phyllosilicate metamorphism and cataclasis. Unfortunately the stresses responsible for this deformation do not appear to have affected the country rocks outside the aureole to any appreciable extent. It is possible that a weak regional stress field may have been particularly effective only in areas where ductility was high due to the heat of the pluton, but this seems somewhat improbable. An alternative theory is that the unusually high-grade regional metamorphic character of the aureole was already localised by a regional 'hot spot' into which the granite was emplaced by passive sheet intrusion prior to the late regional stresses (post-D4) which acted on both granite and envelope alike. The localised nature of the deformation would again result from higher ductility in the vicinity of the granite. This model would require a remarkable spatial coincidence of 'hot spot' and later granite, which apparently rose with such precision that it nowhere transected the boundary of the presumed 'hot spot'. Recent structural studies in Donegal suggest a more plausible answer, invoking emplacement control by a major tectonic lineament. Leake, in his survey of Irish granites, points out that the Main Donegal Granite is reasonably close to, and parallel with, a major tectonic slide which was an early Dalradian fundamental structure, and which in much later times was almost coincident with a zone of major transcurrent faulting. The crust into which the granite was intruded was already a major zone of crustal weakness which underwent repeated or continuing movements. If, as seems likely, the emplacement age is much nearer the mineral cooling age given as around 372 m.y., then there is no need to invoke an early granite crystallisation and aureole metamorphism. The high grade minerals in the schists around the granite were already produced by the regional metamorphism and the aureole is represented by local regrowth of phyllosilicates and the production of cordierite, late garnet, andalusite, and fibrolitic sillimanite. The single schistosity of the envelope which coincides with the intense deformation fabric within the granite could well be a tight regional structure intensified by local movements in the lineament zone subsequent to the granite emplacement. The contrasts between the relatively brittle cleavage in the envelope and the penetrative mineral alignment in the granite might be the result of the marked ductility contrast between the relatively cool country rock and the hot intrusive.

The appinites. Certain of the Donegal Granites are closely associated in space and time with a characteristic assemblage of basic minor intrusions varying from small bosses to dykes and sheets, all intimately associated with intrusion breccias occurring either marginal to the igneous intrusion or as individual breccia pipes. These rocks are mainly varieties of appinite – a dark diorite composed of idiomorphic hornblende set in a ground mass of plagioclase and quartz. Some of the larger bodies show variation from olivine and pyroxene varieties to more leucocratic types with dominant oligoclase. Many such bodies are grouped around the Ardara pluton and a few are found elsewhere in the region. They are also very closely associated with lamprophyre dykes and sills. An analogous situation is seen in the vicinity of the Leinster granite batholith. The intrusion breccias give an insight into the origin of these rocks; the breccias consist of irregular fragments of the various country rock types packed in a finely comminuted matrix showing signs of much metasomatic reaction. The commonly accepted view is that they are the product of a high pressure magmatic gas phase closely associated with the granitic plutons. Close association with the diapiric intrusion of Ardara suggests that the latter opened up fissures in the crust which were then drilled out by the gases and the breccias emplaced by a process of 'fluidisation' in a kinetic environment. In Leinster, appinites range from hornblendites to hornblende-biotite-diorites, and small ultramafic intrusions made up of orthopyroxenes, clinopyroxenes, and hornblende are found in close proximity. The appinites predate the late aplitic and pneumatolytic phase of the granite emplacement, but may be contemporaneous with earlier phases. In fact the association of appinites with granodiorite is a common one in orogenic belts. It seems that the source of the appinites was a basic magma which originated or differentiated under high water pressure. It is possible that the source of the water was the associated granite, for whilst the evidence is against the granite and appinite having been formed co-magmatically it does seem probable that the granite could have supplied a low-melting acid fraction, together with much water.

The Galway and Mayo granites. In this region, permissive plutons with sharp discordant contacts and static hornfels aureoles are found; most are cauldrons or small stocks, and biotite granodiorite and adamellite are the dominant rocks. The Blacksod Granite (or Termon Hill Granite) of Belmullet is one such small stock, about 5 km in extent, and the Corvock Granite in South Mayo is another. The roof of the latter is partially preserved, as are some associated appinite dykes. These two granites have been dated at 383 ± 10 m.y. (Rb/Sr isochron) and 381 ± 19 m.y. (Rb/Sr) respectively.

The Connemara granites include the extensive and complex Galway batholith together with a number of satellite plutons. Of the latter, the Omey Granite

(403 ± 18 m.y.) is a circular cauldron about 6·5 km in diameter, a multiple ring intrusion with biotite adamellite as its main type. The remnants of the Inish Pluton (420 ± 8 m.y.) which remain along the coast suggest that it is similar. The Roundstone Granite (410 ± 85 m.y.) is likewise a circular ring of biotite granodiorite about 7 km across. The western end of the Galway batholith consists of a series of intrusions: the Carna Granite, the Errisbeg Townland Granite, and the Murvey Granite, which range in composition from granodiorite to granite, the terminal phase being the Murvey garnetiferous muscovite granite. Layering indicates gravitational crystal settling in a magma with concommittent differentiation towards potash-enriched types. Emplacement has been by uplift of the overlying strata accompanied by stoping on a large scale. The Errisbeg Townland Granite shows a clear chemical differentiation toward an acid potash-rich granite and the Murvey Granite appears to represent a segregation of residual magma being forced out by the foundering of large stoped blocks of the country rocks into the magma chamber.

The main mass of the Galway Granite, covering some 1000 km², is a composite body dated at 399 ± 1 m.y., intruding the much older migmatitic gneisses and also the lower or possibly upper Ordovician South Connemara Group. The main variety is a porphyritic biotite adamellite with green chloritic ground mass and large pink potash feldspar phenocrysts. Leake points out that the batholith lies on the assumed direct extension of the Southern Uplands Fault across Ireland, a major splay of which probably passed through the ground now occupied by the batholith.

North-east of the main Galway Granite is the Oughterard Granite, a much older pluton which could be a post-kinematic intrusion of the early Caledonian (Dalradian) phase. It post-dates the Dalradian F3 & F4 folds but appears to have been emplaced before the regional metamorphism had completely cooled. It is a massive biotite granodiorite with clear-cut static contacts, and no detectable contact aureole.

The Slieve Gamph Igneous Complex. South-west of Sligo, a syn-kinematic granitic intrusion is emplaced in the high-grade metamorphic rocks of the Ox Mountains inlier. The antiquity of these rocks is unknown but they are overlain by upper Dalradian sediments. It appears that the Igneous Complex (Fig. 8) and the upper Dalradian were deformed together, and that the Igneous Complex was hot, perhaps not fully crystallized during deformation. A Rb/Sr whole rock isochron on the granite gives an age of 477 ± 6 m.y., which not only dates the granite emplacement but must also be a minimum age for the regional metamorphism and local Dalradian deformation.

The granites of Tyrone, Longford and Down. In north-eastern Ireland are more examples of permissive granitic plutons which penetrate non-metamorphic Lower Palaeozoic rocks; they are post-kinematic cross-cutting plutons. The Tyrone Granites of Slieve Gallion and Pomeroy are mostly small stocks with static hornfels aureoles. Some cut through high-grade metamorphic rocks of the Central Inlier, which are probably pre-Caledonian in age, and, though none are seen in the younger Dalradian rocks of the near-by Sperrin Mountains, other granites penetrate the mid-Ordovician Tyrone volcanic rocks and are believed by some workers to have a close genetic relationship to the eruptives. One important example, the Craigballyharky granitic complex is emplaced in the basic plutonic complex, into which it grades marginally and from which it may be derived. In at least one case a granite is unconformably overlaid by Caradoc sediments, and pebbles of the granite are found in basal Ashgill conglomerates near Pomeroy. However, east of Pomeroy, three small granite bodies penetrate the Lower Old Red Sandstone Fintona Group, so that at least part of this Tyrone granitic activity is Devonian, possibly of an age similar to that of the Newry granodiorite. Biotite granodiorite is the main rock type with quartz hornblende tonalite as a marginal reaction facies. Aplogranite bodies are also present. Large masses of country rock found within the granites are thought to be stoped blocks of roof. The granites have steep irregular boundaries which contain many xenoliths and exhibit widespread reaction effects.

In the Longford–Down massif, the Newry Igneous Complex is an elongate batholith extending 40 km along the Caledonoid trend, producing some deflection of the regional strike of cleavage in the Silurian sedimentary host rocks, which have demonstrably been shouldered aside in some places. The batholith may be considered a composite body comprising three contiguous sub-units or plutons which are arranged *en echelon*, slightly oblique to the regional Caledonoid trend. Three major rock types are known: hornblende granodiorite, porphyritic hornblende biotite granodiorite, and a paler biotite granodiorite. Recent work on strontium isotopes appears to suggest that the granodiorite is entirely magmatic and has been derived from an upper mantle or lower crustal source region, perhaps by the differentiation of intermediate magma at depth. Its emplacement has been dated by Rb/Sr isochron at 391 ± 21 m.y. A narrow static biotite-cordierite hornfels aureole is developed. The boundary is irregular, reaction phenomena are conspicuous, and a stoping origin similar to that of the Thorr pluton is suggested, though the marginal reaction phenomena led earlier workers, notably Doris Reynolds, to ascribe the origin to granitisation. At the north-eastern end of the complex is an association of ultramafic biotite pyroxenites with metadiorites, quartz diorites, and monzonites, which were emplaced before the granodiorite. These basic rocks were also regarded as the products of metasomatism by Reynolds, but current workers take the view that the ultramafics and meladiorites are cumulates from an intermediate magma. There is also an association with the lamprophyre dykes which are found in abundance over the whole region. These dykes belong to a swarm which extends from the Ards peninsula across County Down in a north-east to south-west

direction. There appear to be two periods of intrusion, the earlier being syntectonic, the later post-tectonic. A wide variety of lamprophyre types are represented. They may be related to the granitic intrusion in the same way as the appinites and lamprophyres of the Ardara or Leinster granites.

The Crossdowney stock, some 65 km south-west of Newry, is much smaller. About 13 km² in area, it cuts Silurian greywackes with a markedly cross-cutting contact which is sometimes sharp, sometimes diffuse with feldspathisation of the country rock. A substantial hornfels aureole up to 2 km wide is developed. Associated porphyritic rhyolite dykes lose their regular orientation on entering the aureole and appear to have been emplaced synchronously with the heating up and increased ductility of the aureole rocks. The body consists of regular zones of more or less melanocratic granodiorite with some central adamellite.

The Cushendun microgranite boss, which intrudes Dalradian strata on the east coast of Antrim, should be included here. Though undated as yet, this intrusion, together with a number of dykes of quartz-orthoclase porphyry and pegmatite, is thought to be of Caledonian age.

The Leinster Granites. These make up a compound batholith more than 1500 km² in area, together with a number of outlying belts of minor intrusions (Fig. 58). The envelope rocks are Lower Palaeozoic metasediments, crossed by a Caledonian dyke swarm, and folded by the first phase of the main Caledonian deformation. The main plutonic emplacement coincided with a second phase of regional deformation and has been recently dated by an Rb/Sr isochron at 404 ± 24 m.y. A possible cooling period of some 20 m.y. is suggested by K–Ar mineral determination which has given ages of 386 ± 6 m.y. and 392 ± 9 m.y. Upper Old Red Sandstone sediments overlap the pluton at its southern end. The main batholith comprises five oval dome-like units (Figs. 58 and 59), disposed *en-echelon* on a north-north-eastern trend oblique to the main Caledonoid 'grain' and separated by narrow septa of schists. Flow structures within the granites parallel the margins, which are cross-cutting at the terminations but generally concordant on the flanks. In places strong sheeting with associated feldspathisation of the intercalated sediments is seen. The flow pattern and gradational internal boundaries suggest that each dome was intruded as an essentially continuous event. A fine-grained tonalite locally forms a marginal phase, grading in to the main type, which is a coarse adamellite. Late crystallisation of potash feldspar porphyroblasts in quartz tonalite produces a distinctive adamellite, which in some areas is modified by post-emplacement re-crystallisation to a muscovite-porphyritic adamellite sometimes containing tourmaline and garnet. Late aplogranite is abundant and the final

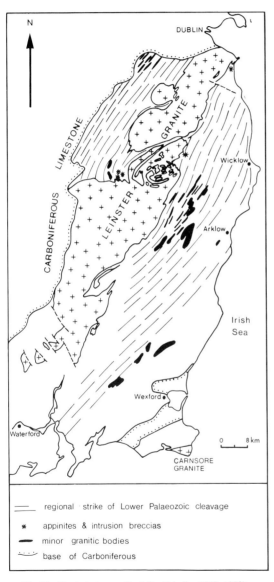

Fig. 58. The Leinster granites (after Brindley 1969, 1973).

Legend:

— regional · strike of Lower Palaeozoic cleavage

* appinites & intrusion breccias

— minor granitic bodies

⌐ base of Carboniferous

phase is of aplitic granite and quartz diorite which was emplaced in a late cauldron subsidence.

Very recent chemical studies in the northern units of the batholith suggest that the most abundant types of granite represent a fractionation series from adamellite to aplite. Early quartz diorite which forms

Fig. 59. The Turlough Hill pumped storage scheme. This electricity generating scheme is located in County Wicklow about 40 km south of Dublin. It is situated in the Northern Unit of the Leinster granite batholith and this view looking north-westward across some 10 km of granite shows the typical rolling upland topography. The lower reservoir, Lough Nahanagan, is a glacial corrie lake; the upper reservoir is man-made. The station, constructed by the Electricity Supply Board, uses the night-time surplus generating capacity of thermal power stations elsewhere in Ireland to pump water up to the upper reservoir and this head of water is then used at peak hours during the daytime to generate electricity.

Photograph courtesy Electricity Supply Board

marginal zones and rafts may represent a separate earlier magma. Some of the granites have been modified by hydrothermal alteration brought about by the migration of alkali-rich solutions through the batholith at a late stage in its consolidation history.

The coarse muscovite schists of the aureole, with andalusite, staurolite, almandine, and biotite porphyroblasts, contrast strongly with the normally low grade metasediments of the region and are comparable with the contact schists of the Ardara Pluton, displaying a strong flattening deformation which developed during the main granite emplacement, by a combination of regional deformation and intrusive stresses. The analogy with Ardara is strengthened by the occurrence of appinites and lamprophyres in the aureole, and of at least one intrusion breccia.

Minor granites form post-tectonic sheet intrusions in belts with Caledonoid trend south-east of the main batholith. They range from quartz porphyries to microgranite and quartz diorite and have biotite-andalusite hornfels aureoles; greissenisation is common at the upper contacts of the sheets. West of the granite are small felsite intrusions in Kildare and to the north is the Rockabill Granite, 6·5 km offshore in the Irish Sea, a granodiorite with again much greisenisation.

The isolated Carnsore Granite, at the south-eastern end of Leinster, has been dated on an Rb/Sr isochron at 520 ± 6 m.y. and should thus be included here, though it intrudes Pre-Cambrian gneisses and is somewhat older than the main group of 'Newer Granites'. It is a homogeneous porphyritic biotite adamellite and has a hornfels aureole, though the actual contact is unexposed. According to gravity surveys, it extends offshore to a dimension of up to 75 km².

Petrogenesis

There has been a rapid advance in recent years in the recognition of magma types and tectonic settings of ancient volcanic rocks, even where the rocks have been subjected to metamorphism, submarine weathering, or spilitisation. Studies of this nature applied to the upper Ordovician volcanic rocks south of the Proto-Atlantic suture in east and south-east Ireland suggest that these rocks were erupted on the margins of a continental plate which thickened in general towards the south-east above a south-eastward dipping subduction zone. The volcanics all belong to the Orogenic Volcanic Series; they show a transition from tholeiitic to dominant calc-alkaline compositions and suggest that the magma generation system was arrested at quite a late stage when compositions approaching the shoshonitic were being erupted. The

field and geochemical evidence is consistent with volcanism on the edge of a fracturing continental plate fringed to the north-west by an arc-trench system. North of the Leinster Granite the volcanics are restricted in composition, being predominantly basalts and basaltic andesites erupted in what was apparently a relatively immature island arc. South-east of the granite a much wider range of compositions is found and acid members predominate. The geochemical characters suggest that whilst the andesites and basalts were probably derived from a partial melt of upper mantle or subducted ocean crust, the rhyolites may have been produced by partial melting of downfaulted thick continental crust. There is indeed a reasonable relationship between faulting and contemporaneous volcanism, but there are as yet insufficient isotopic data to confirm this hypothesis. Figure 60 demonstrates the distribution of the upper Ordovician volcanic rocks in terms of this plate tectonic model.

On the other side of the suture, there is evidence of a somewhat different model of magma genesis, or rather models, since it is far from clear that any single system was in operation over the whole region. In Murrisk, the Tremadoc to Arenig activity shows a progression from early island arc tholeiites to calc-alkaline basalts, indicating the evolution of an active island arc on what was to become the southern margin of the south Mayo trough. The development of this arc was arrested before reaching the dominant andesitic stage. The tholeiitic magma here, as in the Welsh basin, produced acid as well as basic eruptives. The succeeding Arenig activity was essentially bimodal basalt-rhyolite, with an increasing predominance of acid rocks as time progressed. This bimodality is a feature of the other volcanic areas along the Mayo to Tyrone line, and, although an insufficiency of data makes conclusions more speculative than south of the suture, it seems possible that the type of magma was substantially determined by the tectonics along this margin of the north-western continental plate. The Murrisk situation has been likened by Ryan and Archer to that of a Gulf of California type marginal basin. It is noteworthy that the initiation of island arc volcanism was broadly synchronous with, or followed closely after, Dalradian high grade metamorphism and migmatisation in Connemara. It is possible that the syn-kinematic basic and ultrabasic intrusions of Connemara were derived from a magma source similar to that of the Lough Nafooey volcanics, intruded further inland from the trench into the rising mobile core of a geanticlinal thermal dome. Ryan and Archer suggest that the opening of the south Mayo trough was perhaps coincident with the change in the early island-arc volcanism, and the subsequent change to bimodal basalt-rhyolite volcanism may indicate collision of a Proto-Atlantic ridge with the south Mayo trough.

In Charlestown and Tyrone the volcanic association seems similar to that of Murrisk, though if conclusions regarding Murrisk are speculative then those for other regions are even more so since virtually no geochemical data or up-to-date field evidence are available.

South of the Mayo–Tyrone line of volcanics lies the Longford–Down massif of Ordovician and Silurian greywackes in which Caledonian volcanics are entirely mafic, apparently tholeiitic, and erupted into a marine basin accumulating turbidites derived in part at least from the north. Some of the sediment clasts are of blueschist, suggesting a source area which had been involved in subduction and uplift.

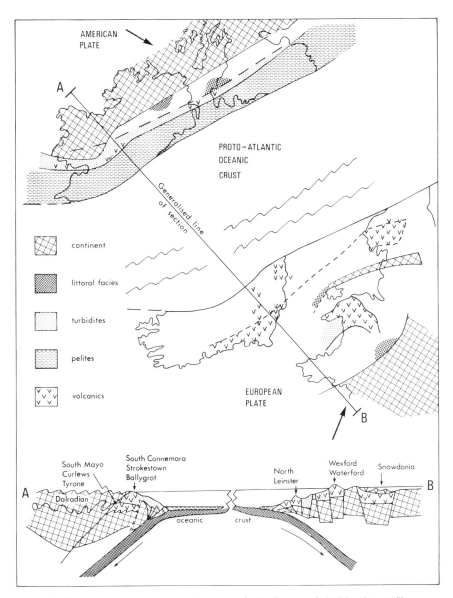

Fig. 60. A suggested palaeogeographical reconstruction for upper Ordovician times to illustrate the tectonic setting of the volcanic rocks (after Phillips, Stillman, and Murphy 1976).

Though the origin and environment of this volcanism may be unclear, it is consistent with plate margin activity and there is little doubt that to the north there lay continental crust, on which the ensialic Dalradian basin sediments were deposited. Caledonian volcanism in this basin appears to relate to rifting of continental crust in early to middle Cambrian times, which permitted the dilational emplacement of tholeiitic basalt dykes. These may have been feeders to the basaltic pillow lavas in the upper parts of the Dalradian succession.

From this diversity two features seem to emerge.

	LEINSTER			NEWRY		GALWAY					DONEGAL				
	1	2	3	4	5	6	7	8	9	10	11	12	13	14	15
SiO_2	71.58	72.52	73.98	63.22	70.30	68.25	69.65	70.44	71.50	74.87	73.1	74.0	74.4	76.4	72.9
Al_2O_3	15.43	15.29	15.17	15.94	15.21	14.71	14.59	14.49	14.06	13.47	14.2	13.8	13.6	13.2	14.7
Fe_2O_3	0.50	0.42	0.27	11.71	0.72	1.42	1.20	1.12	0.87	0.37	0.50	0.56	0.50	0.42	0.57
FeO	1.19	0.77	0.14	2.56	1.48	1.74	1.57	1.50	1.30	0.60	0.93	0.79	0.70	0.22	1.02
MgO	0.67	0.45	0.11	2.87	1.16	1.62	1.37	1.32	1.01	0.48	0.63	0.57	0.52	0.28	0.56
CaO	1.06	0.84	0.37	4.19	2.80	2.55	1.97	2.04	1.80	0.73	1.24	0.97	0.91	0.39	1.52
Na_2O	3.85	3.77	4.96	3.88	4.30	4.01	3.60	3.33	3.62	3.67	4.05	3.91	4.04	3.82	3.85
K_2O	4.03	4.38	3.98	2.89	2.91	3.84	3.87	4.33	4.30	4.77	4.60	4.66	4.62	4.82	4.10
H_2O+	1.11	1.01	0.61	1.04	0.56	1.01	1.03	0.91	0.70	0.54	0.73	0.67	0.70	0.68	0.67
H_2O-	0.07	0.08	0.08	0.38	0.10	–	–	–	–	–	–	–	–	–	–
TiO_2	0.28	0.17	0.02	0.29	0.31	0.39	0.34	0.37	0.28	0.12	0.21	0.19	0.20	0.09	0.23
MnO	0.05	0.05	0.13	0.04	0.05	0.13	0.11	0.14	0.12	0.11	0.03	0.04	0.03	0.04	0.03
P_2O_5	0.15	0.18	0.16	0.88	0.13	0.14	0.16	0.14	0.12	0.03	0.08	0.06	0.07	0.05	0.07
	99.97	99.93	99.98	99.89	100.03	99.81	99.46	100.13	99.68	99.76	100.29	100.22	100.29	100.41	100.22

	DONEGAL											
	16	17	18	19	20	21	22	23	24	25	26	27
SiO_2	75.3	71.9	71.6	63.1	65.4	69.6	65.8	62.9	65.1	70.0	60.5	71.1
Al_2O_3	13.8	15.0	15.0	17.10	16.6	15.0	17.0	17.0	16.6	15.7	18.82	15.3
Fe_2O_3	0.14	0.47	0.52	0.99	0.94	0.96	0.71	1.33	1.12	0.60	1.56	0.40
FeO	0.41	1.27	1.37	2.97	2.50	1.35	2.70	2.98	2.35	1.25	3.15	1.89
MgO	–	0.61	0.64	2.41	1.73	1.32	1.80	1.92	2.07	1.23	1.95	0.92
CaO	0.76	1.95	2.12	3.70	2.77	1.81	2.80	3.48	2.98	1.70	3.65	1.76
Na_2O	3.60	3.74	3.87	4.20	4.14	4.02	3.80	4.41	4.77	5.02	4.71	4.32
K_2O	5.00	4.31	3.80	3.24	4.37	4.89	3.5	4.21	3.47	3.15	3.19	3.12
H_2O+	0.02	0.53	0.57	0.85	0.76	0.60	0.77	0.66	0.72	0.62	0.84	0.72
H_2O-	–											
TiO_2	0.80	0.27	0.32	0.74	0.64	0.42	0.64	0.88	0.60	0.31	0.74	0.18
MnO	0.01	0.03	0.03	0.06	0.05	0.05	0.05	0.08	0.04	0.04	0.09	0.05
P_2O_5	0.27	0.09	0.10	0.26	0.24	0.14	0.19	0.26	0.17	0.09	0.34	0.06
	100.11	100.17	99.87	99.62	100.14	100.16	99.76	100.11	99.99	99.71	99.54	99.82

Table 9

Chemical analyses of some Irish Caledonian granites.

1. Leinster granite, Northern units; Porphyritic-Microcline Type II.
2. Leinster granite, Northern units; Equigranular Type II.
3. Leinster granite, Northern units; Aplite
   Average of analyses from Brück and O'Connorr 1977, table 1.
4. Newry Granodiorite: hornblende granodiorite; Moor Quarries, Newry. Charlesworth, *op. cit.*
5. Newry Granodiorite: biotite granodiorite; Cam Louth, Newry. Charlesworth, *op. cit.*
   6-18. Average compositions of some Galway granites. Wright, P. C. (1964), table 4.
6. Carna Granite.
7. Cuilleen Granite.
8. Callowfinish Granite.
9. Erris Beg Townland Granite.
10. Murvey Granite.
    11-27. Average compositions of parts of the Donegal plutons. Pitcher, W. S. and Berger, A. R. (1972), table 16-2.
11. Rosses Complex G_1-G-A.
12. Rosses Complex G_2.
13. Rosses Complex G_3.
14. Rosses Complex G_4.
15. Trawenagh Bay Pluton: normal.
16. Trawenagh Bay Pluton: marginal.
17. Main Donegal Pluton, north-west.
18. Main Donegal Pluton, south-west.
19. Thorr Pluton: 'strip'.
20. Thorr Pluton: Thorr.
21. Thorr Pluton: Gola.
22. Thorr Pluton: contact.
23. Ardara Pluton: outer monzodiorite.
24. Ardara Pluton: monzotonalite (outer part of central component).
25. Ardara Pluton: grandiorite (inner part of central component).
26. Fanad Pluton.
27. Barnsemore Pluton.

Firstly calc-alkaline suites typical of the Orogenic Volcanic Series are limited, and the more widespread volcanicity is bimodal basalt-rhyolite in which the basic component probably derives from mantle partial melts. Secondly, fractionation may provide some of the acid component; but the more voluminous acid volcanics, particularly in the post-Arenig volcanism, all appear to occur in regions where thick continental crust might have been depressed to the region of partial melting and so provide a source for the magma.

Table 10. Comparison of means, ranges, and standard deviations for chemical features of some upper-Ordovician volcanics from the paratectonic Caledonides.

| Analysis oxide weight % | Central paratectonic belt | | | | | | South-eastern paratectonic belt | | | | | | | | |
| | basalts | | | andesites | | | basalts | | | andesites | | | rhyolites | | |
	range	mean	stand. dev.	range	mean	stand. dev.	range	mean	stand. dev.	range	mean	stand. dev.	range	mean	stand. dev.
SiO_2	40-52	47.8	3.2	53-63	56.6	3.0	40-54	50.2	3.1	54-62	58.3	3.5	70-77	74.1	2.5
Al_2O_3	13-23	16.8	2.5	14-21	17.1	1.7	14-18	16.0	1.2	12-19	16.1	1.8	12-14	13.2	0.7
$FeO+Fe_2O_3$	5.8-13.7	11.0	1.9	5.8-10.5	7.5	1.4	8-18	11.7	2.4	5-12	9.1	2.2	1.1-4.1	2.7	0.8
MgO	2.6-15.9	8.3	3.1	2.1-7.8	4.6	1.9	5.2-16	8.7	3.0	3.1-13	7.1	2.6	0.2-4.5	1.3	1.1
CaO	5.0-11.3	8.3	1.8	0.7-10.4	5.5	3.0	0.4-14	7.2	3.0	1.0-5.0	2.4	1.2	0.05-2.5	0.5	0.5
Na_2O	1.0-6.0	2.2	1.0	2.6-6.5	3.9	1.0	1.5-5.4	2.9	1.0	1.0-4.9	3.3	1.0	1.2-5.4	2.9	0.9
K_2O	0.3-3.0	1.7	0.7	0.2-4.2	2.9	1.1	0.03-2.8	1.2	0.8	0.05-6.7	2.0	1.6	1.3-7.6	4.8	1.6
P_2O_5	0.2-0.5	0.3	0.1	0.2-0.9	0.4	0.2	0.1-0.9	0.3	0.2	0.1-0.9	0.3	0.2	0.1-0.2	0.1	0.1
TiO_2	0.8-1.7	1.3	0.2	0.8-1.7	1.1	0.3	0.1-2.8	1.6	0.6	0.6-2.6	1.3	0.6	0.01-0.6	0.3	0.2
Na_2O+K_2O	2.5-6.3	3.8	1.0	4.4-8.3	6.7	1.2	2.5-7.8	4.1	1.0	3.5-11.6	5.3	2.0	6.1-14	8.2	1.8
Na_2O/K_2O	0.3-3.1	1.3	0.7	0.3-3.9	1.4	0.8	0.5-8.8	3.9	4.0	0.3-8.7	2.1	1.8	0.09-4.3	0.8	0.9
$FeO+Fe_2O_3/MgO$	0.8-4.3	1.5	0.7	0.8-5.4	2.0	1.2	0.7-4.4	1.6	0.8	0.7-3.2	1.5	0.6	0.3-11.7	3.3	2.5
p.p.m.															
Ba	393-1318	756	354.5				11-748	195	215.4	20-928	345	291.0	65-1028	675	354.5
Sr	162-1101	500	25.1	119-1298	491	363	38-528	198	131.2	21-293	139	76.4	22-85	65	25.1
Rb	9-192	42	64.5	5-116	72	34	1-140	45	41.8	4-137	74	44.7	48-220	136	64.5
Y	18-36	25	8.7	14-44	28	9	21-56	45	15.3	15-69	45	20.3	67-89	82	8.7
Nb	1-12	5	0.8	2-23	10	6	1-18	9	4.6	2-14	10	3.9	19-21		0.8
Zr	112-252	150	18.4	54-474	226	137	98-334	207	69.8	113-463	273	110.5	399-432	407	18.4
Cu	44-159	117	9.6				6-143	49	44.3	13-42	23	9.5	1-23	10	9.6
Zn	9-141	112	66.9				31-156	103	39.6	26-111	83	28.1	30-186	97	66.9
V	197-347	285	1.9				202-297	272	42.9	25-361	200	106.0	1-6	3	1.9
Ni	11-91	49	6.9				2-145	38	46.0	5-47	15	16.0	0-19	9	6.9
	(25 analyses)			(14 analyses)			(21 analyses)			(14 analyses)			(18 analyses)		

Data from Downes, K. (1975) and Stillman, C.J. (unpublished). Analysed by Downes, K., Fitton, J.G., Hughes, D.J., and Williams, C.T.

Caledonian volcanic activity reached its peak in the upper Ordovician, whilst the Proto-Atlantic ocean was presumably still closing, and was associated with the appropriate tectonic conditions on the continental margins. The rate of production dropped significantly at the end of the Ordovician, when apparently collision of the two plates first occurred north-east of Ireland. By the end of the Silurian, collision had occurred in Ireland and the main end-Caledonide deformation took place. With it came the uprise and emplacement of the granitoid plutons.

The petrogenesis of the granites has been much discussed and modern theories group around two models, the first and less popular is that the magma is essentially anatectic, derived from an upper crustal remelt; the other that it is produced by partial melt and fractionation of the upper mantle or lower crust. The latter has gained ground with increasing evidence

available from isotopic studies, though the former still has its adherents. Leake in his 1978 review summarised these arguments and the reader is referred to this work for details. In brief it can be said that in general the restriction of granites to areas of continental crust strongly suggests that the origin of granite magma lies in the crust. Those favouring magma genesis by the partial fusion of a depleted lower crust, probably of pyroxene granulite, claim that the low initial $^{87}Sr/^{86}Sr$ isotope ratios which have been invoked as proof of mantle origin can in fact support a lower crustal origin equally well, since much evidence now suggests that the lower crust is severely depleted in Rb compared to the upper crust. Melting such lower crust with its low Rb/Sr ratio would produce a magma with a low $^{87}Sr/^{86}Sr$ ratio since there would have been little contribution of radiogenic ^{87}Sr from the decay of the Rb. Similar ratios may of course be obtained by

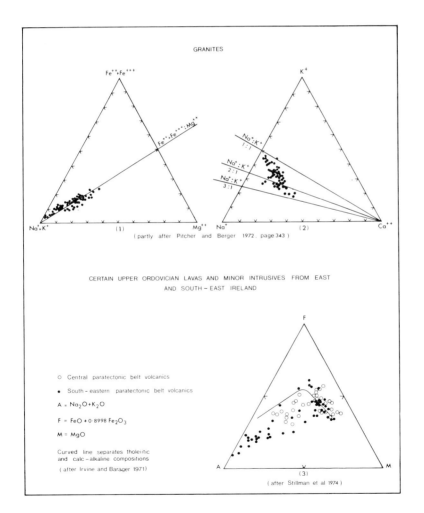

Fig. 61

Some chemical characteristics of Irish Caledonian igneous rocks.

partial melt of basic volcanics, or even of the grey-wackes containing large amounts of recently derived basic material, so that it would be unwise to entirely discount such a source area. Furthermore oxygen isotopes from granite plutons also indicate the possibility of magma derivation from the melting of high $\delta^{18}O$ metasediments or altered volcanic rocks and that the primary (magmatic) water in the batholiths is derived by dehydration and/or partial melting of lower crust or subducted lithosphere.

It remains to discuss the emplacement of the granites relative to their tectonic situation. Isotopic and structural evidence show that they were emplaced late in the process of cratonising and welding together the plates which subsequently became the continental crust of north-western Europe. They are found on both sides of the suture, and with the notable exception of the Newry and Crossdowney plutons, occur in regions where the pre-Caledonian crust was thick. It is perhaps significant that the only major intrusions which show reasonable evidence of evolution by crystal fractionation from a magma more basic than granodiorite is the Newry pluton, situated in the Longford–Down massif where there are no extensive acid volcanics.

As regards their actual sites of emplacement, Leake cogently argues control by deep crustal dislocations which may have extended to the mantle. He suggests that both siting and timing of granite emplacement in Ireland may be controlled by major deep faulting which triggered off the granite episodes so that, although the lower crust would reach partial melting temperatures during the metamorphic climax, the granite emplacement is not restricted to this climax, nor is emplacement a continuous process throughout the orogenic episode.

BIBLIOGRAPHY

BRINDLEY, J. C.   1969   Caledonian and Pre-Caledonian Intrusive Rocks of Ireland. *In* Kay, M. (Ed.). *North Atlantic – Geology and Continental Drift. Mem. Am. Ass. Petrol. Geol.*, **12**, 336–353.

BRINDLEY, J. C.   1973   The structural setting of the Leinster Granite, Ireland – a review. *Scient. proc. R. Dubl. Soc. Ser. A*, 5, 27–36.

BRÜCK, P. M. & O'CONNOR, P. J.   1977   The Leinster Batholith: Geology and Geochemistry of the Northern Units. *Geol. Surv. Ireland Bull.*, 2, 107–141.

HARTLEY, J. J.   1933   The geology of north-eastern Tyrone and the adjacent portions of County Londonderry. *Proc. R. Ir. Acad.*, **41B**, 218–285.

LAMBERT, R. St. J. & MILLS, A. A.   1961   Some critical points for the Palaeozoic time scale from the British Isles. *Ann.N.Y.Acad.Sci.*, **91**, 378–388.

LEAKE, B. E.   1970   The fragmentation of the Connemara basic and ultrabasic intrusions. *In* Newall, G. and Rast, N. (Eds.). *Mechanism of Igneous Intrusion.* Geol. J. Special Issue No. 2, 103–122.

LEAKE, B. E.   1978   Granite emplacement: the granites of Ireland and their origin. *In* Bowes, D. R. and Leake, B. E. (Eds.). *Crustal evolution in northwestern Britain and adjacent regions.* Geol. J. Spec. Issue No. 10, 221–248.

LEGGO, P. J., COMPSTON, W., & LEAKE, B. E.   1966   The geochronology of the Connemara granites and its bearing on the antiquity of the Dalradian Series. *Q. Jl. geol. Soc. Lond.*, **122**, 91–118.

LEGGO, P. J., TANNER, P. W. G., & LEAKE, B. E.   1969   Isochron Study of Donegal Granite and Certain Dalradian Rocks of Britain. *In* Kay, M. (Ed.). *North Atlantic – Geology and Continental Drift. Mem. Am. Ass. Petrol. Geol.*, 12, 354–362.

O'CONNOR, P. J. 1976 Rb-Sr whole-rock isochron for the Newry Granodiorite, (for N. E. Ireland. *Scient. Proc. R. Dubl. Soc. Ser. A*, 5, 407–1975) 413.

PHILLIPS, W. E. A., STILLMAN, C. J., & MURPHY, T. 1976 A Caledonian plate tectonic model. *Jl. geol. Soc. Lond.*, 132, 579–609.

PIDGEON, R. T. 1969 Zircon U-Pb ages from the Galway granite and the Dalradian, Connemara, Ireland. *Scott. J. Geol.*, 5, 375–392.

PITCHER, W. S. & BERGER, A. R. 1972 *The Geology of Donegal: A Study of Granite Emplacement and Unroofing*. Wiley-Interscience, New York and London, pp. 435.

RINGWOOD, A. E. 1974 The petrological evolution of island arc systems. *Jl. geol. Soc. Lond.*, 130, 183–204.

RYAN, P. D. & ARCHER, J. B. 1977 The South Mayo Trough: a possible Ordovician Gulf of California-type marginal basin in the west of Ireland. *Can. J. Earth Sci.*, 14, 2453–2461.

STILLMAN, C. J. & WILLIAMS, C. T. 1978 Geochemistry and tectonic setting of some Upper Ordovician volcanic rocks in east and southeast Ireland. *Earth & Planet Sci. Lett.*, 41, 288–310.

SUTTON, J. 1971 Orogeny. *In* Gass, I. G., Smith, P. J., and Wilson, R. C. (Eds). *Understanding the Earth*. Artemis Press, Sussex (For the Open University), 287–299.

WRIGHT, P. C. 1964 The petrology, chemistry and structure of the Galway Granite of the Carna area, Co. Galway. *Proc. R. Ir. Acad.*, 63B, 239–264.

7

LATE CALEDONIAN DEFORMATION

W. E. A. Phillips and C. H. Holland

At many localities in Ireland an angular unconformity is exposed between folded Palaeozoic rocks and clastic rocks of uppermost Devonian or Lower Carboniferous age (Fig. 75). This unconformity reflects widespread formation of folds, cleavage, and faults in the Caledonides within the period from late Silurian to latest Devonian.

In Galway, the Wenlock sedimentary rocks south of Killary Harbour were folded before the intrusion of microgranite sills which are probably of the same age as the Lower Devonian granites of Connemara (Chapter 6). Similar evidence for late Silurian or early Devonian deformation is seen in south Connemara, where the South Connemara Group (page 56) was folded and cleaved before intrusion of the Lower Devonian Galway Granite. Near Pomeroy in County Tyrone, the Lower Old Red Sandstone sediments of the Fintona block rest with angular unconformity upon folded late Ordovician and Silurian rocks. According to Reynolds, the Newry Granodiorite was emplaced after folding (F1) of the adjacent Silurian greywackes. The pluton has been dated at 399 ± 23 m.y. indicating a Lower-Middle Devonian age; later deformation has produced a strong marginal foliation in the pluton.

There is also evidence of widespread deformation younger than the Lower Devonian. Pre-Carboniferous north-east to south-west trending open folds are developed in the Lower Old Red Sandstone of the Fintona and Curlew Mountains inliers. There are also pre-Carboniferous folds of Caledonoid trend as well as low-angle thrusts in the Middle Devonian rocks near Castlebar in County Mayo.

The style of the late Caledonian deformation varies considerably across Ireland, and it is possible to recognise four distinct structural zones which are named in Figure 62. The Dalradian zone contains the metamorphic rocks of the orthotectonic Caledonides

other than the Connemara inlier. These rocks behaved in a relatively rigid fashion during the late Caledonian deformation; faulting was the main form of strain. Ductile strain in the form of upright locally polyphase folds and cleavage is important in the Murrisk zone. These features were imposed on the lower Ordovician rocks of the orthotectonic Caledonides of Mayo, on the Silurian cover, and to a lesser extent on Devonian rocks. Faulting becomes the more important strain feature in the Dalradian of the Connemara inlier. The Longford–Down zone is typified by steeply dipping, overturned or inverted bedding facing generally north-westwards with strike faulting bringing up older rocks to the north-west. Polyphase folds and cleavages are locally folded into a recumbent attitude, and pre-cleavage folds and strike faults are important. The structural style of the Leinster zone is comparable to that of Murrisk with upright locally polyphase folds and associated cleavage.

Dalradian zone

The most important late Caledonian structure of this zone is the Leannan fault of Donegal and its probable continuation in County Mayo, the Leck fault. The Leannan fault is a composite fracture extending from Killybegs to Malin Head. M. R. Dobson and D. Evans have used geophysical data to trace the fault farther north-eastwards through the island of Islay to join the Great Glen fault of Scotland. In Donegal the fault is marked by a zone of breccia and mylonite up to 200 m wide. Sinistral displacement is indicated by curved mylonitic cleavage, *en echelon* tension veins, and stepped striations on the fault plane. There is also evidence for vertical uplift on the north-west side; this is probably dated by K/Ar biotite ages of 370 m.y. from Inishtrahull. Available evidence is consistent with the hypothesis that the upright D1 synformal axis of central Donegal and Derry is displaced sinistrally by about 160 km to the Clew Bay area (Chapter 3). The fault near Killybegs is unconformably covered by late Tournaisian clastic sediments, whose facies changes indicate a local south-east facing palaeoslope over the fault. The main fault movement was both before and after deposition

of the possibly Lower Old Red Sandstone sediments at Ballymostocker Bay (see page 123). To the east, the north-east to south-west trending Belshade fault shows a 3.5 km sinistral displacement of the Barnesmore Granite.

The Leck fault outcrops between Clare Island and Lough Conn in western County Mayo. On Clare Island the horizontally slickensided vertical fault is

Fig. 62. Late Caledonian structures in Ireland. A A', B B' lines of sections in Figure 65. Ch = Clogher Head, Db = Devilsbit Mountains, In = Inishtrahull, Kd = Kildare, Kh = Killary Harbour, LA = Lough Acanon, N = Navan, NG = Newry Granodiorite, SC = South Connemara Group, Sh = Shercock, SIB = Slieve Bernagh.

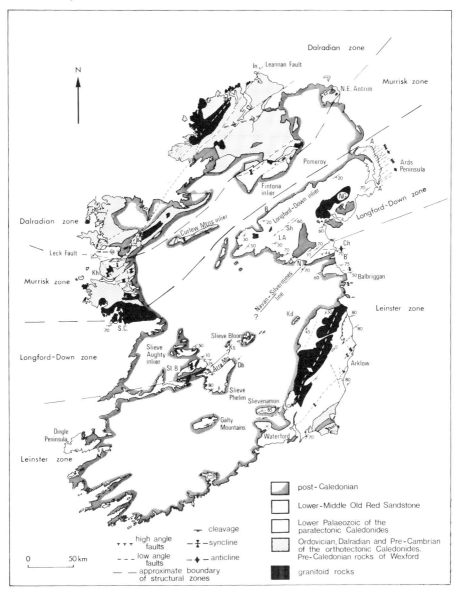

associated with both vertical and low-angle splay faults. Post-Wenlock sinistral displacement is indicated by the apparent removal of the high grade metamorphic source area inferred for the local Silurian rocks. It is also indicated by a 4·8 km sinistral displacement on a sub-parallel splay fault, by the pattern of second-order dextral and normal faults, and by the associated graben and monoclinal (F4) features. Alkaline ultrabasic dykes, sills, and plugs with marginal gas breccias were intruded during faulting. These intrusions are later than an episode of low-angle thrusting and are probably of Middle to Upper Devonian age, for the Middle Devonian rocks near Castlebar are cut by similar low-angle faults. On the south side of Clew Bay another late (F4) monocline in the Silurian rocks, and further small intrusions of alkaline ultrabasic rocks and gas breccias, are associated with the fault. Farther east the fault curves into a north-east to south-west trend in the south-west Ox Mountains, where it consists of a

series of low-angle and vertical fractures which displace rocks as young as Middle Devonian. Here the fault separates the south-easterly striking Dalradian of the North Mayo inlier from the south-westerly striking Caledonian structures of the Ox Mountains inlier (Fig. 63). If allowance is made for 160 km sinistral displacement, then the north-west to south-east strike of the North Mayo inlier and of central Donegal become aligned (Fig. 11). The Leck fault formed a north-facing fault-line escarpment against which is embanked up to 700 m of southerly derived breccias and fluviatile sediments of Tournaisian age. The fault as a whole was probably active during the Wenlock, controlling the local shore line and volcanicity. Later sinistral strike-slip movement was important in Middle-Upper Devonian times and was probably responsible for the north-east to south-west trending folds and faults in the Middle Devonian rocks. There is also a post-Carboniferous vertical downthrow to the north of up to 1·5 km.

Fig. 63. Late Caledonian structures in south Mayo and north-west Galway. A B, C D lines of sections in Figure 64. CG = Corvock Granite, CPS = Croagh Patrick synclinorium, DBF = Derry Bay fault, DRF = Doon Rock fault, ET = Emlagh thrust, Lo = Louisburgh, MF = Maam fault, MPS = Mweelrea-Partry syncline, OA = Oughty anticline, TF = Toormakeady fault.

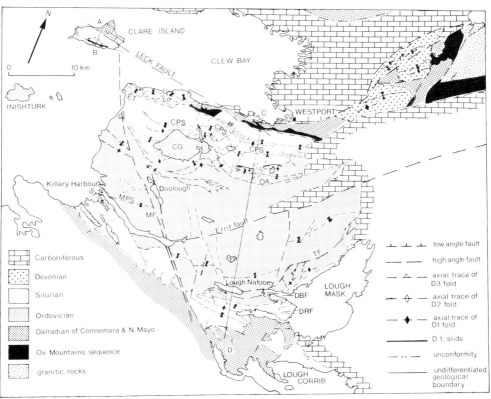

Murrisk zone

The northern boundary of the second zone (Fig. 62) has been drawn to separate the Dalradian zone from the most northerly outcrops of Devonian and Lower Palaeozoic rocks with upright late Caledonian folds. In Scotland this boundary coincides with the Highland Boundary fault, whose Middle Devonian reverse fault movement has downthrown Lower Old Red Sandstone to the south-east, against the Dalradian. There is little justification for the frequent assumption that the late Caledonian component of this fault continues into Ireland. In Antrim there is no evidence for a fault of this age either within the Lower Old Red Sandstone outcrop, or separating it from the Dalradian outcrop to the north. In Tyrone, low-angle faulting appears to be associated with the first deformation of the Dalradian rocks during the Ordovician (Chapter 3). The serpentinites along the south side of Clew Bay and on Clare Island have often been compared with the serpentinites along the Highland Boundary fault in Scotland. However, the early serpentinites of the Clew Bay area are part of the Pre-Caledonian basement of the Ox Mountains sequence (Chapter 2), while the late ultrabasic intrusions and associated monocline are clearly linked to the Leck fault and hence with the Leannan and Great Glen fault system. The northern boundary of the Murrisk zone reflects a southward transition into a more deformed area, and also a transition into an area

where erosion has not yet removed a cover which deformed in a more ductile fashion than its basement.

In the western part of this zone (Fig. 64), the Silurian rocks just south of the Leck fault on Clare Island and in the Louisburgh area (Fig. 63), show upright sub-horizontally plunging east-west buckle folds (F1), with poorly developed cleavage and minor upright F2 folds. These mildly deformed rocks have been thrust southwards during a third, probably Middle-Upper Devonian, deformation, and overlie much more deformed Silurian rocks of the Croagh Patrick synclinorium. The east-west trending Croagh Patrick synclinorium is an upright variably plunging first structure. J. F. Dewey and J. McManus have shown that deformation here started with buckling and flexural slip accompanied by cross-buckling; this produced major culminations and depressions of fold plunge. During imposition of a penetrative first cleavage and growth of muscovite and biotite, strain ranged from a dominant flattening on cleavage in the plunge depressions to stretching upwards at about 40° to the west in plunge culminations. Minor tectonic slides appear to have been formed by local rapid changes in strain across the strike. Emplacement of the Corvock Granite started during D1, for hornfelsic cordierite and biotite grew with the S1 cleavage; however the granite was finally emplaced at the end of the first deformation. A second deformation (D2) produced minor upright folds and a west-north-west to east-south-east trending crenulation cleavage. Bulk

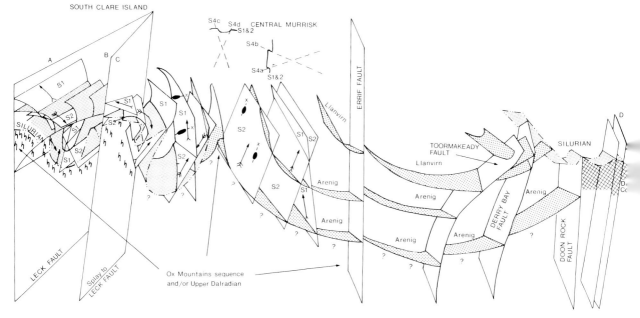

Fig. 64. Structural profile of the Caledonides of south Mayo and north-west Galway. Lines of section on Figure 63.

strain during D2 involved lateral shortening with vertical extension (Table 11). These structures are superposed on the pre-Silurian Mweelrea-Partry syncline in the Ordovician rocks. Their intensity decreases southwards across this Ordovician fold. Simple upright east-west buckle folds with poorly developed cleavage are seen in the Silurian rocks farther south in north-west County Galway. Anticlines often pass down into faults which cut the underlying Dalradian basement here. Later structures are largely confined to the area north of the Mweelrea-Partry syncline. The third deformation here is defined by local vertically plunging east-west folds reflecting a component of east-west sinistral slip along the strike. This was followed by formation of two sets of conjugate normal kink bands which grade into crenulation cleavages (S4a-d) reflecting a phase of vertical shortening and north-south extension. This phase is probably of the same age as the D4 monoclines which rotated earlier upright structures to a flat attitude in the vicinity of the Leck fault and its ultrabasic intrusive suit. Phases of shortening along the strike with lateral expansion produced conjugate kink-bands

(D5) and conjugate wrench faults (D7). Lateral shortening and axial extension caused D6 and D8 conjugate wrench faults which appear to overlap emplacement of Lower Devonian granites in Connemara. In the region of the Croagh Patrick synclinorium the unusual intensity of deformation and the greenschist facies metamorphism may well have developed under the influence of the synkinematic Corvock Granite and of strike slip movement on the Leck fault.

In the Curlew Mountains inlier, the late Caledonian deformation resulted in dips of up to 80° to the south-east in the Silurian and a north-east to south-west trending syncline with an overturned north-west limb in the probably Lower Old Red Sandstone rocks. A comparable syncline and considerable faulting are seen in the Lower Old Red Sandstone of the Fintona block in Counties Fermanagh and Tyrone. Earlier pre-Devonian folds and a south-easterly dipping thrust are seen in the late Ordovician and Silurian rocks of the Pomeroy inlier. Open north-east to south-west trending buckle folds are also seen in the Lower Old Red Sandstone of County Antrim.

Fig. 65. Structural profiles through the Longford-Down inlier. A A′ Ards Peninsula, County Down (T. B. Anderson unpublished information); B B′ Redhills—Clogher Head. Lines of section on Figure 62.

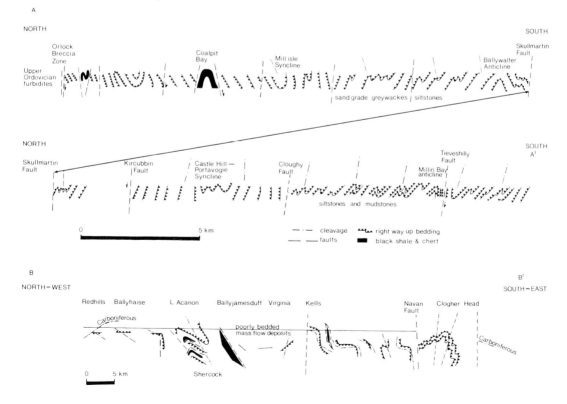

Longford–Down zone

The structural features of this third zone have already been defined. The zone is also distinctive in containing a conformable succession of black shales and greywackes ranging in age from late Llanvirn to late Wenlock. Unlike the situation in the Murrisk zone there is no angular unconformity to mark the early Caledonian deformation of the orthotectonic Caledonides. In Scotland, the northern boundary of the analogous zone (the Southern Uplands) is marked by the Middle Devonian displacement down to the north-west on the Southern Uplands fault. This fault may continue into Ireland lying beneath a Carboniferous

		Leinster zone			Longford–Down zone		Murrisk zone
		south-east Leinster	Leinster Granite	west Wicklow – Slieve Phelim	south central inliers south Longford–Down	north Longford – Down	south Mayo
brittle structures	D9	(inset diagram)					faults oblique wrench sinistral slip along str
	D8						faults primary wrench
	D7						faults secondary wrench
	D6						faults primary wrench granites c.410
	D5	faults secondary wrench	faults primary wrench		faults oblique wrench dextral slip on strike lamprophyre		kinks secondary wrench
	D4	faults primary wrench	kinks secondary wrench	faults primary wrench	F4 & kinks secondary wrench	faults primary wrench	F4 secondary gravity
ductile structures	D3	kinks secondary wrench	F3 secondary gravity	kinks secondary wrench	F3 secondary gravity	kinks F3 secondary wrench	F3 oblique wrench sinistral slip along s
	D2	F2 primary thrust? secondary gravity?	F2 secondary wrench — granite 428+10 m.y	F2 primary thrust? secondary gravity?	F2 secondary gravity lamprophyre	F2 secondary gravity — granite 399+23	F2 primary thrust
	D1	F1 primary thrust or radial	F1 primary wrench	F1 primary thrust	F1 primary wrench	F1 primary thrust	F1 primary thrust primary wrench

Inset diagram (in table): (b) secondary wrench — strike; (a) primary wrench — strike

Table 11. Summary of structural sequences within the paratectonic Caledonides, using the concept of stress regimes:

Primary radical = horizontal shortening normal to strike, both vertical and horizontal extension (flattening).

Primary thrust = horizontal shortening normal to strike, (lateral shortening), vertical extension.

Primary wrench = horizontal shortening normal to strike, lateral shortening). and, horizontal extension parallel to strike, (axial extension). | (a)

Secondary wrench = horizontal shortening parallel to strike, (axial shortening). and, horizontal extension normal to strike, (lateral extension). | (b)

Oblique wrench = horizontal extension oblique to strike, and, horizontal shortening oblique to strike.

Secondary gravity = vertical shortening, and, horizontal extension normal to strike, (lateral extension).

(a) and (b) refer to inset diagram in table.

cover well north of the Longford–Down massif. It is possible that this line continues westwards into the Derry Bay, Doon Rock, and Salrock fault system of north-west County Galway. The post-Silurian pre-Carboniferous displacement here is however an up-thrust to the south. Despite much speculation, there is little justification for extrapolating the Southern Uplands fault to the north side of Galway Bay or to the Dingle peninsula. The northern boundary of the Longford–Down zone may well be a gradational one obscured by a Carboniferous cover.

Detailed structural analysis here is very far from complete at present and it is possible only to give a rather general outline based on a few probably representative areas. In the Ards peninsula, T. B. Anderson has found that the steep or overturned bedding faces predominantly to the north-north-west. Tight upward-facing F1 folds have steeply inclined axial planes emphasised in pelites by a slaty cleavage and in places there is a near-vertical stretching lineation. Folds plunge east-north-eastwards at between 15° and 60°. Despite the overall facing of bedding to the north-north-west, uppermost Llandovery rocks crop out at the southern end of the peninsula and upper Ordovician rocks at the northern end. This anomalous positioning of the older rocks, which is a general feature of the Longford–Down zone, can be accounted for by the effect of strike faults bringing up older rocks north-westwards. Recently D. Cameron and W. E. A. Phillips have found that southwards from the Ards peninsula there is a systematic apparently clockwise offset of the strike of cleavage away from the strike of axial planes of F1 folds (Fig. 66) and the stretching lineation is usually nearly horizontal. It appears therefore that axial extension becomes the main strain pattern towards the south of the zone as a whole. It is also clear that post-F1 deformation is more extensive to the south (Fig. 65). Towards the end of a phase of intrusion of early lamprophyre dykes in the Ards peninsula a second deformation formed small monoclinal folds with an associated crenulation cleavage dipping gently north-eastwards. A third deformation is marked by a vertical set of north-west to south-east sinistral and north-north-east to south-south-west dextral kink bands, which were followed by some strike faulting and intrusion of a younger series of lamprophyre dykes. To the south-west, Anderson has suggested that diapiric rising of the Newry Granodiorite may have caused the steep plunges of F1 folds. The intensity and the polyphase nature of the deformation increase to the south.

Figure 65 shows a structural profile across the Navan–Cavan sector of the Longford–Down massif. J. H. Morris has shown that the earliest structures are pre-cleavage folds and faults inferred from the frequent changes of facing direction of bedding on the first cleavage.

In the Shercock area (Fig. 37), O'Connor has shown that over a distance of at least 15 km across the strike, bedding faces predominantly down at about 50° to the south-east on the first cleavage. It is likely that some of the pre-cleavage deformation was again caused by large-scale slumping. The cleavage is roughly parallel to the axial plane of close to tight F2 folds whose wavelength varies from a few metres to several kilometres as at Lough Acanon to the south-west of Shercock.

In the Navan–Cavan sector as a whole a third deformation produced a series of north-east to south-west trending monoclines which are responsible for alternations between steep and flat attitudes of cleavage. In general these monoclines form a series of steps of bedding and cleavage, which ascend (verge) north-westwards with low dipped limbs becoming dominant in that direction. Though F3 style and orientation are comparable to those of the F2 monoclines of the Ards peninsula, some of these structures are much larger in this central part of the inlier. There is evidence of two phases of monoclines in the south of this section, those with south-easterly dipping axial planes being older than those with axial planes dipping to the north-west. In the Shercock and Lough Acanon areas there is a fourth deformation which formed north-west to south-east trending cross-folds with steep axial planes and wavelengths up to 1 km. Here also, the strike faults bounding the Ordovician pelites appear to be folded by fourth folds.

Farther west in the inliers of south Connemara, Slieve Aughty (Fig. 68), the Arra Mountains and Slieve Bernagh, work in progress has shown that there is a structural regime similar to that of the Longford–Down inlier. Strike faulting of several ages is particularly important in the Arra Mountains and in Slieve Bernagh. Weir has noted that in Slieve Bernagh the Ordovician pelites outcrop in fault-bounded slices within anticlinal cores.

Leinster zone

Although additional work may show that the boundary is not clear-cut, it appears at present that the Navan–Nenagh (Navan–Silvermines) line already referred to in discussion of Ordovician stratigraphy and Silurian palaeogeography (pages 50 and 74) provides a north-western limit for the Leinster zone, to the south-east of which persistent inversion of Lower Palaeozoic strata and nearly flat-lying cleavage are not seen. North-east of Navan this line is actually a fault, separating the Ordovician of the Grangegeeth–Collon inlier from the Silurian rocks to the north.

Within a belt of up to 50 km on either side of the Navan–Silvermines line, there is a distinctive pattern of wrench faults. Sinistral faults strike at about 90° to the line and dextral ones are sub-parallel to it. This pattern is consistent with a major component of dextral strike slip within this belt. Dextral strike slip is also indicated here by the dextral rotation of minor veins (Fig. 67) and lamprophyre dykes on the cleavage in Silurian greywackes along the coast of County Louth.

Caledonian rocks and cleavage to the south-east of this boundary strike regionally approximately west-south-westwards on the coast near Balbriggan, swing south-westwards in the Leinster massif itself, and return to an approximately west-south-westerly orientation in the Galty Mountains and farther west in the Dingle peninsula. Within the southern part of the Slieve Phelim inlier alone R. J. P. Doran has demonstrated local variations in strike of bedding and cleavage, through ninety degrees from north-south to east-west.

The Caledonian cycle in this zone begins with Lower to Middle Cambrian deposition of the Bray Group and its equivalents, followed by the Upper Cambrian to lower Ordovician Ribband Group. The importance of a pre-cleavage soft-sediment deformation has been demonstrated in the Bray Group of Howth and probably also in Wicklow (pages 43 and

Fig. 66

View to west of F1 anticline in Wenlock greywackes on the south side of Clogher Head, County Louth. S1 cleavage fans around the fold but strikes 265°: the axial plane of the fold strikes 256°: the cleavage is not parallel to the axial plane of the fold. The locality is actually a little south of the southern boundary of the Longford-Down zone.

Photograph by A. E. W. Phillips

Fig. 67

Carbonate veins showing dextral offset on S1 cleavage and a dextrally curved kink band. Silurian siltstones, Salterstown coast section, County Louth.

Photograph by A. E. W. Phillips

47). Minor warping and uplift in mid-Ordovician times are marked by the widely recognised unconformity referred to in Chapter 4. This effect is seen to disappear north-westwards. Thus a structural break is absent in the Ordovician successions of Slievenamon and probably also in the area to the north-west of the Leinster Granite. P. M. Shannon suggests that the Ribband Series–Ordovician volcanic group boundary is markedly unconformable in the eastern limb of the major syncline which trends south-westwards between New Ross and Wexford, but that it is, at the least, noticeably less so in the western limb.

The upper Ordovician period is marked by intensive volcanicity described in Chapter 6. The main belt of volcanism extended from Arklow to Waterford and these rocks now form the axial zone of the major syncline referred to above. In Waterford the volcanicity is associated with north-south faulting, downthrowing to the west. Volcanism in this belt ended in the Ashgill but in the Dingle peninsula there is abundant evidence of mid-Silurian volcanicity (pages 75 and 91).

Late Silurian or early Devonian compression produced the regional strike trend already described. North-west of the syncline which passes between Wexford and New Ross a major anticline evidently runs to the west of the main outcrop of the Bray Group, the structure of which Brück has observed to be largely synclinal (page 47). The Leinster granites probably rose along the anticline at a late stage of D1 and before D2. The same anticline may be traceable along the Suir valley underneath the Carboniferous and lying between the Slievenamon inlier (with its Cambrian rocks to the south-east) and the Lower Palaeozoic inlier of the Comeraghs. Thirdly, a major synclinal belt can be traced through the Wenlock inliers of Slieve Bloom and the Slieve Phelim–Devilsbit inliers.

As to the dating of these major (F1) folds, in various areas of the Leinster zone Wenlock rocks are followed unconformably by Upper Old Red Sandstone, the latter extending in age from place to place possibly from high Middle Devonian, through Upper Devonian, to Lower Carboniferous (Chapter 8). In the Dingle peninsula the Upper Old Red Sandstone in places rests unconformably upon the Dingle Group, the latter following directly upwards from fossiliferous middle Ludlow rocks. Thus the movements here can be dated more precisely as post-Downtonian (post-Přidoli) or younger. Middle Devonian would be a reasonable estimate of age.

The major folds have varied plunge and a general flattening strain on cleavage parallel to their axial planes. An axial stretching lineation becomes important near the batholiths. Smaller F1 folds have a scale

Fig. 68

Flute moulds stretched parallel to cleavage-bedding intersection on inverted base of greywacke dipping towards the observer; quarry in Killanena Formation, Silurian, Townland of Knockbeha east of Lough Graney, Slieve Aughty, County Clare.

Photograph by C. H. Holland

Fig. 69. F3 kink-bands affecting S1 in slates of Slate Quarries Formation, Kilmalum, County Kildare. A weakly developed S3 fracture cleavage is seen.

Photograph by P. M. Brück

of a few kilometres downwards and may be symmetrical, isoclinal, or asymmetrical. Again they show variation in plunge. Late D1 conjugate faults are developed in places. The Leinster granites and their associated dykes were emplaced after D1 and caused major lateral and axial extension.

Later structures are variously developed in different areas of the Leinster zone. Near the batholiths axial shortening is reflected by a west-north-west striking steep crenulation cleavage (S2) at a high angle to S1. Away from the batholiths minor F2 folds and steeply dipping crenulation cleavage are sometimes developed striking close to S1 but slightly clockwise from it. Small D3 monoclines and kinks are locally present (Fig. 69), which are co-axial with F1 and reflect a phase of vertical shortening with lateral expansion. Conjugate kink-bands (D4) indicate minor shortening with lateral expansion before a return to the lateral shortening and axial extension shown by conjugate wrench and normal faults.

It must be emphasised that the major consistent characteristic of deformation in the Leinster zone is the development of F1 upright folds with one obvious axial planar cleavage which may or may not be penetrative. The style of deformation is illustrated in sections across the Slieve Phelim and Slievenamon inliers (Fig. 70). The areas are not well exposed, the occasional larger quarry face demonstrating the prevalence of minor faulting in these rocks.

The effects of Caledonian deformation in the Leinster zone decrease to the south-west where, conversely, Hercynian effects are seen to increase in importance. Thus in the Dingle peninsula (Fig. 71) there is no Caledonian cleavage but the regional Hercynian cleavage is present in restricted zones. Here Caledonian folds have been compressed and overturned by Hercynian movements. Parkin has recognised small scale Caledonian chevron folds in the thinly bedded Ludlow rocks of the Derrymore Formation. Steeply inclined Hercynian faults further affect the Silurian rocks of the Dingle peninsula. Eastwards in Slievenamon, on the other hand, there

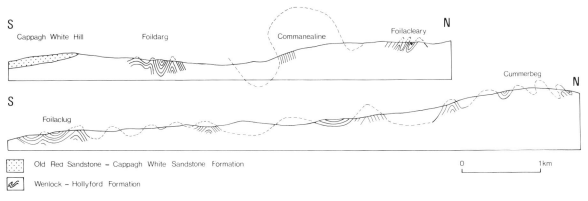

Fig. 70

Above: sections through the Hollyford district, southern part of Slieve Phelim-Devilsbit inlier, County Tipperary (from R. J. P. Doran, unpublished Ph.D. thesis, University of Dublin 1971).

Below: diagrammatic section through part of the Ahenny Formation, Linguan Valley, Slievenamon inlier, county Tipperary (after J. R. J. Colthurst 1974).

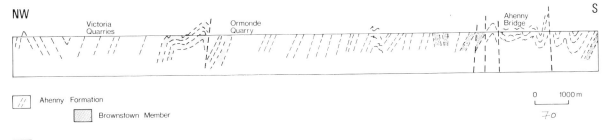

is a well developed Caledonian cleavage (S1) together
with a Hercynian fracture cleavage seen to a variable
extent in the overlying Upper Old Red Sandstone but
not recognisable in the Lower Palaeozoic.

The Dingle Peninsula provides in the south-west
the last that is seen of the Leinster zone. In the south-
east of Ireland the zone has a normal fault bounded
basinal margin, beyond which Lower Palaeozoic
rocks are confined to a small area of Arenig sediments (page 51) which have been gently folded and
faulted, and rest unconformably upon Pre-Cambrian.

An obvious feature of the late Caledonian structures as a whole is the regional swing in strike from
north-east/south-west to about east-west. In north-
west Galway and Connemara, W. A. Morris has
shown from palaeomagnetic evidence that the local
near east-west strike has been rotated by about 30°
clockwise prior to the Upper Devonian. In south-
eastern Ireland the late Caledonian fault pattern
appears to have been rotated with the swing in strike.
It seems likely therefore that a very late Caledonian
deformation is responsible for this swing in strike
throughout the paratectonic Caledonides.

The structural sequences within the paratectonic
Caledonides are summarised in Table 11, using the
concept of strain regimes. Major extension along
strike becomes more important than vertical extension in the vicinity of the Navan–Silvermines line
and to a lesser extent in the regions of the Leinster
granites and of the Leck fault.

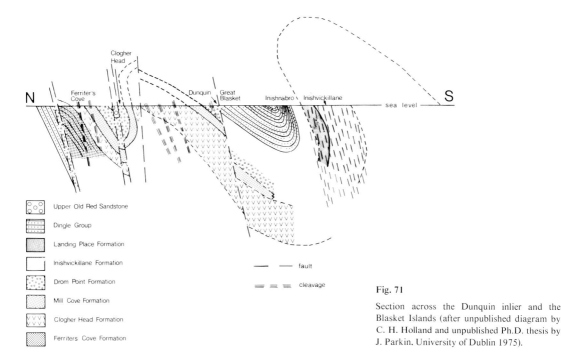

Upper Old Red Sandstone

Dingle Group

Landing Place Formation

Inishvickillane Formation

Drom Point Formation

Mill Cove Formation

Clogher Head Formation

Ferriters Cove Formation

—— fault

≡ ≡ ≡ cleavage

Fig. 71

Section across the Dunquin inlier and the
Blasket Islands (after unpublished diagram by
C. H. Holland and unpublished Ph.D. thesis by
J. Parkin, University of Dublin 1975).

BIBLIOGRAPHY

BRENCHLEY, P. J. & 1970 The stratigraphy and structure of the Ordovician rocks
  TREAGUS, J. E. between Courtown and Kilmichael Point, Co. Wexford.
 Proc. R. Ir. Acad., **69B**, 83–102.

BRÜCK, P. M. 1973 Structure of the Lower Palaeozoic greywacke formations
 west of the Leinster Granite in Counties Kildare and West
 Wicklow. *Scient. Proc. R. Dubl. Soc. Ser. A*, **4**, 391–409.

COLTHURST, J. R. J. 1974 The Lower Palaeozoic rocks of the Slievenamon inlier,
 Tipperary. *Scient. Proc. R. Dubl. Soc. Ser. A*, **5**, 265–276.

CRIMES, T. P. & 1968 The stratigraphy, sedimentology, ichnology, and structure
  CROSSLEY, J. D. of the Lower Palaeozoic rocks of part of north-eastern Co.
 Wexford. *Proc. R. Ir. Acad.*, **67B**, 185–215.

DEWEY, J. F. 1967 The structural and metamorphic history of the Lower
 Palaeozoic rocks of central Murrisk, County Mayo, Eire.
 Q. Jl. geol. Soc. Lond., **123**, 124–155.

DEWEY, J. F. 1969 Structure and sequence in paratectonic British Caledonides. *In* Kay, M. (Ed.). *North Atlantic-geology and continental drift. Mem. Am. Ass. Petrol. Geol.*, **12**, 309–335.

DEWEY, J. F. & 1964 Superposed folding in the Silurian rocks of Co. Mayo,
  McMANUS, J. Eire. *Geol. J.*, **4**, 61–76.

DEWEY, J. F. & 1963 A tectonic profile across the Caledonides of South Mayo.
  PHILLIPS, W. E. A. *Lpool. Manchr. Geol. J.*, **3**, 237–246.

PHILLIPS, W. E. A., 1969 Geologic comparison of western Ireland and northeastern
  KENNEDY, M. J., & Newfoundland. *In* Kay, M. (Ed.). *North Atlantic-geology
  DUNLOP, G. M. and continental drift. Mem. Am. Ass. Petrol. Geol.*, **12**,
 194–211.

PITCHER, W. S. 1969 Northeast-trending faults of Scotland and Ireland, and
 chronology of displacements. *In* Kay, M. (Ed.). *North
 Atlantic-geology and continental drift. Mem. Am. Ass.
 Petrol. Geol.*, **12**, 724–733

VAN LUNSEN, H. A. & 1975 The geology of Howth and Ireland's Eye, Co. Dublin.
  MAX, M. D. *Geol. J.*, **10**, 35–58.

8

DEVONIAN

C. H. Holland

As the opposing shores of the Proto–Atlantic ocean (or seaway) closed and the final phases of the Caledonian earth movements affected the rocks of both orthotectonic and paratectonic Caledonides, the newly uplifted continental areas began to shed their detritus into mountain torrents, into alluvial fans and complexes of meandering or braided streams, into transient lakes, and into areas marginal to the new shallow seas to the south, themselves bordering the newly significant geosynclinal trough, the deposits of which are seen widely across Europe from Brittany to the Harz Mountains and beyond. Corresponding to the marine Devonian deposits of these southern areas, a substantial glimpse of which is available in the south-west peninsula of Britain, were developments of continental deposits related to the new Caledonian lands to the north. These have long been named the *Old Red Sandstone* in contradistinction to the continental deposits of the New Red Sandstone of Permo–Triassic age. They are sometimes thought of as the 'molasse' of the Caledonides. The geography of Devonian times, in which the North American Catskill deposits of similar age seen in New York and Pennsylvania are found to correspond to those of the European Old Red Sandstone, involves a reassembly of the North Atlantic continent as it was before late Mesozoic and Cainozoic continental drift brought about its fragmentation. From such reconstructions it will be seen that what is now Ireland lay within, but close to the margin of, the great Old Red Sandstone continent (Fig. 72).

It is important, but not unexpected, to realise that the onset of these continental Old Red Sandstone conditions came at different times in different places. Thus in the Dingle Peninsula, as in South Wales, there is evidence for their beginning before the end of the Ludlow epoch. Additionally, in relation to the now internationally accepted base of the Devonian System (involving a post-Ludlow, pre-Gedinnian division of the Silurian), the whole of the Downtonian of the Anglo–Welsh basin and its equivalents (such as much of the Dingle Group) elsewhere are probably to be regarded as still within the Silurian System. At the close of the Devonian Period marine conditions became more widespread as the new Lower Carboniferous seas inundated the Old Red Sandstone continent. Again as might be expected, this effect was not instantaneous and thus the change from Old Red Sandstone to marine (and not necessarily Carboniferous as distinct from Upper Devonian) conditions came at different times in different places.

Dingle Group

The transition from fossiliferous marine Silurian sediments to those of Old Red Sandstone type is seen with certainty in Ireland only in the Dingle peninsula where the western inlier (page 76) shows a change at the top of the Croaghmarhin Formation. The marine fauna of this division becomes reduced eventually to a few crinoid ossicles and small rhynchonellid brachiopods, and finally there is a thin unit of resistant, compact, greenish micaceous siltstones above which is a transition into typical purple sediments of the succeeding Dingle Group. The youngest Silurian fossils seen are not younger than middle Ludlow in age and thus the Dingle Group includes upper Ludlow strata and, in view of its thickness, most if not all of the Downtonian. It may well pass up into lowest Devonian rocks of Gedinnian age.

The Dingle Group, over 2,000 m thick, consists of variously coloured – purple, red, greyish, or greenish – sandstones and siltstones, flaggy or more thickly bedded, with conglomerates or massive mudstones particularly at certain horizons. The great thicknesses of purple and red sandstones and siltstones with their conspicuous cross-lamination, cross-stratification, ripple marks, and desiccation cracks contribute to an impression of alluvial sedimentation on the lowlands below the newly arisen Caledonian mountains to the north. The fining-upward sequences, which J. R. L. Allen has described so carefully and convincingly from, for instance, the Lower Old Red Sandstone of the Anglo-Welsh basin, are seen at various levels. They record the repeated change from coarser channel deposits to finer overbank sediments. The conglomerates of the Dingle Group contain pebbles of older sedimentary rocks, rarely with derived Lower Palaeozoic fossils.

These rocks are well seen in the cliffs and mountains of the Dingle peninsula, for example along the precipitous road from Slea Head to the viewpoint across to the Blasket Islands, where the outcrop can clearly be seen to continue into the main mass of the Great Blasket. Another outcrop of these relatively resistant rocks runs through Sybil Head and Inishtooskert. The Dingle Group also forms the mountainous heart of the peninsula above Dingle town and includes Mount Brandon itself, the second highest mountain in Ireland (Fig. 50).

The notion that cross-stratification may be used to indicate the way-up of sedimentary sequences was first published in 1856 by Patrick Ganly, (an assistant to Richard Griffith: see Chapter 19), who, though he may have obtained the idea from observations of a modern river bank in Donegal, referred to its application to these Dingle rocks in a letter to Griffith written in 1838. Together with indications of fining-upwards and from desiccation cracks, it can be used to demonstrate the inversion of the original bedding in many sections along the peninsula. It is evident that Hercynian folding has intensified those folds already developed by Caledonian movements, after the deposition of the Dingle Group but before that of the unconformable Upper Old Red Sandstone shortly to be described.

Eastwards along the Annascaul inlier (Fig. 48), the Dingle Group is faulted against the marine Silurian. Otherwise rocks of this particular age have been thought to be represented only in the Comeragh Mountains, where S. R. Penney has now shown the suggested evidence that the so-called 'Croughaun Beds' are equivalent to the Dingle Group (rather than to the Upper Old Red Sandstone) to be unconvincing. Elsewhere in Ireland there are no clear records of Lower Old Red Sandstone (Downtonian, Dittonian, and Breconian in Anglo-Welsh terms) except in the northern areas of the Curlew Mountains, the 'Fintona block' of Fermanagh and Tyrone, north-eastern Antrim, and County Donegal.

Lower Old Red Sandstone

The fault-bounded synclinal strip of the Curlew Mountains inlier runs east-north-eastwards for some 50 km and is in faulted contact at its western end with the small Lower Palaeozoic area of Charlestown (Fig. 35). The Curlew Mountains rise to about 275 m in the centre of the strip. Poorly developed green sandstones are followed by red pebbly sandstones and conglomerates and then by red sandstones. The succession is some 1,500 m thick. There are igneous rocks, which may be intrusive in origin, associated with the lower sediments and a line of outlying patches of an uppermost division of andesitic lavas and pyroclastic rocks follows the axis of the syncline. During Lower Old Red Sandstone times the area formed part of what has been called the Ulster–Connaught basin, possibly connected to the Caledonian cuvette of Scotland. The latter shows, in what is now the Midland Valley of Scotland, extensive developments of volcanic rocks confined to the Lower Old Red Sandstone, suggesting to H. A. K. Charlesworth that the sequence in the Curlew Mountains may be of the same age. The structures present are certainly more complex than those shown by the

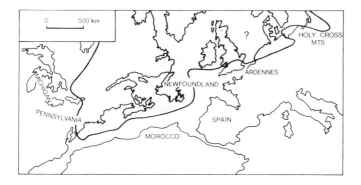

Fig. 72

Map to show position of Ireland in relation to part of the Old Red Sandstone continent in early late Devonian times.

overlying Lower Carboniferous and thus may themselves be regarded as of Middle or Lower Old Red Sandstone age.

About 50 km to the north-east, what has been called the 'Fintona block' comprises some 700 km² of sparsely populated undulating Old Red Sandstone country rising locally to 305 m. The outcrop of the Fintona Group extends from Loch Erne to near Omagh and Pomeroy and is mostly fault-bounded. There is an unconformity with the underlying Silurian near Pomeroy and beds of the Fintona Group are covered unconformably by Lower Carboniferous particularly to the south and east. The Old Red Sandstone is best exposed in the south. The structure of the whole area is roughly synclinal but a wrench fault with substantial dextral movement, the Tempo–Sixmilecross Fault, divides it into differing western and smaller eastern sectors.

A vital indication of the age of these rocks is a small plate of *Pteraspis* cf. *rostrata*, indicative of the Lower Old Red Sandstone, from near the small Silurian inlier of Lisbellaw (Fig. 35), at the south-western corner of the Fintona block. This was originally recorded by J. C. Harper and J. J. Hartley in their description of the Lisbellaw inlier. Pteraspids are much commoner in other areas of Lower Old Red Sandstone, for example in the Anglo–Welsh cuvette, where these stratigraphically useful freshwater vertebrates succeed the marine and brackish water vertebrate faunas of the Downtonian.

In the eastern sector of the Fintona block, local basal conglomerates are succeeded by more than 600 m of red, brown, and green sandstones, some 500 m of flow-banded andesitic lavas, and then by more conglomerates containing greywacke and andesitic pebbles. In the western sector, conglomerates with metamorphic rock pebbles are interbedded with dull purple or reddish brown sandstones and mudstones in changing proportions through the sequence. Cross-stratification, ripple marks, and desiccation cracks are all present.

H. E. Wilson showed that the Old Red Sandstone sediments in the western sector were derived from Dalradian sources farther north, whereas the eastern sediments have contributions from Lower Palaeozoic sediments, from the Tyrone Igneous Group, and from the Dalradian.

Continuing north-eastwards as far as the Antrim coast, Old Red Sandstone rocks are next encountered in the Cushendun–Cushendall district (Fig. 73). About 1,000 m of these rocks succeed the Dalradian unconformably south-eastwards and occupy an area of about 20 km². They provide a good example of sedimentation controlled by post-orogenic uplift adjacent to the basin of deposition.

The lowest beds seen so well at the caves on the raised beach at Cushendun (Fig. 74) are massive conglomerates containing large rounded and cracked boulders of Dalradian quartzite, some over half a metre in size, together with schists, vein quartz, and andesite. The quartzites are not present in the 'Highland Border Ridge' (see also page 202) of Dalradian immediately to the north and must have had a more distant source, before uplift and erosion of Dalradian rocks like those now seen in the adjacent ridge. These conglomerates are some 300 m thick and D. J. Sanderson has shown that near the Glenaan River they divide into four tongues passing laterally south-westwards into sandstones. The south-easterly dip then brings in a much thicker sequence of these red and purple sandstones with cross-bedding, ripple marks, and desiccation cracks. These become increasingly conglomeratic upwards and the amount of volcanic material increases, until finally the rocks are largely andesitic agglomerates containing blocks of andesite up to 2·5 m in size. There are associated ashes, and interbedded lenses of sandstone within this 'volcanic facies' show large scale cross-stratification. There is a small plug of quartz-andesite at Court McMartin near Cushendall which may indicate the position of the original volcanic vent. A larger mass of purplish dacite (the 'Cushendall porphyry') seen on the coast to the east of Cushendall is faulted against the agglomerates. It may represent a succession of lava flows. It consists of quartz, plagioclase, and orthoclase with red jasper along the joints. This in its turn is followed southwards by a conglomerate with boulders of andesite, metamorphic rocks, and of an older apparently Old Red Sandstone conglomerate. H. E. Wilson suggested that the composition and gentler dip of this unit indicate an Upper Old Red Sandstone age. To the south this small patch of conglomerate is followed by bright red Triassic rocks with, once again, a gentler dip. The Old Red Sandstone of the district has been compared very closely with nearby outcrops in the Scottish peninsula of Kintyre.

Little else remains of the (Devonian) Old Red Sandstone in northern Ireland except for a small patch of red beds in a fault trough between the two main branches of the important Leannan Fault system reaching the coast at Ballymastocker Bay, Fanad, County Donegal. This fault system is but a part of a pattern of north-east to south-west faults which affect the Dalradian rocks of north-western Ireland and can be matched in Scotland. Though there may have been earlier movement on these faults the important ones were probably post-Lower Old Red Sandstone and pre-Viséan. A thickness of 250 m of these red rocks rests with a coarse basal conglomerate on the Dalradian. This is followed by sandstones and then by more, torrentially bedded conglomerates. Dalradian boulders, some as much as 1 m in diameter, are accompanied by andesitic ones like the rocks previously referred to from Antrim. H. E. Wilson's studies of the heavy minerals indicate derivation from local Dalradian sources. Though these deposits are comparable with other Lower Old Red Sandstone rocks in northern Ireland and in Scotland, they may have accumulated in a local intermontaine trough in the recently uplifted Caledonides. Alternatively they may have formed part of the larger cuvette which extended from north-eastern Ireland into the Midland Valley of Scotland and from which a branch probably extended northwards to include the Old Red Sandstone of the Lorne plateau of Scotland. A reconstruction of this Caledonian cuvette of Lower Old Red Sandstone times involves a mountain rimmed depression with volcanoes towards its margins. There would be alluvial fans and sometimes temporary pools or lakes on the alluvial flats. A terrestrial plant cover would not yet have evolved. In such circumstances

fluctuation of the water-table would be substantial and there would be relatively brief but intensive floods.

Middle Old Red Sandstone

In the Welsh Borderland and the Midland Valley of Scotland alike, Lower Old Red Sandstone is followed unconformably by Upper Old Red Sandstone (Farlovian). Only in the so-called Orcadian Basin of Old Red Sandstone deposition in north-eastern Scotland and in the Orkneys has a Middle Old Red Sandstone (Orcadian) been clearly recognised. This rests unconformably upon pre-Devonian rocks and is followed unconformably by Upper Old Red Sandstone. Though precise correlation of these various continental deposits is very difficult it would have seemed reasonable to predict the absence of Middle Old Red Sand-

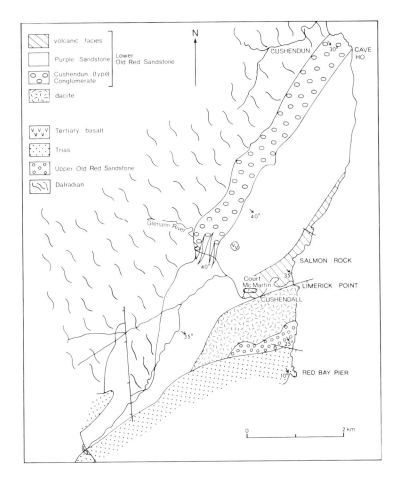

Fig. 73

Geological sketch map of the Cushendall area, County Antrim (after Sanderson 1970).

stone in Ireland; accordingly its recognition in County Mayo is of considerable interest.

East of Clew Bay, to the north-west of Castlebar (Fig. 63), several patches of Old Red Sandstone conglomerates and sandstones are seen over an area of some 20 km². They are folded and faulted and are seen to be in tectonic contact with the Dalradian of the Ox Mountain sequence. At Letter Hill, 8 km west of Castlebar, there is an angular unconformity between Old Red Sandstone conglomerates and more highly deformed andesitic volcanic rocks which may be Silurian or Lower Old Red Sandstone in age. At Glenisland on the south side of Beltra Lough a stream section shows an angular unconformity between red sediments of the basal Carboniferous and steeply dipping Old Red Sandstone conglomerates.

Siltstones from the Old Red Sandstone on the north side of Burren Hill, to the east of the Lough and north of Castlebar, have yielded critical palaeobotanical evidence. J. B. Richardson has identified an assemblage of relatively few spore species which most resemble those of the Middle Old Red Sandstone of the Orcadian Basin. They are associated with tracheids of vascular plants. Evidence for the more precise age of such spore material in terms of Devonian stages is available from marine successions elsewhere. Several of the species present here are known also from the lower part of the Frasnian Stage of the Upper Devonian but the assemblage is different from typical Frasnian ones. In any case, Richardson notes that all of the spores are known from the Orcadian Basin and all but one from the Middle Old Red Sandstone (i.e. Middle Devonian) part of that sequence.

A green micaceous siltstone from the south side of Burren Hill has yielded abundant spores and also a large fossil plant (some 140 mm in size) belonging to the pteropsid genus *Pseudosporochnus*, identified by W. G. Chaloner. He notes that this genus 'may fairly be said to be characteristic of the Middle Devonian'. It is found in north-west Europe, for example in Germany and Scotland, and in North America. It is one of a group of plants first seen at the close of the Early Devonian, which appear close to the stock from which modern ferns evolved. They show the early evolution of a complex vascular system.

During or after Lower to Middle Old Red Sandstone times came the final phase of what may still be grouped as Caledonian earth movements. James Hutton, 'the founder of modern geology' saw unconformities as demonstrating a 'succession of former worlds' and the Upper Palaeozoic world which now follows is marked off very clearly from what went before in Ireland by the often very striking unconformity at which the Upper Old Red Sandstone is seen to cut discordantly across more highly disturbed older rocks (Fig. 75).

Upper Old Red Sandstone

In the northern half of Ireland, north that is to say of a Galway–Dublin line, there are relatively small outcrops of rocks of Old Red Sandstone facies, apart from those already described above, which are probably largely of Lower Carboniferous age, the Carboniferous marine transgression arriving relatively late in these areas.

In the southern half of Ireland, on the other hand, the Upper Old Red Sandstone is much more extensively developed. Its outcrops are seen around the various Lower Palaeozoic inliers (Fig. 35) of the south-central part of the country: Slieve Aughty, Slieve Bernagh and the Arra Mountains, the Slieve Phelim–Devilsbit inlier, the Galty Mountains, Slievenamon, Knockshigowna Hill, Slieve Bloom, and the Kildare inlier. It often forms the highest, more mountainous parts of these areas. The summit of Slievenamon, for example, and the roughly oval elevated rim of the Ninemilehouse tableland of which it forms the western culmination, are of Upper Old Red Sandstone, the Lower Palaeozoic rocks forming the more subdued topography of the central tableland itself. There are also a few small inliers of Upper Old Red Sandstone in eastern County Limerick which have no associated outcrops of older rocks. Finally, there is a more extensive, though still broken, area of Upper Old Red Sandstone outcrop stretching from the Comeraghs in the east to Kerry Head in the west and southwards to the Cork coast (Fig. 2). The splendid Atlantic-type coastline of Kerry and West Cork is formed by rugged peninsulas of these Upper Old Red Sandstone rocks, separated by long bays and valleys floored by the less resistant Lower Carboniferous. The 'Kenmare river' is a good example of one of these Hercynian synclinal strips of Lower Carboniferous rocks alternating with the generally anticlinal belts of Upper Old Red Sandstone (Fig. 127).

Fig. 74. Lower Old Red Sandstone conglomerate with boulders of fractured quartzite, Cushendun, County Antrim.

Photograph Geological Survey of Northern Ireland.

Fig. 75. Unconformity between Upper Old Red Sandstone and Dingle Group, cliff approximately 600 m north-west of Bull's Head, Dingle Peninsula, County Kerry. (Reproduced from Jukes and Du Noyer 1863).

The sub-Upper Old Red Sandstone surface behaves regionally as a plane, folded and faulted by Hercynian earth movements, but of much simpler structure than the Lower Palaeozoic rocks beneath. Thus, for instance, in the southern part of the Slieve Felim–Devilsbit inlier the Upper Old Red Sandstone, referred to in this area as the Cappagh White Sandstone Formation, dips at only a few degrees southwards, the strike swinging slightly as this is really part of a gently domed structure. It consists of red and white sandstones with some finer micaceous red sandstones. The Lower Carboniferous is seen to follow conformably at Gortdrum Mine (now closed), to the north of Tipperary town. The much more tightly folded Wenlock rocks beneath have been secondarily stained red by solutions penetrating downwards from the Old Red Sandstone to a depth as much as 240 m.

The Cappagh White Sandstone Formation was, at the beginning of the 1970s, very unusual in terms of Old Red Sandstone stratigraphy of the central Irish inliers in that R. J. P. Doran had established palynological evidence for its age. A lithologically distinctive grey siltstone in the lower part of the formation yields an assemblage of miospores including the stratigraphically significant form *Spelaeotriletes [Hymenozonotriletes] lepidophytus*. This is widely distributed geographically in latest Devonian strata. In Europe it attains its maximum development in the Strunian (Tn1a) though it ranges from uppermost Famennian to lower Tournaisian (Tn1b). The succeeding Gortdrum Formation provides evidence of the transition from continental Old Red Sandstone to fully marine Carboniferous Limestone conditions. It contains spores indicative of the middle part of the Tournaisian. In other words the Old Red Sandstone facies probably continues into the Carboniferous in this area, most of the Cappagh White Sandstone Formation possibly being Strunian in age.

In detail the unconformity here as elsewhere is seen to involve irregularities of a few centimetres. In some other areas the irregularity is of the order of several metres, the Upper Old Red Sandstone occupying channels cut into the Lower Palaeozoic or Dingle Group rocks below. This is the case in the cliff section near Bull's Head to the south-east of Dingle town (Fig. 75), which provides one of the best views of this important feature in southern Ireland.

Pre-Upper Old Red Sandstone relief on a still larger scale has been convincingly demonstrated in the Galty Mountains inlier (Figs 46 and 76), where, though dips are gentle over the broad Hercynian anticlinal crest, there is evidence in the eastern part of the inlier of an east-west cliff line or scarp feature, evidently representing a stage in the northward retreat by pediplanation of the old Caledonian topography which was being eroded and then gradually buried by the accumulating detritus of the Old Red Sandstone.

The Upper Old Red Sandstone successions in the central inliers of Slieve Aughty, Slieve Bernagh and the Arra Mountains, Slieve Phelim–Silvermines–Devilsbit, Knockshigowna Hill, and Slieve Bloom are all of the same general order of thickness, somewhat less than 300 m in total. A short distance to the south, in the Galty Mountains, the thickness is about 1,000 to 1,500 m. In this last area the breccias of the Pigeon Rock Formation associated with the scarp feature mentioned above are overlapped by the red sandstones of the Galtymore Formation and then, forming a capping to the highest summit of Galtymore, comes another conglomeratic formation: the Galty Formation. This is followed southwards by red and pale sandstones which are overlain conformably by the Lower Carboniferous rocks of the Mitchelstown valley. This highest sandstone formation is similar lithologically as well as in thickness to the Cappagh White Sandstone Formation, representing the whole Old Red Sandstone succession in the southern part of the Slieve Felim–Devilsbit inlier. So another significant topographical feature beneath the Old Red Sandstone may be present in the vicinity of what is now Tipperary town. It is the steep northern margin of what has been called the *Munster Basin* of Upper Old Red Sandstone sedimentation (Fig. 77). This subsiding basin is closed off to the east and north-east

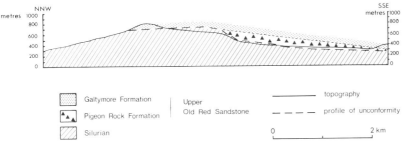

Fig. 76

Section through Black Rock Glen, Galty Mountains, showing the profile of the sub-Old Red Sandstone surface. Lithologies are projected into the line of section (after Doran, Holland, and Jackson 1973).

C. H. HOLLAND

Fig. 77. Isopachyte map of the
Old Red Sandstone of southern
Ireland demonstrating the pre-
sence of the elongate Munster
Basin (data from various sources).

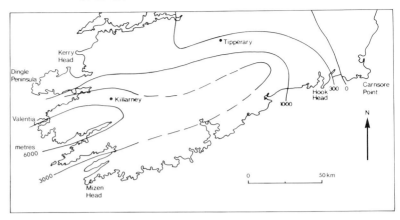

where very thin successions of red beds, of Lower
Carboniferous rather than Devonian age, are associated for instance with the western margin of the
Lower Palaeozoic outcrop of the Leinster block in
Kildare. In the Wexford Syncline a possibly uppermost Devonian and Lower Carboniferous clastic succession rests unconformably upon rocks of the Cullenstown Group of late Pre-Cambrian age or on the
older Rosslare Complex. These basal conglomerates
and sandstones, white, buff, or often reddish in colour,
are some 40 to 80 m thick.

In the Hook peninsula (Fig. 26), about 15 km to
the west-south-west of the Wexford outcrop, a belt of
Upper Old Red Sandstone is present to the north
of the Lower Carboniferous rocks which form the
narrowest part of the peninsula towards Hook Head
itself and there are additionally small outliers to the
north-west along the coast of Waterford Harbour.
There are some excellent coastal sections on both
sides of the peninsula. Details of the uncomfortable
relationship between the Old Red Sandstone and the
underlying Cambrian and/or Ordovician rocks of the
Duncannon area to the north are seldom visible. At
the southern side of one of the small outliers of Upper
Old Red Sandstone near Arthurstown, P. R. R.
Gardiner has described a basal breccia resting irregularly upon truncated folds in the Ordovician sediments below. The total thickness of the Old Red
Sandstone in the Hook area is of the order of 360 m.
A basal conglomeratic unit, the Templeton Formation, very variable in thickness and stratified in places,
is followed by siltstones and sandstones with conspicuous channeling. The sequence passes up transitionally from these red beds, through a tidal
sequence, into the higher shallow water marine sediments of the Lower Carboniferous. Details of this
very well displayed transition are appropriate to the
next chapter of this book as micropalaeontological

evidence indicates that the Devonian/Carboniferous
boundary should probably be taken at about 46 to
68 m below the top of the red fluviatile sandstones
and siltstones, which thus continue into the Carboniferous. The highest occurrence of the *Spelaeotriletes
lepidophytus* (PL) spore zone (page 145) at Hook is
approximately 68 m below the top of the red beds.
Spores of the succeeding *Verrucosisporites nitidus*
Zone (VI Subzone) occur some 46 m below the top of
the red beds.

The basal Old Red Sandstone elsewhere in the
Waterford–Wexford region shows variations in clast
content, a variety of local rocks giving place to quartz
pebbles to the east. A striking view of the unconformity below the Upper Old Red Sandstone is
familiar to those looking up from the river to the steep
slope above Waterford railway station, where the
gently dipping purple and reddish brown, massive
quartzose conglomerates of the Old Red Sandstone
are seen to cut across the underlying steeply inclined
Ordovician.

But at Hook we have already entered the domain
of the Munster Basin and the typical thick Upper Old
Red Sandstone towards its centre may best be illustrated by consideration of the sequence in the Comeragh Mountains area, between the Suir valley near
Clonmel and the Lower Carboniferous lowland of
Dungarvan. A broad, flatly crested, but more steeply
margined anticline, plunging to the west, here exposes
an Upper Old Red Sandstone succession whose
maximum thickness exceeds 3,000 m. The inconspicuous summit is at about 790 m but an impressive
escarpment faces eastwards. Cut into this is the well
known and austerely beautiful corrie of Coumshingaun (Fig. 78), its cliffs nearly 400 m high, all in Old
Red Sandstone. The succession in the Comeraghs
was divided by J. G. Capewell into four 'groups' better
regarded as formations as follows:

(4) Kiltorcan Formation (240–340 m)
(3) Nier Sandstone Formation (610–2,260 m)
(2) Comeragh Conglomerate – Sandstone Formation (0–730 m)
(1) Coumshingaun Conglomerate Formation (0–340 m)

The Old Red Sandstone succession rests unconformably upon the Lower Palaeozoics, beginning, in general, with very coarse sediments and becoming transitionally finer upwards. It passes conformably upwards into the Lower Carboniferous. The almost unbedded cobble conglomerates of the lower part of the Coumshingaun Conglomerate Formation are seen in the lower 200 m of the corrie cliff. Green cobbles are predominant in a brownish red sandy matrix. There are clasts of felsite, quartz porphyry, tuff, greywacke, slate, quartzite, with granite and tourmaline-

Fig. 78. Corrie in Upper Old Red Sandstone, Coumshingaun, Comeragh Mountains, County Waterford. The corrie cliffs are some 400 m high, the lower half of Coumshingaun Conglomerate Formation, the upper Comeragh Conglomerate-Sandstone Formation, which also forms the summit ground above the corrie.
Photograph by J. K. St Joseph, Cambridge University Collection: copyright reserved.

bearing rocks comparable with the Leinster Granite and its aureole. Commonly clasts may be matched with the local Lower Palaeozoic rocks. Quartz clasts become conspicuous upwards. The formation is probably substantially thicker than as indicated above.

The next formation, which makes the highest ground in the Comeraghs, comprises quartz-pebble conglomerates, again with a variety of other clasts, and fine silty sandstones. The succeeding Nier Sandstone Formation is of purple, fine silty sandstones, containing some lenticular conglomerates. The Kiltorcan Formation is of buff, white, greenish, and less commonly purple coloured, medium to fine sandstones and siltstones with plant debris. The wider significance of this uppermost division will be referred to shortly.

The conglomerates are to be regarded as coarse piedmont fans, with the finer sandstones representing alluvial deposits and perhaps playa lake areas. Indications from sedimentary structures are of an easterly derivation. There is local material but the not infrequent feldspathic and micaceous clastic sediments are perhaps from a more distant granitic source or from Pre-Cambrian basement. There are striking thickness changes in the lower part of the sequence and a section (Fig. 79) shows that away from the central Comeraghs there is a rapid thinning and dying out, consistent with our wider picture of the Munster basin.

The Old Red Sandstone of the Knockmealdown Mountains to the west remains less well known but is now under investigation. Dominated by purple silty sandstones with sporadic quartz conglomerates, the succession does not seem to include (or perhaps does not reach down to) the impressive lower conglomerates of the Comeraghs. A similar picture obtains around the Slievenamon inlier (Fig. 80), where J. R. J. Colthurst has shown that the Old Red Sandstone succession can be subdivided into a formation of purple sandstones and siltstones with quartz conglomerate lenses overlain by a formation of yellow sandstones and red and green mudstones which locally, as at Kiltorcan, contain plant fossils. The sediments of the older Carrigmaclea Formation (Fig. 81) were deposited in an alluvial fan and braided stream environment by southward flowing streams. Those of the overlying formation were deposited by southward and westward flowing low sinuosity rivers.

The Kiltorcan Formation already referred to as forming the highest part of the Old Red Sandstone succession in the Comeraghs is so named in conformity with these widespread 'Kiltorcan Beds' or 'Yellow Sandstone Series', recognised by the original geological surveyors from Kerry Head and Slieve Mish, through the Galty Mountains into County Kilkenny, and southwards through Waterford and east Cork. Named from the famous locality of Kiltorcan, County Kilkenny, near the north-eastern corner of the Slievenamon inlier, these fine sandstones are separately indicated on the older Geological Survey maps as a thus much restricted *Upper* Old Red Sandstone. Their general order of thickness is 150 to 300 m. At Kiltorcan, the pale yellow or greenish shales and greenish, brownish, or yellow micaceous, variably fine sandstones have yielded a rich flora (first discovered in the middle of the nineteenth century) associated with arthropods, a freshwater bivalve, and fish. The ancient plants include the fern-like *Archeopteris* (Fig. 82) and lycopods related to those which formed the great forests of later Carboniferous, Coal Measure, times. Certainly terrestrial vegetation had evolved rapidly during the Devonian Period. Professor W. G. Chaloner provides the following revised list of the Kiltorcan flora: *Archaeopteris hibernica* (Forbes) Dawson 1861, *Cyclostigma kiltorkense* Haughton 1860, *Ginkophyllum kiltorkense* Johnson 1914, *Sphenopteris hookeri* Bailey 1861, *Lepidodendropsis* sp., cf. *Rhacopteris* sp., and *Bythotrephis* sp. *Archaeopteris* is one of a group of early fossil plants (the progymnosperms) which have some characters associated with the gymnosperms but have

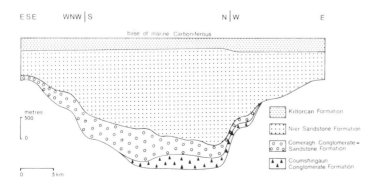

Fig. 79. Thickness variations in the Old Red Sandstone of the Comeragh Mountains (based upon Capewell 1957).

Above: white to yellow quartz arenites showing epsilon and zeta cross-stratification, Kiltorcan Formation, railway cutting south of Ballyhale.

Fig. 80. Upper Old Red Sandstone, north-east of Slievenamon inlier, County Kilkenny.
Photographs by J. R. J. Colthurst

Below: base of a sedimentary cycle overlying red mudstones, Carrigmaclea Formation. Carrigatna.

really not attained this status. *Archaeopteris* is a large (sometimes more than 1 m long) frond but has been found elsewhere in the world associated with stems which assume the proportions of forest tree trunks as much as 1·5 m in diameter. The fronds are in some cases known to be heterosporous and thus to be pteridophytes rather than seed plants. The genus is important as demonstrating an early stage of evolution of leaves. *Cyclostigma* again is present at Kiltorcan as a compression secondarily replaced by chlorite, and careful examination by Chaloner has shown close details of the cone, leaf scars, sporangia, and spores of this plant. It was the first Devonian

lycopod to be figured and described and is actually closer to the well-known Carboniferous forms than to other Devonian members of the lycopods. To the already remarkable floral record from Kiltorcan, Chaloner, Hill, and Lacey have now added the description of chloritised compressions of the seed *Spermolithus devonicus* Johnson 1917. This material is believed to represent 'not only the earliest seed plants known from the British Isles, but also the earliest seeds with apparently platyspermic symmetry'. In view of the closeness in age of the Kiltorcan material to that of the late Devonian and Carboniferous *Archaeosperma*, of radiospermic character, a 'more or less synchronous origin of radiospermic and platyspermic gymnosperms' is favoured.

The association of this rich flora with a fauna including fossil fish such as *Coccosteus*, eurypterids, xiphosura, crustacea, and a large freshwater mussel *Archanodon jukesi* similar to the modern *Anodonta* (Swan Mussel) is indicative of a freshwater lacustrine environment, doubtless in proximity to a forested area. It may be that the local Kiltorcan environment, with its particularly rich and varied fossil record, was restricted in some additional way from the wider area of sedimentation represented by the Kiltorcan Formation as a whole, in which the fine sandstones elsewhere contain a more meagre record of plant fragments.

The revised flora according to Chaloner invites

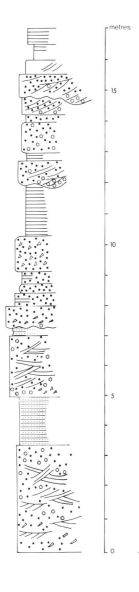

red shale

sandstone

flaggy sandstone

pebbly sandstone

vein quartz, quartzite conglomerate

conglomerate, local clasts

bed with erosive base

cross-stratification

Fig. 81

Measured section in the Carrigmaclea Formation of the Upper Old Red Sandstone of the Slievenamon inlier, at Carrigmaclea Hill about 2 km west of Ninemilehouse, to show the cyclic sequence from scouring coarse conglomerates and sandstones to flaggy and laminated purple sandstones or red shales. Seven cycles are indicated (data kindly supplied by J. R. J. Colthurst).

comparison with a closely similar *Cyclostigma–Archaeopteris* flora from Bear Island in the Arctic. The latter has a spore flora indicating an early Tournaisian age, suggesting that the Kiltorcan flora may approximate to the Devonian/Carboniferous transition beds rather than to the Frasnian/Famennian age which it has been given in the past. Additionally, Dr G. Clayton and his associates have now obtained evidence from miospores and conodonts that the Old Red Sandstone in the area extends as high as the VI Subzone (see page 145), that is into the mid-Tournaisian (Tn 1b–Tn 2), and that the marine transgression reached here not earlier than late VI Subzone times.

In a report of 1869 W. H. Baily referred to the original quarry in the Kiltorcan Formation near Ballyhale as 'this celebrated fossil locality' already variously scientifically visited. He had applied to the British Association for a grant of £40 to allow of further excavations there. '£20 was, however, the only amount voted'. He accepted the smaller sum with hesitation, but 'aided by the Geological Survey', embarked on the task 'accompanied by an efficient and zealous assistant, Mr A. M'Henry, and provided with tools, such as bars and picks, for excavating with vigour. We were engaged for a fortnight, working most laboriously; and fortunately we had very favourable weather, except that it was extremely hot in this exposed situation for the heavy work we were occupied upon.

We engaged the services of two men, who ably assisted in removing the superficial soil and unproductive strata to the depth of about four or five feet, which was carted away at once; and we calculated

Fig. 82

Fossil plants from the Kiltorcan Formation, Upper Old Red Sandstone, Kiltorcan 'Old Quarry', County Kilkenny (see text).

Above: *Archaeopteris hibernica* (Forbes) Dawson; a progymnosperm; part of a large leafy shoot. (Scale below in centimetres). (Irish National Museum Collection, T48/8).

Below: *Sphenopteris hookeri* Baily; part of a frond, $\times 2 \cdot 0$; a probable pteridosperm. (University College Dublin, Geology Dept. Collection, 2793).
Photographs kindly supplied by Professor W. G. Chaloner

that the total quantity removed in this manner and excavated by us amounted to at least 200 loads of stone and rubbish.

The character of the beds beneath this superficial covering, a fine-grained greenish sandstone, admitted of great facility in working [*cf.* Fig. 83], splitting up into layers, sometimes of large size . . . . Some of the surfaces of these layers are covered by plant-remains; and when first opened the fossils are most beautifully exhibited, as, from the dampness of the stone, their darker colour makes them appear very conspicuously'.

As might be expected the thicker Upper Old Red Sandstone successions of the Munster Basin show much lateral and vertical variation in facies. The western and southern coastal areas of Kerry and Cork are attractive in their plentiful exposure as well as in their scenery and the Old Red Sandstone rocks of these areas have been investigated by many individuals. The result, unfortunately, is that an already involved picture has been complicated by individual

Fig. 83. A modern re-excavation of Kiltorcan 'Old Quarry', County Kilkenny in 1976. The party from Birkbeck College, London; University College, Bangor; and Trinity College Dublin was under the direction of Professor W. G. Chaloner. Roadstone Limited provided valuable assistance in excavating the site.
Photograph by C. H. Holland

nomenclatures developed in separate areas (and in some cases in the same area). In the absence of macrofossils and the as yet very restricted use of the limited possibilties of palynology, correlation has been largely in terms of lithological resemblance and comparison of thickness – a notoriously unreliable procedure.

At Kerry Head (Fig. 93), an east-north-easterly plunging anticline, south of the Shannon estuary, provides the most westerly of the more or less isolated inliers of Old Red Sandstone in south-central Ireland. The inlier, about 15 km in length, is of hilly country with a cliffed coastline to the west and an area of Lower Carboniferous lowland enclosing it to the east. The base of the Old Red Sandstone is not seen but comparison with other areas has suggested that erosion has nearly reached it. M. F. H. Khan divided the dominantly arenaceous succession into three groups better treated as formations as follows:

(3) Kilmore Sandstone Formation (110 m or possibly more)
(2) Inshaboy Mudstone Formation (150 m)
(1) Glandahalin Sandstone Formation (370 m)

The lowest formation forms the higher ground in the west and the cliffs of Kerry Head. It is of grey and red cross-stratified sandstones with mainly rounded pebbles of quartz and quartzite with lesser gneiss, schist, quartz porphyry, granite, chert, and sandstone. The red and mottled mudstones of the Inshaboy Mudstone Formation, seen on the north coast, allow subdivision of the succession as there is a return to arenaceous sediments in the succeeding Kilmore Sandstone Formation, with its yellow, grey, and green sandstones mapped by the Geological Survey as their 'Yellow Sandstones'. There are plant fossils reminiscent of those at Kiltorcan. There is already some palynological evidence that Old Red Sandstone conditions continued into the Carboniferous.

A similarly plunging anticlinal structure is strikingly expressed at the landward end of the Dingle peninsula where the Old Red Sandstone of the Slieve Mish range forms an elevated topography, itself dying away eastwards under the surrounding and softer

Lower Carboniferous rocks of the Vale of Tralee. J. G. Capewell had divided the Upper Old Red Sandstone succession here into what are in effect five formations:

(5) Lack Formation (180 m)
(4) Gearhane Sandstone Formation (370–550 m)
(3) Castle Hill Conglomerate Formation (15–120 m)
(2) Coumbrack Sandstone Formation (0–180 m)
(1) Inch Conglomerate Formation (0–610 m)

Addition gives a total thickness of some 570 to 1,650 m, already showing a substantial increase southwards from Kerry Head. The Inch River provides a good section in the southern limb of the Slieve Mish anticline.

The Inch Conglomerate Formation, well displayed on the shore to the west of Inch Strand, is a remarkable piedmont deposit of metamorphic provenance. It is a poorly sorted sediment with rounded to angular clasts usually a few centimetres in size but sometimes exceeding ·5 m, set in a matrix of coarse purple sandstone. The clasts include greenish schist, phyllite, and gneiss, with granite, chert, jasper, and vein quartz. The very common soft schist pebbles imply a source originally close at hand – perhaps a strictly local elevation. The succeeding Coumbrack Formation is a cross-stratified purplish or yellowish sandstone, again showing substantial thickness variation in sections taken across the peninsula (Fig. 84). R. R. Horne ascribes these very well sorted fine sandstones with their large and characteristic fore-set beds to an aeolian (dune belt) origin. The individual cross-stratified units are from 1 to 12 m in thickness and there are alternating water-laid deposits sometimes showing desiccation cracks indicating their temporary atmospheric exposure in this continental basin. These beds are well seen in Kilmurry Bay between Inch and Dingle.

The Castle Hill Conglomerate Formation, in contrast to the Inch Conglomerate is of well-rounded quartz and jasper clasts in a red sandstone matrix.

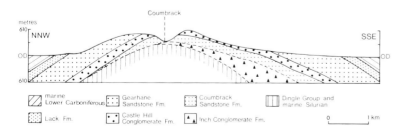

Fig. 84

Section across the Slieve Mish anticline (after Capewell 1965).

It oversteps the formations previously mentioned. The younger red Gearhane Siltstone Formation forms the highest summits of the Slieve Mish range. It is followed by green and purplish fine sandstones and siltstones of the Lack Formation which appear to be the local equivalent of our now familiar Kiltorcan Formation. Brown and yellowish-grey sandstones appear in the succession for the first time.

With the dying out of the conglomerate formations northwards, the northern side of the peninsula shows successions dominated by massive and cross-stratified sandstones with irregular lenses and beds of quartz jasper conglomerate at different horizons. The direction of wedging of the conglomerates, the orientation of the pebbles, and the attitude of the cross-stratification all suggested to Capewell an origin of the Old Red Sandstone of Slieve Mish from the palaeogeographically predictable north, though Horne suggests that the source of the Inch Conglomerate Formation actually lay in a ridge to the south, along what is now Dingle Bay. The minor irregularities of the sub-Old Red Sandstone surface are well seen, for example, along Derrymore Glen; but the supposed old cliff line to be seen in the corrie wall at the head of the glen is a fault affecting Old Red Sandstone and underlying Lower Palaeozoic rocks alike, the former also making its clear unconformably capping of the splendid mountain of Caherconree.

Some of the best scenery in Ireland is made by Old Red Sandstone rocks and within it we move now from the Dingle peninsula to the mountains of the broader Iveragh peninsula to the south of Dingle Bay and to the country around Killarney. At the inland head of the peninsula these rocks form the highest mountains in Ireland in McGillycuddy's Reeks (Fig. 85), with their summit of Carrauntoohil at approximately 1,040 m. The Old Red Sandstone is well displayed in the glacially scoured mountainous country and in the Caragh Valley. Some 3,600 m are present, though the base of the succession is not exposed and the total subsidence of the local floor of the Munster Basin must have been even greater. A mainly arenaceous sequence was divided by P. Walsh mainly upon colour changes into five formations as follows:

(5) Upper Purple Sandstone Formation (90 m)
(4) Ardnagluggen Sandstone Formation (90 m)
(3) Lower Purple Sandstone Formation (about 1,500 m)
(2) Grey Sandstone Formation (about 900 m)
(1) Green Sandstone Formation (about 1,200 m)

The typically bright green, massive, cross-stratified, medium sandstones of the basal formation are exposed in the glaciated Gap of Dunloe and near the Upper Lake of Killarney. They are seen very well from the Killarney–Kenmare road: with their torrential bedding, channels, and lenticles of quartz jasper conglomerate. The poorly sorted, dull grey or purplish grey, medium or fine sandstones of the next formation are monotonous in their lithology, owing their colour to the association of a much lower content of chlorite and the presence of ferric oxide. They form the eastern peaks of the Reeks. After a transitional alternation there follow the very thick sandstones of the Lower Purple Sandstone Formation. These have a wide outcrop along the northern foothills of the Reeks and are well displayed in the Caragh Valley and the Gap of Dunloe. Some quartz jasper conglomerates are present, for example at the latter locality. The relatively thin development of pale greenish and buff sandstones of the Ardnagluggen Sandstone Formation, seen along the north shore of Muckross Lake, allows separation of the reddish purple, medium to fine sandstones of the Upper Purple Sandstone Formation, seen only in the Muckross Demesne. Greenish sandstones also are present in this highest formation and the succession finally passes upwards into the 'Lower Limestone Shales' at the base of the Carboniferous Limestone. At Kilgarvan near the head of the narrow inlet of the Kenmare River, less than 10 km south of the Killarney area, the total thickness of the Upper Old Red Sandstone has been estimated as reaching some 6,500 m.

A possible correlation of the Upper Old Red Sandstone rocks of Kerry Head, Slieve Mish, and Killarney is given in Figure 86, which also includes successions westwards along the Iveragh peninsula. The Lower Slate Formation shown tentatively on the section at Killarney was described by Capewell in the Sneem district (Fig. 127) on the north side of the Kenmare River, where its dull, purplish-grey, silty shales form the basal 900 m of the succession. The higher formations of green and then purple sandstones in the neighbourhood of Sneem are similar to those at Killarney except that the intervening grey sandstone unit is not developed and their total thickness is some 500 m greater than at Killarney. Green sandstones form the striking Derry ridge to the south-west of Sneem and the higher purple sandstones are seen on the coast around the entrance to Sneem Harbour and in the ridge to the south-west of Doon.

At the western end of the Iveragh Peninsula, spectacular cliffs to the south of Dingle Bay, mountainous country including the summit of Coomacarrea (775 m), and lower rocky terrain along the Kenmare River contrast with the ill-exposed, drift and bog covered country of the Inny Valley, inland from Waterville. The purple siltstones of the Valentia Slate Formation show well developed axial planar cleavage in Valentia Island. They were widely used in the nineteenth century, the large slabs forming an admirable roofing and flooring material. The same formation is seen about Cahirciveen. Along the south-eastern side of the peninsula another anticlinal structure carries it from the Sneem area to Lamb's Head to the south of Derrynane Bay. The succeeding St Finan's Sandstone Formation is of greyish rocks, rather, as Capewell has shown, than the conspicuous green of their equivalents farther east. Purple sandstones follow. K. J. Russell has made most important discoveries of fish beds from the western end of the Iveragh Peninsula, the lowest within the Valentia Slate Formation. The vertebrates include the widespread genus *Bothriolepis*, suggesting a maximum age for the lower part of the Valentia Slate close to the Middle/Upper Devonian boundary.

Contemporaneous volcanic rocks occur within the Upper Old Red Sandstone in the wider area around Killarney. Ashes and rhyolitic lava occur in the mountains to the south-east but remain poorly known. The quarries at Glenflesk about 10 km east-south-east of Killarney display ashes and other volcanic rocks associated with green sandstones and cut by intrusive felsite. The Old Red Sandstone sequence here is thrust over the Carboniferous which forms the very obviously subdued topography to the north. In the vicinity of Valentia Harbour probably intrusive columnar dolerites are associated with interstratified pyroclastics.

There remains the tract of Upper Palaeozoic country to the south of an approximate Kenmare–

Fig. 85. Upper Old Red Sandstone scenery: Macgillycuddy's Reeks in winter. The view is towards the Kenmare River, glimpsed in the top of the picture.
Air photograph by Daphne Pochin Mould

Cork line, conveniently referred to as the *South Munster Basin*. This is of particular interest as the change from Old Red Sandstone fluviatile conditions, through a tidal regime, into a fully marine situation here occurs before the end of the Devonian (Fig. 93). The whole area has been much investigated in piecemeal fashion and one enters a welter of confused nomenclature.

South of the Kenmare–Cork line the Old Red Sandstone is followed not by Lower Limestone Shales and then Carboniferous Limestone as to the north, but by a thick (up to 2,400 m), mainly marine, clastic sequence of Famennian to Namurian age given the informal name 'Cork Beds' by D. Naylor, who has established divisions of this sequence on the Old Head of Kinsale (Fig. 87), some 30 km south-west of Cork Harbour. This narrow peninsula extends some 5 km south-south-eastwards providing complete and largely

accessible sections through the Cork Beds, a synclinal axis crossing the landward end of the peninsula. Naylor and his associates consider that the divisions used at Old Head can be recognised more widely, but that the equivalent sequence in west Cork is sufficiently different as to merit the maintenance of a separate nomenclature. Other workers on these rocks have used, and continue to use, different classifications. For example Gardiner and Horne have reviewed and suggested revisions of Devonian and Carboniferous stratigraphical classification throughout the area south from Kerry Head and the Comeraghs.

The Old Head Sandstone Formation on the Old Head of Kinsale is dominated by marine sandstones and there are records of marine macrofossils, such as the well-known brachiopod *Cyrtospirifer verneuili*. The non-marine Old Red Sandstone is not exposed

Fig. 86. Possible correlation of Upper Old Red Sandstone successions at Kerry Head, Slieve Mish, and from Killarney westwards along the Iveragh peninsula. Formations are as follows:

1. Glandahalin Sandstone Formation	12. Lower Purple Sandstone Formation
2. Inshaboy Mudstone Formation	13. Ardnagluggen Sandstone Formation
3. Kilmore Sandstone Formation	14. Upper Purple Sandstone Formation
4. Inch Conglomerate Formation	15. Lower Slate Formation
5. Coumbrack Sandstone Formation	16. Chloritic Sandstone Formation
6. Castle Hill Conglomerate Formation	17. Purple Sandstone Formation
7. Gearhane Sandstone Formation	18. Transition Formation
8. Lack Formation	19. Valentia Slate Formation
9. Lower Slate Formation	20. St. Finan's Sandstone Formation
10. Green Sandstone Formation	21. Ballinskelligs Formation
11. Grey Sandstone Formation	

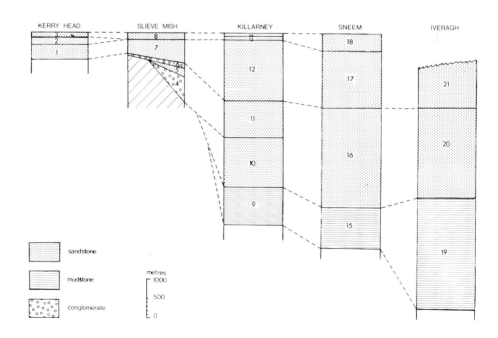

below but is seen on Seven Heads peninsula, 13 km to the west-south-west. Here a 'transitional facies' (185 m), now referable to the Toe Head Formation, occurs between the Old Red Sandstone and the Old Head Sandstone Formation. Within it sandstones with erosive bases and evidence of bioturbation de-

Fig. 87. Old Head of Kinsale, County Cork. Folded rocks of the Bream Rock Member of the Devonian Old Head Sandstone Formation form the foreground. The succeeding Holeopen Bay Member occupies the narrow neck of the peninsula. Beyond are the higher Carboniferous beds of the Kinsale Formation.
Aerofilms photograph

Fig. 88. Sand-dominant heterolithic facies showing flaser bedding. The structure is here presumably due mainly to wave action. Old Head Sandstone Formation, Upper Devonian, Carrigadda Bay, south of Cork.

Photograph by A. van Gelder

Fig. 89. Mud-dominant heterolithic facies showing lenticular bedding. The internal structure of the small lenses points to a bipolar current system related to tidal action. The ripples at levels A and B show oppositely directed foresetting. Old Head Sandstone Formation, Upper Devonian, Carrigadda Bay.

Photograph by A. van Gelder

The author is grateful to Professor J. F. M. de Raaf for comments on Figures 88 and 89.

crease upwards, and green to grey colours become dominant, as sediments of a coastal plain gradually give way to those of a marine tidal environment.

The Old Head Sandstone Formation at Old Head of Kinsale can be divided into two members, of which the lower, Bream Rock Member comprises some 435 m of sediments. Greenish grey, fine to medium sandstones with minor scouring effects are inter-bedded with flaser bedded units – that is sandy beds containing fine films of muddy material – and with beds of mud with silt or sand lenses. A group of Dutch sedimentologists, Professor J. F. M. de Raaf and his associates, who have been studying the sedimentation of Upper Palaeozoic successions in south Cork in very great detail have been able to make close comparison between structures in the Cork Beds and those found forming at the present time in the tidal deposits of the Dutch coast. Cross-lamination indi-

Fig. 90

Desiccation cracks drawn out along the Hercynian cleavage, Caha Mountain Formation, Upper Old Red Sandstone between Kenmare and Glengarriff.

Photograph by C. H. Holland

cates a bipolarity of current direction (Figs. 88, 89) with a north-south orientation and a dominance of flow from the south, a clear indication of tidal currents in this inshore environment.

The succeeding Holeopen Bay Member forms the narrowest and least accessible part of the Old Head of Kinsale, where marine erosion and subsequent collapse have created passages through the peninsula, after which the easterly bay is named. The member consists of some 460 m of massive sandstones separated by mudstones with variable sandy laminae. There are indications that the environment represented is now of higher energy tidal conditions, large-scale cross-stratification replacing the small-scale cross-laminated units.

The Old Head Sandstone Formation is now known to thicken considerably from localities farther south. Thus in the south limb of the Skibbereen syncline it is 230 to 250 m thick as compared with the 895 m of the type section. The effect has been related to the northern, possibly faulted, margin of a positive basement structure, the Glandore High.

Farther northwards, however, the marine strata of the Old Head Sandstone Formation pass laterally into Old Red Sandstone facies in Cork Harbour, where 'Lower Limestone Shales' follow directly upon Upper Old Red Sandstone. In the north limb of the Ringa-

bella syncline, to the south-west of the entrance to the harbour, the equivalent of the Old Head Sandstone Formation is only about 67 m thick, though if it is defined as beginning at the first occurrence of silt-streaked mud instead of above the highest red bed the thickness is more than doubled. It remains, however, very much thinner than on the Old Head of Kinsale.

Returning to the type section, above the Old Head Sandstone Formation, the overlying Kinsale Formation (more than 760 m) begins with an approximately 200 m thick uniform grey pyritic mudstone. The characteristic ripple-lensed laminae of sand and silt in grey mudstone of the formation as a whole were deposited in shallow marine conditions, a pro-delta slope having been invoked. Higher in the formation de Raaf has identified a pattern of onlap-offlap cycles in superposition.

In the Bantry area of west Cork thick Old Red Sandstone is followed by Cork Beds. Here Coe and Selwood recorded some 6,700 m of Upper Old Red Sandstone, divided into the Caha Mountain Formation (approximately 5,500 m) and the West Cork Sandstone Formation. The basal member of the former is characterised by fining-upwards cycles but the bulk of the formation is of uncertain origin. The Caha Mountains were said to 'embosom as many lakes as there are days in the year.' The rocks are well exposed on the scenically beautiful mountain road from Kenmare to Glengarriff which in places is tunneled through them. They form the core of an anticlinal structure plunging west-south-westwards, the outcrop disappearing just north of Castletownbere. The strata are uniform purple and green siltstones and slates, thickly bedded and rarely laminated. Some pale siltstone and fine sandstone bands show the bedding in relation to the well developed and sometimes markedly refracted Hercynian cleavage. The beds may have been deposited in a low energy continental environment perhaps involving temporary lakes. There is some evidence of desiccation (Fig. 90).

The predominantly arenaceous West Cork Sandstone Formation is well seen on both sides of the entrance to Glengarriff Harbour. It forms the western end of the peninsula which separates the Kenmare River from Bantry Bay and the heart of the Sheep's Head and Mizen Head peninsulas farther south. In all three cases there are narrow more or less interrupted outcrops of Cork Beds along the coasts at each side. The formation is mostly of very fine sandstone and coarse siltstone, with some coarse sandstones and conglomerates forming the lower parts of the characteristic fining-upwards cycles. The siltstones are purplish grey to greenish grey with the sandstones somewhat paler in colour. There is an erosion surface lightly channeled at the base of each

Fig. 91. Schematic representation of types of bedding in the Ardaturrish Formation, Ardaturrish Point, west of Bantry Bay (after P. C. Jones 1974).

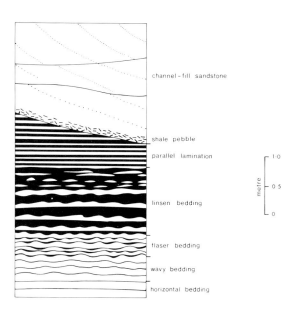

channel-fill sandstone

shale pebble

parallel lamination

linsen bedding

flaser bedding

wavy bedding

horizontal bedding

metre

1·0

0·5

0

unit. Large scale cross-stratification is the most obvious sedimentary structure. Plant fragments are the only fossils.

The Glengarriff Formation, which comprises the lowest 530 m of the Cork Beds, consists of greenish-grey siltstones with lesser light grey quartzitic sandstones and conglomerates arranged in fining-upwards cycles which on average are a little over 30 m thick. Higher in the succession the conglomerates disappear and the proportion of siltstone increases. Poorly preserved plant fragments are present and there is evidence of drifted logs as much as 1·8 m in length. A low energy alluvial plain environment is postulated, similar to that of the Old Red Sandstone below. Cross-stratification indicates currents from the north and north-west, its variability possibly related to the meandering of the original stream courses. The clean sands are rich in other sedimentary structures such as ripple marks, washouts, load moulds, convolution, and slump structures, the last perhaps being related

to the steep sides of shifting channels. High in the formation interbedded dark grey shales and rippled silts appear. The first thickly bedded dark grey laminated slates (greater than 30 cms) indicate the base of the succeeding Ardaturrish Formation. Coe and Selwood used the old stratal term 'Coomhola' for both these formations, together with the younger Reenagough Formation. Gardiner and Horne employed the formational name 'Coomhola' in a slightly different sense.

The Ardaturrish Formation, about 550 m thick, its base being approximately that of the Carboniferous, is mainly of thinly bedded sandstones or siltstones and dark shales, with some thickly bedded sandstones. The interbedded sandstones, siltstones, and shales are characteristically heterolithic in their associations, that is to say they show variation between two end members: flaser bedding (of mud streaks in sand) and linsen bedding (of sand streaks in mud). Such associations (Fig. 91) are characteristic of

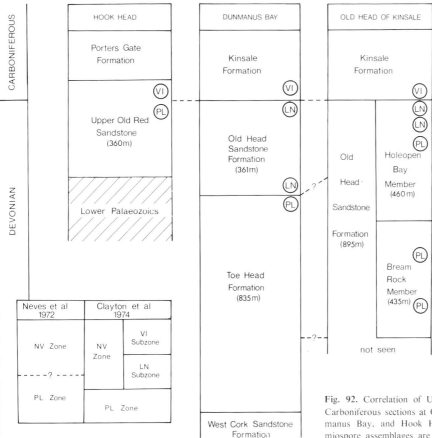

Fig. 92. Correlation of Upper Devonian and basal Carboniferous sections at Old Head of Kinsale, Dunmanus Bay, and Hook Head. Positions of critical miospore assemblages are indicated. For further explanation and sources of data see text.

tidal flat sedimentation and there is additional evidence. Ripple marks are ubiquitous, some of them flat-topped; there are bioturbated dark grey silty mudstones; channel fillings and desiccation cracks are present in places; there are carbonised plant remains and sparse marine infaunal bivalves such as *Edmondia* and *Nuculoidea*. Also characteristic is the so-called 'herring bone cross stratification', its bipolarity indicating the two directions of flow of tidal currents.

Details of the facies variations of the Old Red Sandstone and Cork Beds between the south Cork sections and Bantry Bay are gradually becoming clearer. The outcrop of Old Red Sandstone crossing Glandore Harbour and running north of Toe Head (Fig. 93) to Sherkin Island and Clear Island is distinct from the successions farther north. Graham and Reilly have here defined a basal Sherkin Formation

which extends for 40 km along the core of the Rosscarbery anticline. It comprises some 1,050 m of drab grey and green sandstones interbedded variously with drab and pale purple mudstones. The most common sedimentary structure is large-scale cross-stratification of the sandstones and measurements on Sherkin Island and Clear Island suggest current flow a little south of eastwards, though there is considerable spread. Alluvial muds evidently alternate with the deposits of high energy, possibly braided, rivers. A development of considerable stratigraphical significance is the recognition by Clayton and Graham of miospore assemblages from the Sherkin Formation of Clear Island which are late Givetian or early Frasnian (Middle/Upper Devonian) in age. The succeeding Castlehaven Formation (750 m) differs from the West Cork Sandstone Formation. Though it includes cross-stratified channel sandstones it is dominantly of

Fig. 93. Facies map for the Upper Devonian and lowest Carboniferous of southern Ireland (PL and basal VI times), to demonstrate northward marine transgression across the Old Red Sandstone continent. For details see text (after Holland 1979: data from various sources). The map also shows some localities referred to in the text.

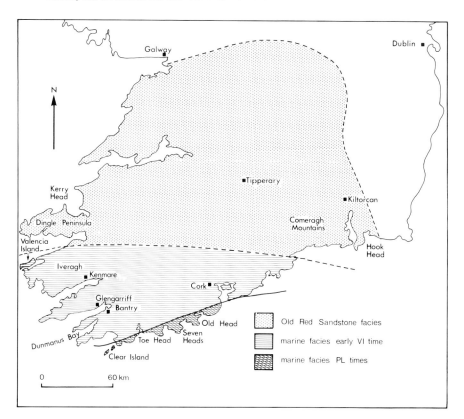

purplish mudstones of overbank and flood plain environments. The Toe Head Formation follows.

Farther north in Dunmanus Bay. Naylor's detailed mapping and logging of sections along the northern coast of the Mizen peninsula provides a useful link with the Bantry Bay sections. A thick development of the Toe Head Formation (835 m) here follows the West Cork Sandstone Formation. It is dominantly of massive, cross-stratified sandstones, largely green and grey in colour and probably deposited under coastal plain conditions. Cyclothems are recognisable, the base of each defined by a major sandstone. Above comes the heterolithic sequence of the Old Head Sandstone Formation, here 361 m thick.

All these changes become meaningful in terms of an evolving palaeogeography when a time scale can be applied to them. Here, as examples have already shown, palynology is beginning to provide valuable evidence of the gradual northward spread of marine conditions through late Devonian and early Carboniferous times. The combination of modern studies of sedimentation (in comparison with present day models) combined with the setting up of a palynologically controlled time scale provides a comprehensive and detailed picture which would be surprising to those who, in the past, were justifiably inclined to regard the Old Red Sandstone and 'Carboniferous Slate' as drab, thick, unfossiliferous, monotonous, and unrewarding sequences of strata.

Clayton, Kuijpers, and their associates have shown that in southern Ireland there is an assemblage of spore species between that of the *Vallatisporites pusillites–Spelaeotriletes lepidophytus* (PL) Zone and that of the younger *Verrucosisporites nitidus–Vallatisporites vallatus* (NV) Zone, which contains the elements of each but in which *V. pusillites* and *S. lepidophytus* are far less common. They refer to this transitional assemblage as the *S. lepidophytus–V. nitidus* (LN) Subzone of the NV Zone, which latter is

then completed by another subzone: the *Vallatisporites vallatus–Retusotriletes incohatus* (VI) Subzone. The LN/VI boundary now provides a workable Devonian/Carboniferous boundary.

Many samples have been obtained from grey mudstones and shales from the Old Head Sandstone Formation and some from the underlying strata and from the overlying Kinsale Formation. Despite the cleavage the spores are well preserved. As a result the Devonian/Carboniferous boundary within the Cork Beds in south Cork can be drawn approximately at the base of the Kinsale Formation (Fig. 92) in the Old Head and Ringabella sections. Comparing this dating with those obtained at Hook Head (where Sleeman suggests that the LN Subzone is represented by part or all of the interval of 22 m of barren strata between the samples previously referred to), at Kerry Head, and from Tipperary, we obtain an approximate timetable for the advance northwards of the marine shore line across what was originally the continental environment of the Munster Basin (Fig. 93). It also now appears that the Old Head Sandstone Formation is diachronous, being younger in south-west Cork than at the Old Head of Kinsale, there being perhaps a westerly as well as a northerly component to the marine transgression. Thus the Dunmanus Bay section has yielded samples suggesting that the PL/LN junction approximates to the boundary between the Toe Head Formation and the Old Head Sandstone Formation. The coastal plain sediments of the former would thus be time equivalents of the tidal sediments of at least the lower member of the Old Head Sandstone Formation at the Old Head of Kinsale. We have seen that the Toe Head Formation is much thicker at Dunmanus (835 m) than at Seven Heads (185 m). The base of the Kinsale Formation appears to maintain approximately the same age from Old Head to Dunmanus Bay.

BIBLIOGRAPHY

BRÜCK, P. M.   1971   A note on some 'Old Red Sandstone' rocks at Forenaghts
                                       Great, Co. Kildare. *Ir. Nat. J.*, **17**, 17–19.

CAPEWELL, J. G.   1975   The Old Red Sandstone Group of Iveragh, Co. Kerry.
                                       Proc. R. Ir. Acad., **75B**, 155-171.

CHALONER, W. G.   1968   The cone of *Cyclostigma kiltorkense* Haughton, from the
                                       Upper Devonian of Ireland. *J. Linn. Soc. (Bot.)*, **61**, 25–36.

CHALONER, W. G.,   1977   First Devonian platyspermic seed and its implications in
   HILL, A. J., &   gymnosperm evolution. *Nature*, **265**, 233–235.
   LACEY, W. S.

CLAYTON, G.,   1977 Tournaisian miospores and conodonts from County Kil-
  COLTHURST, J. R. J.,   kenny. *Geol. Surv. Ir. Bull.*, 2, 99–106.
  HIGGS, K., JONES, G. Ll.,
  & KEEGAN, J. B.

CLAYTON, G., HIGGS, K.,   1974 Palynological correlations in the Cork Beds (Upper Dev-
  GUEINN, K. J., &   onian – ?Upper Carboniferous) of southern Ireland. *Proc.*
  VAN GELDER, A.   *R. Ir. Acad.*, **74B**, 145–155.

COE, K. & SELWOOD, E. B.   1968 The Upper Palaeozoic stratigraphy of West Cork and parts
                                      of South Kerry. *Proc. R. Ir. Acad.*, **66B**, 113–131.

COLTHURST, J. R. J.   1978 Old Red Sandstone rocks surrounding the Slievenamon
                                      inlier, Counties Tipperary and Kilkenny. *J. Earth Sci. R.*
                                      Dubl. Soc., **1**, 77–103.

DORAN, R. J. P.,   1973 The sub-Old Red Sandstone surface in southern Ireland.
  HOLLAND, C. H., &   *Proc. R. Ir. Acad.*, **73B**, 109–128.
  JACKSON, A. A.

GRAHAM, J. R. &   1972 The Sherkin Formation (Devonian) of south-west County
  REILLY, T. A.   Cork. *Geol. Surv. Ir. Bull.*, **1**, 281–301.

HIGGS, K.   1975 Upper Devonian and Lower Carboniferous miospore
                                      assemblages from Hook Head, County Wexford, Ireland.
                                      Micropaleontology, **21**, 393–419.

HORNE, R. R.   1975 The association of alluvial fan, aeolian and fluviatile facies
                                      in the Caherbla Group (Devonian), Dingle Peninsula, Ire-
                                      land. *J. sedim. Petrol.*, **45**, 535–540.

HOUSE, M. R.,   1977 A correlation of Devonian rocks in the British Isles. *Geol.*
  RICHARDSON, J. B.,   *Soc. Lond. Spec. Rep.*, **8**, pp. 110.
  CHALONER, W. G.,
  ALLEN, J. R. L.,
  HOLLAND, C. H. &
  WESTOLL, T. S.

KUIJPERS, E. P.   1975 Continental and coastal plain deposits of the uppermost
                                      Old Red Sandstone complex of southern Ireland. *Geologie*
                                      Mijnb., **54**, 15–22.

MAWHINNEY, K.   1974 Valentia Slate Quarries. *Technology Ireland*, **6**, 42.

NAYLOR, D.   1975 Upper Devonian–Lower Carboniferous stratigraphy along
                                      the south coast of Dunmanus Bay, Co. Cork., *Proc. R. Ir.*
                                      Acad., **75B**, 317–337.

NAYLOR, D., HIGGS, K., &   1977 Stratigraphy on the north flank of the Dunmanus syncline,
  BOLAND, M. A.   West Cork. *Geol. Surv. Ir. Bull.*, **2**, 143–157.

NAYLOR, D., JONES, P. C.,   1974 Facies relationships in the Upper Devonian–Lower Car-
  & MATTHEWS, S. C.   boniferous of southwest Ireland and adjacent regions.
                                      Geol. J., **9**, 77–96.

PENNEY, S. R.   1978 Devonian lavas from the Comeragh Mountains, County
                                      Waterford. *J. Earth Sci. R. Dubl. Soc.*, **1**, 71–76.

RUSSELL, K. J.   1978 Vertebrate fossils from the Iveragh peninsula and the age
                                      of the Old Red Sandstone. *J. Earth Sci. R. Dubl. Soc.*, **1**,
                                      71–76.

WALSH, P. T.   1968 The Old Red Sandstone west of Killarney, Co. Kerry, Ire-
                                      land. *Proc. R. Ir. Acad.*, **66B**, 9–26.

WILSON, H. E.   1953 The petrography of the Old Red Sandstone rocks of the
                                      north of Ireland. *Proc. R. Ir. Acad.*, **55B**, 283–320.

9

LOWER CARBONIFEROUS

G. D. Sevastopulo

The Carboniferous is an extremely important system in Ireland because it occurs at the surface or beneath Quaternary deposits over nearly half the land area of the country, and also forms the host to most of the major sulphide orebodies discovered to date. Despite this importance, our knowledge of Irish Carboniferous stratigraphy is sketchy and uneven. The following account should not be regarded as more than a first approximation.

In Ireland, as in other parts of north-west Europe, the Carboniferous is conveniently split into a Lower and an Upper division (Dinantian and Silesian sub-systems respectively); the latter, which in the British Isles includes the Millstone Grit and Coal Measures, is described in Chapter 10.

During the Dinantian, Ireland lay near the equator and was the site of a generally shallow sea, which was bounded to the north by a much diminished Old Red Sandstone continent and which extended eastwards to Central Europe (Fig. 94), and possibly westwards to the maritime provinces of Canada. The carbonate sediments which accumulated in the shallow parts of this sea lithified to form the familiar Carboniferous Limestone of Ireland and Britain, the Calcaire Carbonifère of Belgium and northern France, and the Kohlenkalk of Germany. A contrasting facies called *Culm*, which is characterised by little autochthonous carbonate, is widely developed in Germany and in south-west England; a similar facies occurs in south Munster.

Within the generally shallow water regions there were marked lateral changes of facies and thickness, with thick deposits accumulating in subsiding basins and thinner deposits on structural highs and more extensive stable shelves. The facies varied not only in space but also with time. W. H. C. Ramsbottom has shown that the vertical facies changes were cyclical in nature and has suggested that the sequence of

facies within a single cycle can be interpreted as reflecting progressive shallowing (Fig. 95). Since individual cycles can be recognised over large areas, they may have been caused by eustatic movements of sea-level.

The biostratigraphical scheme (see Table 12) which became the most generally applied in Britain and Ireland was formulated by A. Vaughan in 1905 (and subsequently developed by him and others) and was based on the sequence of brachiopod and coral faunas in the section exposed in the Avon Gorge, at Bristol, England. Bristol lay on the southern flank of a regional high which extended from Belgium (Massif de Brabant) to Wales and possibly into eastern Leinster (Fig. 94). The cyclical nature of the succession is particularly evident in this region, and in the Avon section the boundaries between successive cycles are marked by important non-sequences. Attempts to accommodate faunas, absent through non-sequence in the type section, within Vaughan's zonal scheme have forced so many modifications to the meaning of the zonal symbols that their continued use has led to confusion. A fresh approach to subdivision of the Lower Carboniferous in Britain and Ireland has resulted in the definition of six chronostratigraphical stages, reflecting the six major cycles of sedimentation recognised by Dr Ramsbottom; the base of each stage is defined in a stratotype section. The relationship of the stages to the previous stratigraphical nomenclature is shown in Table 12.

Brachiopods, corals, goniatites, bivalves, foraminifera, conodonts, and plant miospores have been the most widely used fossils for correlation. The degree to which Lower Carboniferous successions can be divided by biostratigraphical means varies, depending on which fossil groups are used and also the age and facies of the sequences under study. For example, foraminifera, which are of little biostrati-

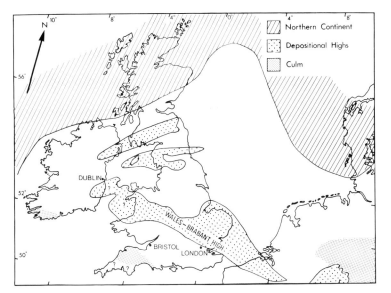

Fig. 94

Generalised Dinantian palaeogeography of North-West Europe, showing the probable extension of depositional highs, shelves, or blocks into eastern Ireland. Carboniferous Limestone and associated facies shown blank (compiled from various sources).

graphical use in the Courceyan, allow great precision from the Chadian onwards. Conodonts, on the other hand, can be used to make a detailed division of the Courceyan but are of limited use in the Chadian, Arundian, and Holkerian. Goniatites may be used to recognise a large number of zones within the Brigantian but are commonly found only in deep water and very shallow water limestones and shales, and very rarely in sublittoral bioclastic limestones. Much remains to be done to improve our knowledge of the stratigraphical distribution of the fossil groups mentioned above and to realize the potential of others such as the bryozoans, ostracodes, and tribolites.

Courceyan Stage

This stage takes its name from the Barony of Courceys, which contains the boundary stratotype section on the western side of the Old Head of Kinsale, County Cork (Fig. 87). Its upper and lower boundaries are slightly younger than those of the Tournaisian Series of Belgium and it probably represents a longer period of time (perhaps as much as 10 million years) than each of the five succeeding stages. The base of the stage has been chosen at a level which is thought to be consistent with the currently accepted biostratigraphical concept of the base of the Carboniferous, that is the base of the zone of *Gattendorfia subinvoluta*, a goniatite which so far has not been found in Britain and Ireland. Biostratigraphical correlation around this level in Ireland, both in marine and non-marine facies, has been carried out through

the use of plant miospores. G. Clayton and his co-workers have shown that the base of the Courceyan in the stratotype section (Fig. 96, Column 7) coincides with the boundary of two miospore assemblages (see also page 145); the lower LN assemblage contains the widely distributed spore *Spelaeotriletes lepidophytus*, whilst the succeeding VI assemblage lacks that form.

At the end of the Devonian, an alluvial plain traversed by mainly southerly flowing rivers lay between upland source areas in Ulster and Connacht and a shallow sea in south Munster (Fig. 93). During the Courceyan, the sea transgressed northwards as illustrated in Figures 96 and 97, so that by the beginning of the succeeding Chadian Stage it had reached into Ulster. For ease of description the Courceyan is treated in two parts. Over much of the south of the country, a convenient division of the lithological

Fig. 95

Generalised sequence of Dinantian rock types reflecting upwards shallowing.

EVAPORITES	Dessiccation polygons	
DOLOMICRITES	Bird's eye vugs	
MICRITES	Stromatolites, oncolites	
PELMICRITES	Restricted fauna –bivalves gastropods, ostracodes, serpulids	
OOLITES	Cross-stratification Vertical and U-shaped burrows Generally sparse fauna of brachiopods and solitary corals	
PALE THICKER–BEDDED BIOCLASTIC LIMESTONES	Diverse fauna including colonial corals	
DARK THINNER–BEDDED BIOCLASTIC LIMESTONES	Diverse fauna; corals mainly solitary	
MUDSTONES	Goniatites and pectinoid bivalves	

Sea level _ _ _ _

Increasing depth

succession can be made at the base of a widespread grey non-calcareous mudstone and siltstone marker unit, which has become known as the Ballyvergin Shale; this level has been found to mark a change in the conodont microfaunas which also occurs at the boundary between the Middle and Upper Tournaisian rocks of Belgium.

Early Courceyan

During latest Devonian and early Courceyan times, and indeed throughout the Dinantian, an important facies divide and hinge was sited along a line drawn from Cork Harbour to the Kenmare River (Fig. 96). The region to the south of this line, which will be described first, has already been referred to as the South Munster Basin. During the latest Devonian, this basin, in contrast to areas to the north, was already accumulating marine sediments; the thick sequences of sandstones and mudstone of the Old Head Sandstone Formation were deposited in shallow water under the influence of tidal currents (see page 141). The beginning of the Courceyan was marked almost everywhere within the basin by an abrupt change of facies. At the boundary stratotype section on the Old Head of Kinsale (Fig. 96b, Column 7) unusually coarse sandstones at the top of the Old Head Sandstone Formation are sharply overlain by dark, probably off-shore, mudstones (Castle Slate Member) of the Kinsale Formation. Similar changes are found in sections around the coast westwards to Dunmanus Bay and eastwards into Cork Harbour, where on both limbs of the Ringabella syncline (Fig. 96b, Column 6) the base of the Courceyan (identified using the LN/VI spore boundary) coincides with a change from pebbly sandstones to dark mudstones. This regional synchronous change of facies possibly reflected a general, but perhaps slight, rise in sea level, which would have resulted in a northward movement of the strand line. Above the Castle Slate, which varies from 10 to 60 m in thickness, the Kinsale Formation consists of sparsely fossiliferous mudstones, siltstones, and subordinate sandstones, all probably of shallow marine origin. In the Bantry area

BELGIUM	VAUGHAN's ZONES	RADIOGENIC DATES m.y.	BRITISH AND IRISH STAGES	BRACHIOPODS AND CORALS	MICROFOSSILS	GONIATITES
Viséan (V)		325				P_2 c Sudeticeras costatum
						b Neoglyphioceras subcirculare
V3c	D_2		BRIGANTIAN	Productus productus (Br)*	Asteroarchaediscus (F)*	a Goniatites granosus
						d Goniatites koboldi
V3b (part)				Lonsdaleia floriformis (Co)*	Gnathodus nodosus (C)*	P_1 c Goniatites elegans
						b Goniatites falcatus
						a Goniatites crenistria
V3b	D_1		ASBIAN	Davidsonina septosa (Br)	Howchinia (F)*	Bollandites castletonense Goniatites*
				Dibunophyllum (Co)*	Gnathodus bilineatus (C)*	
V3a V2b	S_2		HOLKERIAN	Davidsonina carbonaria (Br)		
V2a V1b	C_2S_1	345	ARUNDIAN	Delepinea carinata (Br)	Archaediscus (F)*	
				Lithostrotion (Co)*	Koninckopora inflata (A)*	
V1a	C_1 (part)		CHADIAN	Levitusia humerosa (Br)	Eoparastaffella (F)*	Pericyclus kochi
				colonial rugose corals*	Mestognathus (C)* lycospores*	
Tournaisian (Tn) Tn3 Tn2 Tn1b (part)	C_1 (part) Z K	360	COURCEYAN	Unispirifer tornacensis (Br) Caninophyllum patulum (Co)	Scaliognathus anchoralis (C) Siphonodella (C)	Muensteroceras* Pericyclus princeps Gattendorfia

Table 12. British and Irish Dinantian Stages, their correlation with Vaughan's Zones and Belgian stratigraphical notation, and occurrence of selected characteristic macro- and microfossils. Brachiopods identified by (Br), corals by (Co), foraminifera by (F), conodonts by (C) and algae by (A). Goniatite zones P_{1a}, P_{2a}, etc. shown at the left of the goniatite column. An asterisk indicates that the taxon indicated first appears in a particular stage, but ranges upwards. Radiometric dates from George et al. 1976, p. 76.

(Fig. 96b, Column 9) the early Courceyan succession has been interpreted by P. C. Jones as representing a progression from low energy tidal flats, lagoons, and

interdistributary bays (Ardaturrish Formation: see page 143), through deltaic shoreface sandbars and flats (Reenagough Formation), to subtidal environ-

Fig. 96. (a) Early Courceyan section north of the South Munster Basin.
        (b) Early Courceyan section within the South Munster Basin and comparative succession at
            Whiting Bay.
        (c) Early Courceyan palaeogeography, just before the deposition of the Ballyvergin Shale.
        (Data from Gardiner and Horne 1976; from references given in George *et al.* 1976; and from
        unpublished sources).

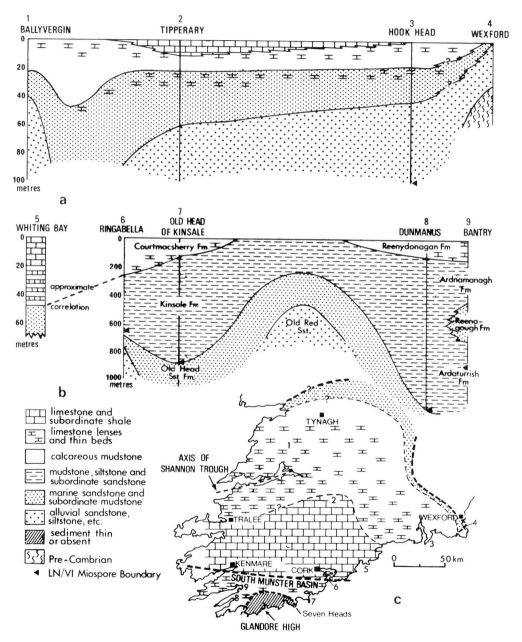

ments (Ardnamanagh Formation). The pattern of thickness variation of the Kinsale Formation and its equivalents through the South Munster Basin is imperfectly known as most of the information is derived from coastal sections. However, an area of thinning between the Seven Heads and Dunmanus Bay (Fig. 96c) has been termed the Glandore High by D. Naylor. Successions the same age as the Kinsale Formation north of the Cork/Kenmare line are considerably thinner than in the South Munster Basin (see below, page 152).

In the eastern part of the basin, the incoming of limestones and calcareous mudstones of the Court-macsherry Formation (Fig. 96b) marks an abrupt change of facies. At Ringabella (Fig. 96b, Column 6) the basal limestones sharply overlie muddy sandstones of the Kinsale Formation and contain numerous phospatic nodules some of which appear rolled. The fauna of brachiopods, bryozoans, simple corals, and crinoids indicates open marine conditions; conodonts occur, including the biostratigraphically important form, *Siphonodella*, which suggests correlation with late Lower or Middle Tournaisian rocks of Belgium. A similar change of facies occurs in the Bantry area where fossiliferous limestones of the lower part (Member 1) of the Reenydonagan For-

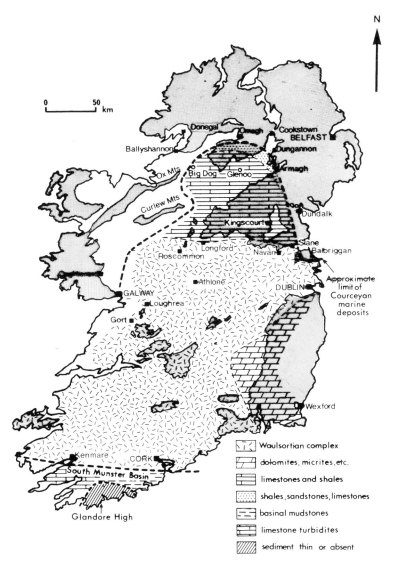

Fig. 97

Late Courceyan palaeogeography. (Fine stipple in this and succeeding maps represents pre-Upper Old Red Sandstone and post-Carboniferous rocks).

mation overlie mudstones of the Ardnamanagh Formation. The incoming of carbonate sedimentation appears to have been synchronous throughout much of the basin; this may reflect a further northward advance of the strand line and consequent reduction in the clastic supply. Probably at this time the basin began to deepen, particularly away from the northern margin. Fossiliferous limestones at the base of the Courtmacsherry Formation rapidly give way upwards to sparsely fossiliferous calcareous mudstones. How much of these are of early Courceyan age is unknown, and the thicknesses shown in Figure 96b are conjectural. In the Bantry area (Fig. 96b, Column 9), the early Courceyan part of the Reenydonagan Formation (Member 1) retains its shallow water aspect throughout, but at Dunmanus (Fig. 96b, Column 8) the carbonate content is much reduced. It appears that over the Glandore High equivalents of the early Courceyan parts of the Reenydonagan and Courtmacsherry formations are extremely reduced or absent, since only a few metres of dark mudstones occur between the Kinsale Formation and beds with Brigantian goniatites.

North of the Cork/Kenmare line, successions of early Courceyan age (beneath the Ballyvergin Shale) are much thinner than those of the South Munster Basin (Fig. 96a). In general they thicken southwards, but unusually thick successions are also present in the Shannon Trough (Fig. 96c), a region of persistent downwarp through most of Dinantian and Namurian time.

The successions shown in Figure 96a start in northerly derived sandstones and red siltstones and mudstones of alluvial origin. The position of the base of the Courceyan has been established within this facies at Hook Head (Fig. 96a, Column 3 and see also p. 128) and it is now known that in each of the successions shown, alluvial sedimentation continued into the Courceyan. The transition to marine conditions is recorded in grey sandstones and dark mudstones which show flaser bedding, cross-stratification, and vertical and horizontal burrows. Towards the top of the sandstone unit shown in Figure 96a, bioclastic limestones and oolites, often containing the brachiopod 'Camarotoechia', were developed in some areas, probably as off-shore bars. In various sections along the south-east coast and inland, the sandstones contain pebble and granule conglomerates with pebbles of vein quartz, mylonite, jasper, and igneous material. A striking example is exposed at Whiting Bay, Ardmore, County Waterford (Fig. 96b, Column 5), where some 20 m of pebbly sandstones include one bed which has a megarippled surface with a veneer of white quartz pebbles. The origin of the pebbly beds has been a subject of debate. I. A. J. MacCarthy and his coworkers have suggested that they were derived from a

suddenly uplifted Pre-Cambrian source region off and parallel to the present south-east coast. Others have suggested a northerly or north-easterly source. Less spectacular granule and pebble conglomerates occur in sandstones in County Clare and south County Galway and are probably not rare in similar facies elsewhere. Shallowing at the top of the sandstones was widespread as shown by the common occurrence of a unit of laminated and sand-lensed mudstones with deep desiccation cracks, which must have formed on intertidal mudflats. The contact between the sandstones (and associated facies) and the overlying calcareous shales shown in Figure 96a is usually very sharp. Thin, coarse, sometimes hematite-rich, limestones, at or close to the base of the shales, contain an open marine fauna of crinoids, brachiopods, and bryozoans. They resemble the basal limestones of the Courtmacsherry Formation in containing rolled phosphatic granules and pebbles, and preliminary biostratigraphical correlation suggest that they are of approximately the same age. There is little doubt that in each succession the change from sandstones to calcareous shales represents deepening, but whether the contact is regionally diachronous, resulting from a continuous transgression, or synchronous, reflecting a single rapid transgression, is not yet known. The calcareous shales which contain a diverse fauna of brachiopods, common simple rugose corals, and tabulates such as *Michelinia* and *Syringopora*, become more limey upwards and in some areas grade into dark bioclastic limestones. They also become more limey southwards and at Whiting Bay (Fig. 96b, Column 5) are completely replaced by limestones. Figure 96c illustrates the distribution of facies shortly before Ballyvergin Shale times. The extent of the inshore sand facies is largely speculative. Preliminary results from the Wexford region (Fig. 96a, Column 4) indicate that sandstones and pebbly beds there are equivalent to calcareous shales at Hook Head.

Late Courceyan

During the later part of the Courceyan, the sea transgressed across the midlands into Ulster and considerable facies differences existed between different areas (Fig. 97). The succession developed in County Limerick (Fig. 98, Column 2) may be taken as a standard for comparison with other areas. The lowest unit, the Ballyvergin Shale, consists of distinctive non-calcareous grey-green mudstones with thin silt lenses and laminae and has a maximum thickness of 10 m; it is a widespread marker unit which is known from a crudely triangular area with corners at Tynagh, County Galway, Tralee, County Kerry, and Whiting Bay, County Waterford (Fig. 96c); it probably resulted from a rapid influx of sediment from the north-west. Above the Ballyvergin Shale are dark well-bedded limestones with varying amounts of shale, which have been mapped as the Ballysteen Limestone. The limestones originally were muddy skeletal sands and gravels made up of disarticulated crinoids and the skeletons of other invertebrates, which accumulated in moderately shallow water (perhaps less than 100 m deep). A diorama of this environment would show crinoids (particularly the camerates *Dialutocrinus* and *Platycrinites*) forming dense stands with some individuals reaching perhaps as high as half a metre from the sea floor. Other conspicuous inhabitants would be the horn-shaped zaphrentid corals, bushy colonies of the tabulate *Syringopora*, and the lower, saucer-like colonies of *Michelinia*. Brachiopods would be abundant on the sediment surface, particularly *Unispirifer*, *Schellwienella*, and productaceans. Less conspicuous might be the numerous small and delicate twig-like or lacy colonies of bryozoans. Gastropods, trilobites, and ostracodes would be shown as moving over the sediment surface, whilst the sediment itself would be highly burrowed by the infauna, including bivalves and probably annelids and crustaceans. Small fish and the enigmatic conodont animals might be shown as swimming in the bottom waters.

The Ballysteen Limestone in many areas becomes particularly cherty and shaly towards its top and is overlain by a succession of distinctive, generally massive, limestones. The similarity of the latter to limestones at Waulsort in Belgium has long been recognised and in the literature they have generally been referred to as Waulsortian 'reefs'. As A. Lees has shown, the term 'reef' is inappropriate for these limestones; they are here referred to as Waulsortian Mudbank Limestones (bank limestones).

The bank limestones are very pure, light to dark grey in colour, and fine-grained (mud and silt grade) in texture, but often also contain skeletal material which is probably mainly *in situ*. Original cavities now filled with fibrous and blocky sparry calcite may form half or more of the volume of the rock. They are of differing form and origin: some are the interior of shells while some are bounded by fronds of fenestrate bryozoans; others have no obvious bounding framework and have been called stromatactis, a name originally applied to soft bodied organisms, whose moulds the cavities were supposed to be. Most of the cavities are floored with internally sedimented lime mudstone (micrite). The limestones form mound or sheet-like build-ups whose growth forms can be established by detailed mapping of bedding surfaces and of stromatactis cavities whose maximum dimensions approximately parallel bedding surfaces. Original depositional dips of 40° are quite common on the flanks of the mounds. Associated with the bank limestones are cherty or shaly thin-bedded limestones which have been referred to as 'lagoonal' limestones. Individual mounds were usually not more than 15 m high and probably not more than a few hundred metres in diameter but they grew one on another and inter-fingered with the 'lagoonal' rocks to form a considerable thickness of limestones here called the Waulsortian Limestone Complex.

Evidence as to the origin of the lime muds making up the bank limestones is scanty. Algae containing fine carbonate crystals within their soft tissues are a possible source, but recognisable algal remains of any kind are extremely scarce. The stromatactis cavities may have originated by the decay of masses of organic tissue, possibly algal holdfasts, below the water-sediment interface. The collapse of the surrounding fairly cohesive sediment would have resulted in the production of an open-textured structure which would

Fig. 98. Late Courceyan section in Munster and South Connacht (data from references given in George *et al.* 1976).

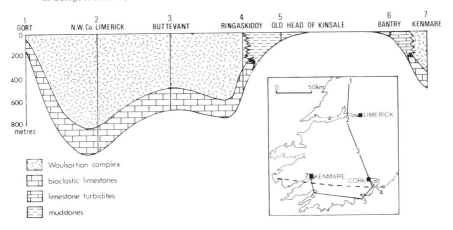

have become progressively modified by the depositon of mud within cavities and the precipitation of sparry carbonate cements. There is no direct evidence as to the depth of water covering the banks. They do not appear to be capped by algal stromatolites and there seems little evidence of strong wave or current action apart from some flank beds which contain soft pebble conglomerates.

The fauna from the Waulsortian Limestone Complex is diverse. The fossils in some places occur in pockets which may represent original clusters; brachiopods and bivalves are often preserved with valves articulated and with little sign of transport. Perhaps the most striking aspect of the fauna is the abundance of molluscs. Among the cephalopods, orthoconic nautiloids, *Vestinautilus*, and the goniatites *Muensteroceras* and *Pericyclus* are common. Gastropods and bivalves are represented by numerous genera including *Straparollus* and *Conocardium*. Brachiopods are some of the commonest fossils; typical genera are the productaceans *Dictyoclostus* and *Antiquatonia*, rhynchonellaceans such as *Pugnoides*, spiriferaceans including *Brachythyris* and *Syringothyris*, and terebratulaceans such as *Dielasma*. Fenestrate bryozoans are a dominant constituent of some, but not all, bank limestones. They are often preserved relatively unfragmented, sometimes as complete cone-shaped zoaria. Trilobites include *Phillipsia* and *Brachymetopus*. The ostracodes are mainly smooth shelled forms amongst which examples of the myodocopid genus *Entomoconchus* are notable for their large size. There appears to be a real difference between the faunas of the bank and 'lagoonal' limestones, which is apparently highlighted by the relative abundance of solitary rugose corals in the latter. The only corals found with any frequency in

the bank limestones have been recorded as *Amplexus*. To what extent they represent amplexoid growth forms of typical 'lagoonal' rugosans requires investigation. Although echinoderm material is present in most bank limestones, it seems more abundant in the 'lagoonal' facies. In some cases it appears that crinoid stands with rarer blastoids occupied the tops and flanks of mounds on which carbonate mud deposition had diminished. In such cases the flank beds may have been made largely of coarse crinoid gravels amongst which thecae of camerate crinoids such as *Platycrinites* and *Amphoracrinus* are fairly common.

Despite the rich faunas available, the age of the Waulsortian Complex of the Limerick region is difficult to determine. The whole complex is here treated as being of Courceyan age although it is recognised that some of the upper part may eventually be established as Chadian. The north-west Limerick succession with some variations in thickness may be traced southwards to the Cork/Kenmare line (Fig. 98). However, equivalent rocks within the South Munster Basin are of completely different character. At Bantry (Fig. 98, Column 6) the upper part of the Courceyan is represented in the Reenydonagan Formation by 10 m of black pyritous mudstones (Member 2) and a thin succession of limestone turbidites (Member 3), which, according to P. C. Jones, were derived from the north-east. The Glandore High seems to have been a region of non-deposition, whilst at the Old Head of Kinsale it is probable that dark deepwater mudstones of the higher parts of the Courtmacsherry Formation accumulated (unfortunately there is no fossil evidence available and the section shown in Fig. 98, Column 5 is speculative). It seems likely that the balance between rapid subsidence and rapid sedimentation within the basin, which had led to the

Fig. 99. Late Courceyan section in Ulster and Leinster (data from references given in George *et al.* 1976).

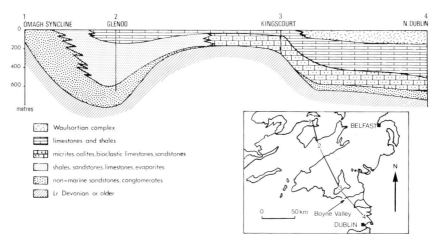

development of thick sequences of shallow water sediments in the early Courceyan, was upset in the late Courceyan by a reduction in the clastic supply caused by the northward movement of the strand line and onset of carbonate sedimentation north of the basin. By the time Waulsortian mudbanks were well established to the north, the basin was effectively starved of all except the finest argillaceous sediment and re-sedimented carbonate.

On the northern side of the Shannon (Fig. 98, Column 1), the north-west Limerick succession is much reduced in thickness. Between Gort and Loughrea, County Galway (Fig. 97) the Waulsortian Limestone Complex appears to be absent; in this region the equivalents of the Ballysteen Limestone contain intercalations of sandstone hinting at a north-western land area.

In the triangular area to the south-east of Loughrea bounded by the Lower Palaeozoic inliers of Slieve Aughty, the Arra Mountains, Devilsbit, and Slieve Bloom, the upper Courceyan appears similar to that of County Limerick but is probably thinner. To the east the Waulsortian limestones become thinner and the equivalents of the Ballysteen Limestone contain considerable thicknesses of oolite. Closer to the Leinster Granite and Lower Palaeozoics, (Fig. 97), Waulsortian limestones are apparently absent and the poorly known Courceyan successions are thought to consist of bioclastic limestones, dolomites, and oolites. This region corresponds with part of the East Leinster High recognised in Namurian palaeogeography (Fig. 112). Whether by latest Courceyan times (Fig. 97) it had been completely submerged or whether some of it remained as land is debateable.

To the north, the upper part of the Courceyan overlaps the lower part (compare Figs. 96c and 97) to rest on Lower Devonian or older rocks. Waulsortian limestones of varying thickness, but locally at least 300 m thick, form the upper part of the successions as far north as the southern margin of the Longford–Down Lower Palaeozoic region. They are usually underlain by very shallow-water limestones and sandstones. Typical examples of such a succession are developed in the Boyne Valley between Navan and (to the north-east) Slane (Fig. 99). There, variably thick red beds resting on Lower Palaeozoics are overlain by siltstones and sandstones deposited by tidal currents and argillaceous limestones. They are followed by a distinctive suite of grey fine-grained limestones, micrites, oomicrites, and pelmicrites; some of the micrites are burrowed and contain 'bird's eye' calcite-filled vugs and others are full of the calcified tubes of codiacean algae, which have formed algal nodules (oncolites). The fauna is not very diverse and includes ostracodes, bivalves, gastropods, and rare brachiopods. The original lime muds

were deposited in very shallow water, possibly in lagoons, and some beds may have been exposed on intertidal and supratidal flats. They are overlain by sandstones, sandy oolites, and bioclastic limestones which contain brachiopods, particularly *Schellwienella* and *Tylothyris*. The sandstones and sandy limestones may have formed as off-shore bars. The upper part of the succession is commonly cut out by unconformity in the Boyne Valley, but where it remains, it consists of rather shaly bioclastic limestones overlain by a thin development of Waulsortian bank limestones. The Boyne Valley succession with some variations can be traced westwards along the south side of the Longford–Down Lower Palaeozoic region at least as far as Longford. Similar successions, but with thicker developments of Waulsortian bank limestones are known as far south as Athlone and probably extend into the Dublin region, where, however, sandstones are not developed except at the base. There is little doubt that the lithological units within these successions are diachronous. Preliminary studies suggest that a north-south transect in late Courceyan times would have passed from lagoonal micrites near the southern margin of the Longford–Down massif through offshore sands to bioclastic limestones in the south Midlands and Waulsortian mudbanks in Counties Kerry and Cork. Variation in late Courceyan successions northwards is shown in Fig. 99. In the Kingscourt outlier (Fig. 99, Column 3), the succession is similar to that in the Boyne Valley but considerably thinner, and the mudbank limestones are replaced by well-bedded bioclastic limestones. The thinning may reflect the existence of the Southern Uplands High identified in Namurian palaeogeography (Fig. 112). Certainly the successions to the north, which have been investigated by D. J. R. Sheridan, are very much thicker.

In the Glenoo well (Fig. 99, Column 2) Courceyan dark bioclastic limestones and interbedded shales are underlain by a thick sequence of sandstones, shales, and micrites with substantial intervals of anhydrite. Similar sandstones, shales, and micrites (which crop out both on the north-western margin of the Longford–Down massif and farther north) contain an impoverished fauna, typically of ostracodes, bivalves, and 'serpulid' tubes (now thought to be vermetiform gastropods). Older Carboniferous rocks, scarcely penetrated by the Glenoo and other deep borings, crop out north-west of Glenoo near Fivemiletown, County Tyrone, where at least 200 m of red conglomerates, sandstones, and siltstones overly the Lower Devonian of the Fintona block.

The Courceyan sea may have advanced as far north as Omagh, County Tyrone, but its limit is difficult to fix accurately because the facies developed are poorly fossiliferous conglomerates, sandstones, and siltstones. In the north-east of the Omagh syncline (Fig. 99, Column 1) the Omagh Sandstone rests unconformably on Dalradian schists and is reported to be 600 m thick. It thins rapidly westwards. A lower unit of conglomerates and sandstones, some of them red, which were deposited by rapidly flowing rivers from the north, is overlain by an upper unit of conglomerates, sandstones, shales, and seat earths with rare fossil bands containing bivalves, ostracodes, and 'serpulid' tubes which accumulated in marginal marine environments. In the past, all of the Omagh Sandstone and parts of the overlying Claragh Sandstone have been assigned to the Courceyan; this reading of the stratigraphy leads to a palaeogeographical reconstruction with the shore line considerably north of that drawn in Fig. 97, which has as its basis the belief that only the lower unit of the Omagh Sandstone is Courceyan. There is some hope that palynological studies will eventually provide a firmer biostratigraphy on which to base palaeogeographical reconstructions in the Omagh syncline.

From the Omagh region, the margins of the late Courceyan sea may be traced both eastwards and westwards with varying degrees of confidence. The north-western limit must have lain to the east of the Ox Mountain–Ballyshannon area (Fig. 97) where T. N. George and D. H. Oswald have shown that Chadian limestones rest almost directly on metamorphic basement. However, D. J. R. Sheridan has suggested that a tongue of the Courceyan sea may have extended westwards into the north-east corner of the Donegal syncline. If the rocks in question (sandstones, shales, and micrites, with stromatolites and evaporitic horizons) are confirmed to be of Courceyan age, the map in Figure 97 will have to be altered accordingly.

The lack of Courceyan strata on the Ox Mountain–Ballyshannon High contrasts with the succession recorded by D. J. R. Sheridan 20 km to the south-east of Ballyshannon in the Big Dog well (Fig. 101, Column 4) which penetrated at least 600 m of Courceyan limestones, shales, sandstones, dolomites, and anhydrites without reaching the basement. Thick successions (more than 300 m) of Courceyan rocks similar to those in the Big Dog well are known from other subsurface sections in Counties Leitrim and Fermanagh (Macnean and Owengarr wells).

A very considerable facies change must occur between the western end of the Longford–Down massif and the eastern end of the Curlew Mountains, where the Boyle Sandstone Formation which is predominantly non-marine in origin is overlain by Chadian limestones. South of the Curlew Mountains, Waulsortian-bank limestones are known around the town of Roscommon (Fig. 97) and to the west. They appear to be thin and to lie not far above sandstones

at the local base of the succession. Control of the western limit of the late Courceyan sea in this region is poor. The lowest limestones in the area around Oughterard, County Galway, are known to be Chadian in age while the most westerly known Courceyan sequence occurs a few kilometres west of Loughrea, County Galway. The position of the eastern margin of the Courceyan sea in Ulster is uncertain. Around Cookstown and Dungannon, County Tyrone, the oldest dated strata are post-Courceyan and they are thought to overlie undated basal clastic rocks. Farther south, around Armagh, some 90 m of red siltstones with occasional conglomerates are overlain by 130 m of very shallow marine and marginal marine sandstones, conglomerates, grey shales, and sandy limestones, some of which may be Courceyan. On the south side of Belfast Lough at Cultra, red sandstones about 180 m thick are overlain by grey shales, dolomites, and thin limestones of 'cementstone' facies. If these are Courceyan as has been reported, they probably formed in a separate shallow gulf which opened eastwards; however, they are more likely to be post-Courceyan. The shoreline lay to the west of the small outliers west of Dundalk (Fig. 97) in which the basal limestones are probably Chadian, but its position farther south is less certain. An alternative to Figure 97 would show the coast line swinging eastwards on the south side of Dundalk Bay to form the northern margin of a broad gulf connecting the Kingscourt region with the Solway Firth on the other side of the Irish sea. The Balbriggan inlier, which was certainly upstanding, would have formed an island.

Chadian to Brigantian Stages

These stages, defined in boundary stratotype sections in England and Wales (Table 12), span an interval of about 25 million years, during which most of Ireland was covered by the sea. The great range of facies developed are described on a regional basis: the palaeogeographical maps and stratigraphical sections are intended to provide a link from one region to another.

North-west Region

The north-west region lies north and west of a line drawn from Belfast Lough along the margin of the Longford–Down Lower Palaeozoic area to Galway (Fig. 100). Its northern part lay close to, or included, the margin of marine deposition from Chadian times onwards; as a result very little limestone was ever deposited north of Cookstown, County Tyrone, and the Omagh and Donegal synclines (see Fig. 97 for locations). The thickest successions are found between the north-eastern Ox Mountains, which formed part of the Ox Mountains–Ballyshannon High (Fig. 101), and an eastern shelf area between Armagh and Cookstown. For much of Chadian and Arundian times (Fig. 100), the north-west region was the site of carbonate deposition, except around the marginal areas where terrigenous sediments predominated. The limestones were mapped by Griffith's surveyors and the Geological Survey as the Lower Limestone; they have subsequently received local names. A typical succession (described by W. G. E. Caldwell) is developed in the Carrick syncline (Fig. 101, Column 6). The dark bioclastic Kilbryan Limestones (Chadian) are sandy close to the underlying Boyle Sandstones and are overlain by the Oakport Limestones, whose

lower (? Chadian) part, predominantly fine-grained peloidal micrites and oolites with horizons rich in blue-green and red algae, is clearly of very shallow water origin. The upper part of the Oakport Limestone (Arundian) was originally a crinoidal muddy carbonate sand, containing amongst others the stratigraphically important dascycladacean alga *Koninckopora* and archaediscid foraminifera. Similar successions are found to the west at Oughterard, County Galway (where intercalations of sandstones may reflect a western shore line) and along the length of the Ox Mountains. In general the limestones are underlain by northerly or north-westerly derived fluviatile sandstones, probably partly of Courceyan age, although in some areas on the Ox Mountains–Ballyshannon High (for example Ballysadare, County

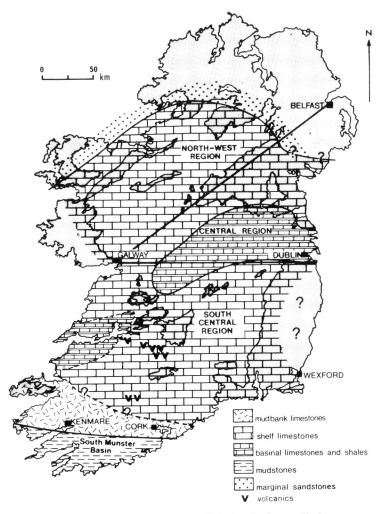

Fig. 100. Chadian palaeogeography and delimitation of regions used in the text.

Sligo, and Ballyshannon, County Donegal) they rest almost directly on the metamorphic basement. In those areas where marine sandstone deposition had been established during the Courceyan, the base of the Chadian lies within or at the base of the Lower Limestone.

The passage from limestones into marginal clastic facies has been clearly demonstrated by T. N. George and D. H. Oswald in the Donegal syncline (Fig. 101), where thick deposits accumulated in an actively subsiding graben, possibly controlled by the north-east to south-west trending Killybegs (Leannan) Fault between Largymore and Bruckless (Fig. 101, Columns 1 and 2) and a similar fault east of Donegal town. The Bruckless Grits represent environments ranging from subaerial fanglomerates near the base to marginal marine just below the fully marine Calhame Limestone (Chadian), which may be regarded as a northwards thinning tongue of Ballyshannon (Lower) Limestone. Alluvial sandstones and red and green siltstones with casts of *in situ* tree stumps and roots occur above the Calhame Limestone and they pass upwards through transitional facies into the fossiliferous shaly limestones of the Rinn Point Beds (Arundian). The coarse nature of much of the Bruckless Grits and the common large fresh feldspar grains suggest rapid transport from a source area which lay to the north or north-west according to the orientation of foresets in cross-stratified sandstones. North of Donegal, the Arundian succession is even less

carbonate rich and the thick Bannagher Hill Grits may be the equivalent of part of the Rinn Point Beds.

A similar passage from limestones to clastic facies takes place westwards from the Ox Mountains to the coast of North Mayo, where alluvial conglomerates, sandstones, and red and green siltstones are overlain by sandstones, shales, and fine-grained limestones deposited in marginal marine environments. Higher limestones and shales contain channel-form sandstones with casts of drifted tree trunks; the whole succession is of deltaic aspect.

The Ballyshannon (Lower) Limestone (Chadian and Arundian) can be traced from Ballyshannon (Fig. 101, Column 3) northwards into the Omagh syncline where it has been mapped as the Pettigo Limestone (Fig. 102, Column 1). It is there underlain by the thick Claragh Sandstone; foraminiferal evidence suggests that much of the Claragh Sandstone in the north correlates with the Ballyshannon Limestone farther south. The Newtownstewart outlier, 15 km north of Omagh, contains a thick clastic succession which may in part be Chadian and Arundian in age.

South of Lough Erne (Fig. 101, Columns 4, 5) the Lower Limestone includes sandstones, thought to be a tongue of the Claragh Sandstone. Equivalent successions of the eastern shelf area (Fig. 100) are poorly known but appear to be relatively thin sandstones or shallow-water limestones. The Lower Limestone and its near-shore equivalents contain a diverse fauna and flora. Most conspicuous are corals, particularly

Fig. 101. Section across the Ox Mountain-Ballyshannon High into counties Fermanagh and Leitrim, (data from references given in George *et al.* 1976).

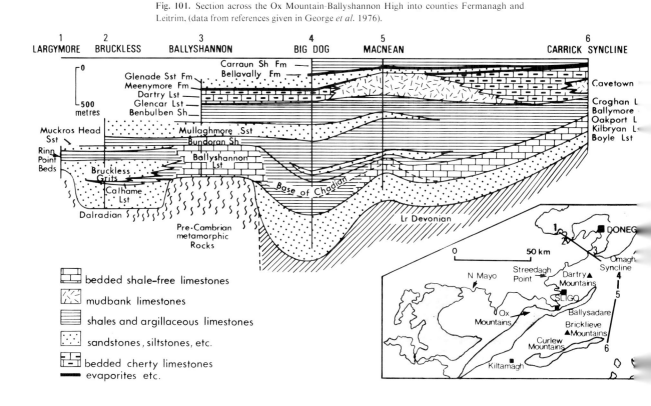

caniniids, *Lithostrotion*, and *Syringopora* and the large stratigraphically useful brachiopods *Daviesiella* and *Delepinea*. Many of the limestones are largely made up of crinoid ossicles and also contain algae, bryozoans, foraminifera, and ostracodes. Some of the more shaly facies yield scarcer fossils such as crinoid crowns, complete echinoid tests, and trilobites. The activities of the infauna are preserved in rich suites of trace fossils including *Chondrites*, *Diplocraterion*, *Teichichnus*, and *Zoophycos*.

Throughout much of the north-west region, the Lower Limestone is overlain by Arundian dark, fossiliferous shales, the lower part of the Calp or Middle Limestone recognized by Griffith. The shales have subsequently received local names (*e.g.* the Bundoran Shale of the Sligo syncline); they extend in a broad belt from Counties Donegal and Sligo eastwards to the Clogher Valley (Fig. 102). Northwards and on the eastern shelf they probably pass into sandstones and limestones, while to the south they are increasingly more calcareous, becoming mainly limestones in and to the west of the Carrick syncline.

The influx of terrigenous material represented by the Bundoran Shales reached a maximum with the widespread introduction of sandstones; these were termed the Calp Sandstone by the Geological Survey but have subsequently received local names, such as

the Mullaghmore Sandstone of the Sligo syncline (Fig. 101, Column 3). The evidence for the Holkerian age assigned to the sandstones is slight and they may eventually be found to be Arundian. The sandstones are feldspathic and also include thin fossiliferous shales and rare limestones. They may be traced eastwards from the coast of north Mayo, through the Sligo and Donegal synclines, into the Omagh syncline, where they are mapped as the Clonelly Sandstone (Fig. 102, Column 1), and the region south and east of Lough Erne as far as south-east County Tyrone (Fig. 103). They are thickest in the north, and thin and become finer grained southwards. In the south and south-west of the region, and probably also in the east, they pass into limestones.

Detailed sedimentological studies of the Carrowmoran (Calp) Sandstone of western County Sligo by J. A. E. B. Hubbard have established its deltaic origin. Cross-stratified sandstones, which are commonly slumped are thought to have formed on the delta top and its seaward margins. They contain drifted lycopodian plant material and the sandstone casts of *in situ* lepidodendrid stumps and rootlets. A thin shale just above a bed with *in situ* plant material has yielded a brackish water ostracode fauna. Thin-bedded sandy and silty shales which are commonly ripple-marked and contain a sparse fauna of ostracodes, sponge

Fig. 102. Post-Courceyan section in Ulster and Leinster (data from references given in George *et al.* 1976).

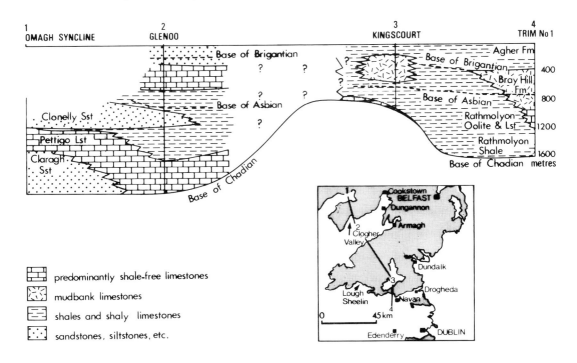

spicules, and 'serpulid' tubes, may have been deposited at the seaward margin of the delta top and on the delta slope. Thinly bedded calcareous shales with abundant trace fossils, including *Rhizocorallium*, *Teichichnus*, and *Chondrites* accumulated seawards of the delta slope. They contain bivalves, gastropods, orthoconic nautiloids, and ostracodes. Cross-stratified oolitic limestones probably formed away from the areas of active terrigenous sediment supply. The repetition of these lithologies in vertical sequence resulted from the impersistence of clastic sedimentation at any one place due to the migration and abandonment of distributary streams flowing from the north and north-west. The southward advance of the clastic facies must have been in response to a regionally important event, either uplift in the source regions or a relative lowering of sea level. The latter hypothesis is attractive in view of the persuasive evidence for eustatic movements of sea level elsewhere within the Dinantian.

Throughout most of the region the deltaic sandstones are overlain, in most places abruptly, by dark fossiliferous shales, the upper part of Griffith's Calp, now given local names such as the Benbulben Shale in the Sligo syncline (Fig. 101, Column 3). The change from deltaic sandstones to fully marine shales seems to indicate a regional deepening of the sort that occurred at the start of each of the six major sedimentary cycles recognised by W. H. C. Ramsbottom and referred to earlier (page 147). However, the lower part of the Benbulben Shale is thought to be of Holkerian age; thus the major sedimentological change in the Calp succession lies within the Holkerian, unless, as hinted above, the Calp Sandstones are Arundian in age.

Carbonate sedimentation was gradually re-established in the previously deltaic areas; in the Sligo syncline (Fig. 101, Column 3) the Benbulben Shale (mainly Holkerian) is overlain by the Asbian argillaceous Glencar Limestone, which contains large caniniids and *Lithostrotion* colonies, spectacularly displayed on wide bedding planes at Streedagh Point (Fig. 104) and Serpent Rock, County Sligo. The overlying Dartry Limestones (the upper Limestone of Griffith and the Geological Survey) includes two distinct facies: well-bedded, pale-coloured, often very cherty, limestones with *Lithostrotion*, such as make up the scarp and terrace scenery of the Bricklieve Mountains and the well-known feature of Ben Bulbin (Fig. 105), and unbedded or poorly-bedded 'reef' or mudbank limestones, well displayed in the Dartry Mountains. The mudbank limestones are locally very fossiliferous with diverse productacean brachiopods, occasional goniatites such as *Beyrichoceras* (of the B2 zone), and in some thin-bedded flank beds, very common blastoids. Corals are generally rare, in con-

Fig. 103. Distribution of Calp Sandstones and equivalent strata in north-west Ireland (adapted from Sheridan 1972).

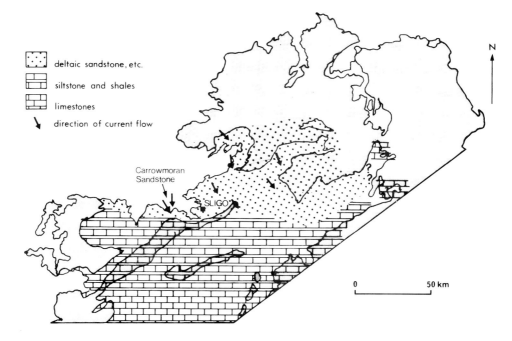

strast to the rich and stratigraphically important faunas of *Lithostrotion*, *Clisiophyllum*, *Dibunophyllum* and other solitary forms found in the bedded facies.

Strata equivalent in age to the Glencar and Dartry Limestones are absent through erosion in the Donegal and Omagh synclines, but in counties Leitrim and Fermanagh, shales and limestones grading up into pale cherty biomicrites are widely represented (Fig. 101). On the eastern shelf between Armagh and Cookstown, County Tyrone, equivalent successions are shale-free bioclastic limestones and oolites. There is also a decrease in argillaceous material towards the south, and bioclastic limestones of this age through Counties Roscommon, Mayo, and Galway contain little shale. The factors which controlled the distribution of the carbonate mudbanks are not clear; in some cases the sites of mudbank formation appear to

have been related to active faults and structural highs, as for instance on the north-western flank of the northern Ox Mountains and along the northern fault-bounded side of the Curlew Mountains, but in other instances, there is no obvious structural control.

Throughout much of the region, there was a marked change in conditions in late Asbian time with the development of widespread very shallow water environments which persisted into the Brigantian (Fig. 106). A. Brandon and his co-workers have described the stratigraphy and sedimentology of this interval.

The Meenymore Formation (Fig. 101) includes laminated dolomites and micrites, with desiccation cracks and pseudomorphs after anhydrite and gypsum, which probably formed in supratidal coastal sabkhas. Thin fossiliferous limestones and shales with B2 zone goniatites, brachiopods, and bivalves accumulated in shallow subtidal situations.

Fig. 104. Streedagh Point, County Sligo. Asbian *Siphonophyllia* (*Caninia*), up to 0.6 m long. A. B. Wynne, one of the geologists of the Geological Survey of Ireland, wrote in 1864 of these 'grand assemblage(s) of corals . . . ., many of which lie about, and project from the largely-exposed slightly-sloping beds, like stumps in a cabbage-garden, and one is almost disappointed to find that they cannot pull them up, ...'

Photograph by G. D. Sevastopulo

The Glenade Sandstone Formation consists of a southerly thinning wedge of northerly-derived sandstone which may have been deposited under terrestrial conditions in the north of its outcrop. In some areas where the Dartry Limestone is developed in carbonate mudbank facies, the Meenymore Formation is absent and the Glenade Sandstone rests on dolomitised limestones which had been left emergent by a drop in sea level. The age of the Glenade Sandstone is not known; it is assigned here to the Brigantian on the basis of faunas found above it, but possibly is better regarded as being of latest Asbian age. The Bellavally Formation represents a return to environmental conditions similar to those of the Meenymore Formation, and contains goniatites indicative of the P1b zone. The Carraun Shale Formation does not contain evaporites although some limestone bands within it include oncolites (algal nodules) which suggest fairly shallow water environments. The rich goniatite faunas range upwards to the P2c zone.

In the Slieve Beagh uplands of Counties Fermanagh and Tyrone (Fig. 107) a thick succession of sandstones and interbedded shales have B2 and P1 zonal goniatites near their base. The lower part of the sandstones apparently passes laterally into well-bedded pale coloured coral-bearing limestones around Armagh. Near Dungannon, County Tyrone, similar Asbian and Brigantian limestones which contain the foraminifer *Saccamminopsis* are overlain by the Rossmore Mudstones which range from low in the P2 zone into the Namurian.

South of the main outcrops of counties Leitrim, Cavan, and Fermanagh, rocks of late Asbian and Brigantian age have mostly been removed by erosion. Near Kiltamagh, County Mayo, (Fig. 107) shaly limestones underlying the shales and sandstones of the Namurian outlier contain goniatites thought to be of low P2 age. The Glenade Formation is apparently not represented.

North of Dungannon, County Tyrone, a narrow belt of Carboniferous sandstones, shales, and thin coals stretches northwards to Lough Foyle. Their age is not known with certainty but it is unlikely that they include a great thickness of pre-Asbian strata; a borehole at Magilligan, County Derry (Fig. 107) penetrated thin coals which yielded late Dinantian spores.

Fig. 105. Ben Bulbin, County Sligo, viewed from the west-north-west. The scarp face is cut in Asbian Dartry and Glencar Limestones, and the scree covers the lower part of the Glencar Limestone and the Benbulben Shale. See also page 160.
Bord Failte photograph

The successsion seen at Ballycastle, County Antrim and described by H. E. Wilson and J. A. Robbie, is similar to that developed in the Macrihanish coalfield in Kintyre, Scotland. Sandstones and conglomerates are overlain by basaltic lavas and tuffs. The higher succession of sandstones, shales, and coals includes two marine bands; the fauna of the higher (Main Limestone) contains Brigantian brachiopods, and it is unlikely that the base of the succession is older than Asbian.

Central Region

The central region lies between the north-west region and a line drawn from Galway to Dublin (Fig. 100). Fossiliferous shelf limestones along its north-western margin are similar to those of the adjoining parts of the north-west region. In parts of the Midlands and the Dublin area, dark limestones and shales of basinal aspect predominate.

The Dublin area is perhaps the best known part of

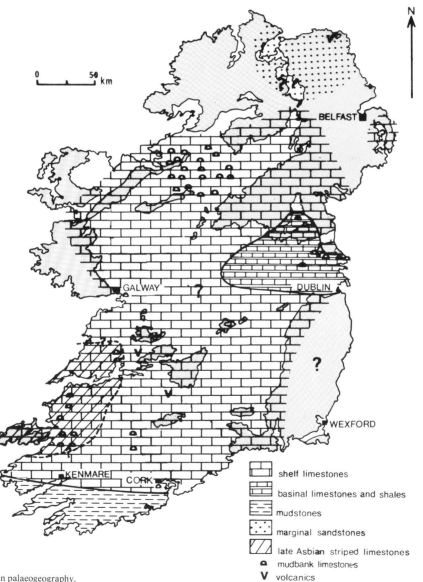

Fig. 106. Asbian palaeogeography.

the region, and has been studied by many leading Carboniferous stratigraphers including G. Delépine, R. G. S. Hudson, L. B. Smyth, J. S. Turner, and A. Vaughan. It illustrates a complexity of facies and thickness changes which may occur elsewhere masked by glacial sediments and bog. Between the Balbriggan Lower Palaeozoic inlier and the northern end of the Leinster granite (Fig. 108), post-Courceyan strata are almost all of basinal character, apart from a small strip of shelf limestones, south of Skerries.

The lowest unit of the basinal facies in the long coastal section between Rush and Loughshinny is the Rush Slates (Fig. 108, Column 2). The slates are poorly fossiliferous and only slightly calcareous but contain horizons with large limestone boulders and towards their top, thin channel-form lenses of limestone, which probably originated as turbidites. The upper part of the slates contains goniatites, such as *Merocanites*, *Muensteroceras*, and *Pericyclus*, and the limestone turbidites include Chadian foraminifera and shallow water algae. The overlying Rush Conglomerates are probably mainly of Chadian age and consist of spectacular beds of conglomerates interleaved with beds of shale and sandy limestone. The clasts are extremely varied and include vein-quartz pebbles; rounded cobbles and pebbles of Ordovician igneous rocks, particularly andesites; boulders, cobbles, and pebbles of varied shallow water Carbon-

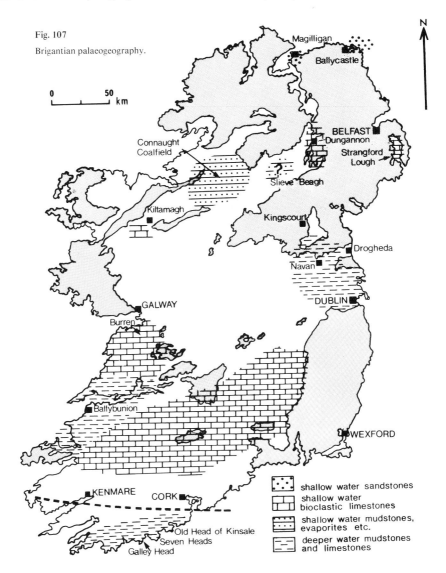

Fig. 107

Brigantian palaeogeography.

0   50 km

N

Magilligan
Ballycastle

Connaught Coalfield

BELFAST
Dungannon
Strangford Lough

Slieve Beagh

Kiltamagh

Kingscourt

Drogheda

Navan

DUBLIN

GALWAY

Burren

Ballybunion

WEXFORD

KENMARE   CORK

Old Head of Kinsale
Seven Heads
Galley Head

· · · shallow water sandstones
⊔⊔ shallow water bioclastic limestones
: ⁘ : shallow water mudstones, evaporites etc.
⊟ deeper water mudstones and limestones

iferous limestones including oolite; and rarer quartz-ites. Carboniferous marine fossils occur as pebbles and rare examples of silicified Ordovician halysitid corals have also been found. The conglomerates, which have been investigated by W. D. Gill and his students, were deposited by turbidity currents, pro-bably on a submarine fan similar to those found at present at the toes of submarine canyons. Transport was from the east and the grain-size and content of exotic clasts decrease as the formation is traced south-westwards inland. The source of the clasts was a shallow carbonate shelf, possibly with islands of Courceyan limestones and Ordovician igneous rocks and limestones similar to Lambay Island at the present day. The basin margin must have had con-siderable topographical expression which probably resulted from active faulting.

The Arundian Carlyan Limestone is an oolite and contains levels with exotic rock fragments. The re-mainder of the succession consists of dark argil-laceous, often cherty, limestones and shales, the lower part of which contains exotic rock fragments. The Cyathaxonia Beds (Asbian and Brigantian) include limestone boulder conglomerates and breccia beds. The Posidonomya Limestones with P1 age goniatites and the bivalve *Posidonia becheri* consist of inter-bedded shales and limestones many of which are graded and show other features of turbidites. The Loughshinny Black Shales with P2 goniatites are probably secondarily decalcified thin cherty limestone and shale alternations. Thin beds of sandstone appear towards the top of the P2 succession inland.

The shelf equivalent of the Rush–Loughshinny suc-cession is exposed on the coast between Loughshinny and Skerries (Fig. 108, Column 1), where the Chadian shallow-water Lane Limestone probably rests on a Lower Palaeozoic floor and contains lenses of quartz and greywacke pebbles. The Lane Conglomerate is non-calcareous and consists of closely packed slabby cobbles and boulders of Lower Palaeozoic grey-wackes similar to those in the Balbriggan inlier to the north. It rests on an irregular weathered surface of Lane Limestone and is of subaerial origin. A return to shallow marine conditions is represented by the overlying Arundian Holmpatrick Limestone which consists of oolites and bioclastic limestones.

The boundary between shelf and basin on the coast section is at the contact between the Lane Limestone (Chadian) and a complicated slumped succession of late Asbian or Brigantian pale grey micritic lime-stones of mudbank type, conglomerates containing Lower Palaeozoic greywacke fragments, and dark limestones and shales. The orientation of stromatactis cavities in some of the masses of mudbank limestones shows that the latter are transported blocks, and the whole complex suggests mass movement down a southerly directed palaeoslope. Inland, a number of mudbank limestone occurrences lie in an east-west

Fig. 108. Post-Courceyan section in the Dublin Region (data from references given in George *et al.* 1976).

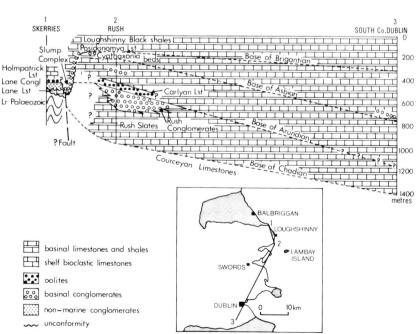

line which may mark the shelf-basin boundary (Fig. 106). Much of the southern margin of the Balbriggan inlier is a fault contact, close to which strata similar to the Cyathaxonia Beds of the coast section are underlain by Arundian limestones containing Lower Palaeozoic rock fragments.

In County Dublin south of an east-west line through Swords (Fig. 108), the post-Courceyan succession described by J. S. Turner consists of poorly fossiliferous dark argillaceous and cherty limestones and shales for which Richard Kirwan in about 1794 coined the name Calp. These limestones have been widely used in buildings and walls in Dublin City. A particularly fine range of representative rock types are displayed in the walls of the Old Library, Trinity College. Not far north of the faulted contact of the Carboniferous and Leinster granite, Asbian limestone turbidites contain angular fragments of granite and slate (Fig. 108, Column 3). The orientation of slumps at this level indicates movement down a northward facing palaeoslope, which probably resulted from active faulting.

Thick basinal successions occur to the south of the Longford–Down Lower Palaeozoic area (Fig. 102). In some places there is a marked uncomformity above the Courceyan; in others there appears to be a conformable passage. Around Navan, County Meath, a channel which in places is over 100 metres deep and probably a kilometre or more wide has been cut into the underlying Courceyan limestones. It is floored with closely packed limestone boulder conglomerates and contains dark shales and limestones, some of which show well-developed graded units and are clearly turbidites. To the west of Navan dark agrillaceous and cherty limestones and shales with rarer intervals of clean limestone, continue into the P2 zone (Fig. 107) where thin sandstones enter, as in the Dublin area. Some of the Arundian limestone turbidites contain oolites, *Koninckopora* and other algal material which presumably were derived from a shallow-water shelf. This source area has not yet been identified but may be farther to the east around Drogheda, where the succession consists of relatively shale-free pale coloured limestones. The shelf margin shown in Figure 106 is close to a number of Asbian carbonate mudbank occurrences.

In the Kingscourt outlier (Fig. 102, Column 3), which has been studied by J. S. Jackson, Chadian shelf-facies bioclastic limestones are overlain by Arundian and probable Holkerian basinal shaly limestones similar to those of the Navan area. Very fossiliferous mudbank limestones and associated lithologies occur in the Asbian. The Brigantian (Fig. 107) is represented mainly by goniatite-bearing black shales and thin limestones which range into P2c.

Farther north, the small outliers around Dundalk (Fig. 107) provide some link with the successions in the east of the north-west region, in that basinal facies

Fig. 109. Post-Courceyan section across the Shannon (data from references given in George *et al.* 1976).

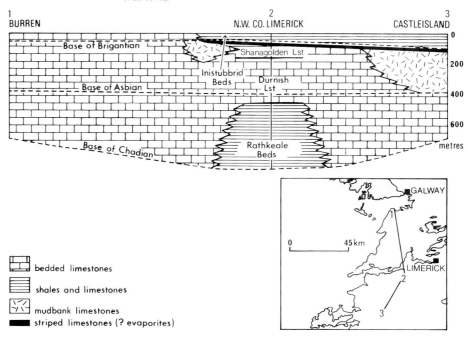

appear to be absent. Probable Chadian sandy bio-clastic limestones and 'bird's eye' micrites are suc-ceeded by Arundian and younger shelf bioclastic limestones. Brigantian shelf limestones which contain the large nautiloid, *Rayonnoceras*, occur at Castle Espie in Strangford Lough.

Basin facies occur to the west of Navan (Figs. 102 and 106), but near Lough Sheelin fossiliferous shelf limestones similar to those of the Carrick-on-Shannon area are predominant.The change from shelf to basinal conditions may have been gradational both in the north and west of the region.

To the south, there are considerable differences in the successions, brought out by comparison of the Trim well section (Fig. 102, Column 4) and the sequence in the neighbourhood of Edenderry, County Offaly, where a considerable thickness of Chadian oolites is overlain by dark, cherty, basinal limestones and shales. The cherty limestones at Croghan Hill, 12 km west of Edenderry, are overlain by basic ashes and lavas. In the Trim No. 1 well, the Rathmolyon Shales appear to be similar to the Rush Slates of the Dublin area. The Rathmolyon oolites are apparently younger than the Edenderry oolites and are overlain by bioclastic limestones and the Asbian Bray Hill Formation, a thin complex of mudbank limestones. The Brigantian Agher Formation consists of basinal limestones and shales.

South-central Region

The south-central region lies between the central region and the South Munster Basin (Fig. 100). In post-Courceyan times it was for the most part a carbonate shelf but more basinal facies tended to develop around the Shannon estuary and in south

Fig. 110. The Burren, County Clare. Looking north-north-westwards across Asbian limestone pavement to the Asbian limestone terraces on Ceappagh na Bhaile. In the background is Galway Bay with its north shore formed of Galway Granite.
    Bord Failte photograph

County Galway. In the south there were thick developments of carbonate mudbanks.

In north Clare and south-west County Galway (Fig. 109, Column 1) shelf bioclastic limestones, which now form extensive areas of pavement, persisted from the Chadian to the Brigantian. The apparent uniformity of the succession masks detailed changes of lithology which are related to variations in the depth of the sea. For example, the base of the Arundian is marked by a distinctive unit of peloidal limestones which probably accumulated in shallower water than the normal bioclastic limestones. Subtle lithogical changes are brought out in the terraced topography of the Burren region of County Clare (Fig. 110), which reflects the cyclical nature of the Asbian and Brigantian succession. The Asbian/Brigantian boundary there has been found by C. V. MacDermot to coincide with a very irregular bedding surface which certainly indicates a hiatus and possibly emergence. Southwards towards the Shannon (Fig 109), the lower part of the succession becomes more argillaceous and the well-bedded Asbian limestones pass into massive mudbank limestones and associated facies which are best seen on the islands in the Fergus estuary and the adjacent mainland. Overlying the bank limestones is a unit of distinctive striped limestones which is widely distributed to the south of the Shannon. The striped beds consist of alternating light and dark laminae of sparry carbonate; in some cases they grade into limestones with features similar to macrocell structure and they are associated with limestone breccias. It seems likely that they were originally evaporites which have become completely replaced by carbonates and they may reflect the regression which has been widely recognised at the Asbian/Brigantian boundary. The overlying Brigantian Inistubbrid Beds, described by F. Hodson and G. C. Lewarne, are basinal limestones and shales with goniatites which contrast with the shelf bioclastic limestones with corals which are their equivalents in the Burren.

On the south side of the Shannon in north-west County Limerick (Fig. 109, Column 2), where the stratigraphy has been described by E. R. Shephard-Thorn, the Rathkeale Beds (Chadian and possibly Arundian) are poorly fossiliferous very argillaceous limestones. The Durnish Limestones consist of coral-bearing bioclastic limestones. The dark Shanagolden Limestones are probably the bedded equivalent of the bank limestones of the Fergus estuary, since they are overlain by the Parsonage Beds which include striped limestones. Overlying limestones and shales are similar to the Inistubbrid Beds.

The succession around Castleisland, County Kerry (Fig. 109, Column 3) is similar to that of the Fergus estuary, particularly in the occurrence of Asbian

carbonate mudbanks overlain by striped limestones. This association may be traced into the areas around Tralee and Ballybunion (Fig. 106), where the overlying basinal limestones and shales, equivalent to the Inistubbrid Beds, are over 200 m thick and contain Brigantian goniatites. West of Tralee, thick successions of mudbank limestones were deposited in the Chadian.

Between Limerick city and Tipperary town (Fig. 111, Column 1) volcanic rocks, mainly of Chadian and Asbian age, are particularly well developed. They have recently been described by P. Strogen. The lower volcanics are mainly basaltic in composition and include lavas, tuffs, and agglomerates. Several centres were active and in those cases that have been investigated so far, lava flows were preceded by the formation of low angle tuff cones which built up in a shallow submarine environment. Limestones associated with the tuffs include oolites and well-washed biosparites; in at least one case there is evidence of subaerial deposition of tuff in spatter-and-cinder cones. Eruption of the lavas probably occurred when the vents were emergent but many lavas flowed some distance under shallow water. However, at Boughilbreaga, some 13 km south-south-east of Limerick city, subaerial flows occur. Many of the lavas have brecciated bases which include tongues and discrete bodies of limestone derived from below. The brecciation is believed to have resulted from the submarine flow of lava over partially lithified water-logged carbonate sediment. Steam generated from the pore fluids would have brecciated the base of the flow which then foundered in the semi-lithified sediment. The lower volcanics are overlain by Arundian and Holkerian limestones which at some levels are oolitic. On the southern and eastern sides of the Limerick volcanic basin further volcanic activity occurred in the Asbian with the production of basaltic ashes and lavas. Volcanics of the same age are known in County Clare.

In north County Cork (Fig. 111, Column 2), where the stratigraphy has been described by R. G. S. Hudson and M. E. Philcox, tuffs occur in the Chadian and early Arundian. The remainder of the sequence compares fairly closely to that at Castleisland, except that the Asbian carbonate mudbanks are covered by Asbian and Brigantian bedded bioclastic limestones.

At Little Island, County Cork, very thick sequences of mudbank limestones occur, as they do elsewhere in the southern part of the south central region, for example, around Tralee. The dating of the mudbank sequences is not certain and it seems likely that the published succession for Little Island (Fig. 111, Column 3) requires modification. Reconnaissance studies suggest that mudbank limestones occur in the Courceyan and Chadian and also in the Asbian, the two developments probably separated by Arundian and Holkerian bedded limestones. At the top of the lower mudbank development there is a useful local marker horizon, the Cork Red Marble, which has been described by W. E. Nevill. It consists of reddened conglomeratic limestones with goniatites and reddened mudbank limestones and has been widely used as an ornamental marble. Excellent polished surfaces of the marble are to be seen in St Finbarr's Cathedral in Cork.

The upper bank limestones are overlain by Asbian coral-bearing limestones which at one level contain clay bands, which may have originally been fine volcanic ash.

Successions in the eastern part of the region are poorly known. Bioclastic limestones are the most abundant rock type in the areas surrounding the Leinster and Slieveardagh coalfields, but other shallow-water types occur, particularly micrites in the Chadian and Arundian. Brigantian bioclastic limestones containing the coral *Lonsdaleia* become very cherty at their top. In the Wexford syncline, described by T. N. George, varied Chadian micritic limestones which were deposited in shallow subtidal and possibly intra- and supratidal conditions are overlain by probable Arundian bioclastic limestones.

South Munster Basin

Post-Courceyan successions in the South Munster Basin give no hint of the thick carbonate sequences to the north. The equivalents of the Little Island limestones at the Old Head of Kinsale, described by D. Naylor (Fig. 111, Column 4), are less than 200 m of mudstones with very rare thin bioclastic limestone beds and unfossiliferous massive mudstones which contain considerable amounts of iron-rich dolomite. These form the upper part of the Courtmacsherry Formation and are overlain by 436 m of mudstones which contain beds of sandstone, and bioclastic and ankeritic limestones, the Lispatrick Mudstone Formation. Goniatites from some 30 m above the base of the formation are Brigantian (P1d zone) in age while another fauna from 45 m below the highest beds seen is probably of P2 age. Farther west at the Seven Heads and Galley Head (Fig. 111, Column 5) the base of the Lispatrick Formation with Brigantian faunas rests on an even more attenuated succession.

Farther west in the basin little of the post-Courceyan succession has been preserved. In the Bantry Bay area, most of the succession lies underwater between the head of the bay and Whiddy Island, but the Chadian and much of the Arundian are contained within less than 50 m of fine-grained limestone turbidites and cherty mudstones.

A comparison of the Kinsale and Little Island successions suggests that starved-basin conditions continued in the South Munster Basin until late Asbian times. However, in the Brigantian, there may have been a reversal of thickness relationships north and south of the Cork/Kenmare line.

Fig. 111. Post-Courceyan section in eastern Munster (data from references given in George *et al.* 1976).

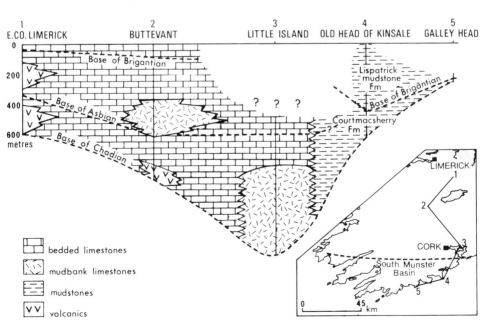

BIBLIOGRAPHY

DIXON, O. A.   1972 Lower Carboniferous rocks between the Curlew and Ox
                                     Mountains, Northwestern Ireland. *Jl. geol. Soc. Lond.*,
                                     128, 71–101.

GEORGE, T. N.,   1976 A correlation of Dinantian rocks in the British Isles. *Geol.*
     JOHNSON, G. A. L.,   *Soc. Lond. Spec. Rep.*, **7**, pp. 87.
     MITCHELL, M.,
     PRENTICE, J. E.,
     RAMSBOTTOM, W. H. C.,
     SEVASTOPULO, G. D., &
     WILSON, R. B.

GEORGE, T. N. &   1957 The Carboniferous rocks of the Donegal syncline. *Q. Jl.*
     OSWALD, D. H.   *geol. Soc. Lond.*, **113**, 137–179.

GRAHAM, J. R.   1975 Analysis of an Upper Palaeozoic transgressive sequence in
                                     southwest County Cork, Eire. *Sedim. Geol.*, **13**, 267–290.

HUBBARD, J. A. E. B.   1966 Facies patterns in the Carrowmoran Sandstone (Viséan) of
                                     western Co. Sligo, Ireland. *Proc. Geol. Ass.*, **77**, 233–254.

HUBBARD, J. A. E. B.   1966 Population studies in the Ballyshannon Limestone, Ballina
                                     Limestone, and Rinn Point Beds (Viséan) of N. W. Ireland.
                                     Palaeontology, **9**, 252–269.

HUDSON, R. G. S.,   1966 The palaeoecology of a lower Viséan crinoid fauna from
     CLARKE, M. J., &   Feltrim, Co. Dublin. *Scient. Proc. R. Dubl. Soc. Ser. A*, **2**,
     SEVASTOPULO, G. D.   273–286.

HUDSON, R. G. S. &   1966 A borehole section through the lower Tournaisian and
     SEVASTOPULO, G. D.   Upper Old Red Sandstone, Ballyvergin, Co. Clare. *Scient.*
                                     Proc. R. Dubl. Soc. Ser. A, **2**, 287–296.

JONES, P. C.   1974 Marine transgression and facies distribution in the Cork
                                     beds (Devonian–Carboniferous) of west Cork and Kerry.
                                     Proc. Geol. Ass., **85**, 159–188.

LEES, A.   1964 The structure and origin of the Waulsortian (Lower Car-
                                     boniferous) 'reefs' of west-central Eire. *Phil. Trans. Roy.*
                                     Soc. Lond., **B247**, 483–531.

NAYLOR, D.   1966 The Upper Devonian and Carboniferous geology of the
                                     Old Head of Kinsale, Co. Cork. *Scient. Proc. R. Dubl.*
                                     Soc. Ser. A, **2**, 229–249.

NAYLOR, D., JONES, P. C.,   1974 Facies relationships in the Upper Devonian–Lower Car-
     & MATTHEWS, S. C.   boniferous of southwest Ireland and adjacent regions.
                                     Geol. J., **9**, 77–96.

OSWALD, D. H.   1955 The Carboniferous rocks between the Ox Mountains and
                                     Donegal Bay. *Q. Jl. geol. Soc. Lond.*, **111**, 167–186.

PHILCOX, M. E.   1971 A Waulsortian bryozoan ('cumulative biostrome') and
                                     its off-reef equivalents, Ballybeg, Ireland. *C. R. 6me Cong.*
                                     int. Strat. Géol. Carb., Sheffield 1967, **4**, 1359–1372.

RAMSBOTTOM, W. H. C.   1973 Transgressions and regressions in the Dinantian: a new
                                     synthesis of British Dinantian stratigraphy. *Proc. Yorks.*
                                     geol. Soc., **39**, 567–607.

SHEPARD-THORN, E. R.   1963 The Carboniferous Limestone succession in north-west
                                     County Limerick, Ireland. *Proc. R. Ir. Acad.*, **62B**, 267–
                                     294.

SHERIDAN, D. J. R.   1972 Upper Old Red Sandstone and Lower Carboniferous of
                                     the Slieve Beagh Syncline and its setting in the northwest
                                     Carboniferous basin, Ireland. *Geol. Surv. Ireland. Spec.*
                                     Pap., **2**, pp. 129.

SLEEMAN, A. G., JOHNSTON, I. S., NAYLOR, D., & SEVASTOPULO, G. D.   1974   The stratigraphy of the Carboniferous rocks of Hook Head, Co. Wexford. *Proc. R. Ir. Acad.*, **74B**, 227–243.

SMYTH, L. B.   1930   The Carboniferous rocks of Hook Head, County Wexford. *Proc. R. Ir. Acad.*, **39B**, 523–566.

SMYTH, L. B.   1939   The Lower Carboniferous of south-east Ireland. *Proc. Geol. Ass.*, **50**, 305–319.

STROGEN, P.   1973   Brecciated lavas from County Limerick, Ireland, and their significance. *Geol. Mag.*, **110**, 351–364.

STROGEN, P.   1973   The volcanic rocks of the Carrigogunnel area, Co. Limerick. *Scient. Proc. R. Dubl. Soc. Ser. A*, 5, 1–26.

TURNER, J. S.   1950   The Carboniferous Limestone in Co. Dublin, south of the River Liffey. *Scient. Proc. R. Dubl. Soc.*, 25, 169–192.

WEST, I. M., BRANDON, A., & SMITH, M.   1968   A tidal flat evaporitic facies in the Viséan of Ireland. *J. sedim. Petrol.*, **38**, 1079–1093.

WILSON, H. E.   1972   *Regional geology of Northern Ireland.* Ministry of Commerce, Geol. Surv. Northern Ireland. Belfast, H.M. Stationery Office, pp. 115.

10

UPPER CARBONIFEROUS

G. D. Sevastopulo

The Upper Carboniferous (Silesian) of Western Europe is divided into Namurian (including the Millstone Grit of Britain), Westphalian, and Stephanian Series. Of these, the Namurian is the most widely represented in Ireland; Westphalian rocks are preserved only in the Leinster, Slieveardagh, Crataloe, Kanturk, and Coalisland coalfields and in the Kingscourt outlier; no Stephanian sedimentary rocks are known. The extensive areas of Coal Measures shown in Munster and County Leitrim on the current revised 3rd edition of the 1:750,000 Geological Map of Ireland are now known to be Namurian in age, not Westphalian as their name suggests; also, the 'Yoredale and Pendleside Series' (Upper Avonian Shales and Sandstones), of the map include both Dinantian and substantial amounts of Namurian-age rocks.

Namurian Series

The map in Figure 112a shows the generalised setting of Britain and Ireland in Namurian times. In Ireland, sands, silts, and muds derived from northerly and south-westerly or westerly source areas were deposited in actively downwarping troughs and basins (Fig. 112b) which accumulated thick successions of sediment, and on structural highs which subsided much less rapidly and accumulated thinner successions. The seas were populated at certain times by goniatites, which now provide a means of very precise correlation, both on a regional scale within Ireland and farther afield with successions in Britain, continental Europe, and elsewhere. Nineteen goniatite zones are recognised in England (Table 13) and eleven of them have been divided into a total of twenty five subzones. All the zones and most of the subzones have been recognised in Ireland. Seven

Namurian stages (Table 13) have been erected with reference sections designated in goniatite-bearing facies in the Pennine region of England and in County Leitrim.

The most extensive Namurian outcrops occur in Munster in a crudely north-south belt from the Burren area of County Clare across the Shannon to Mallow, County Cork and Killarney, County Kerry (Fig. 113). Within this area three major lithological divisions may be recognised: the lowest consists of shales; the middle of greywackes and siltstones; and the highest of a number of cycles, each with a marine band at its base, and sandstones and sometimes a coal at its top.

The lowest division, the Clare Shale Formation, is recognisable throughout almost all the outcrop belt. The shales are grey to black in colour; some part into thin leaves whilst others, usually slightly silicified, split or weather into platy beds between 10 and 100 mm thick. Clay-ironstone bullions occur at some levels and are generally unfossiliferous. Thin calcareous beds and horizons of bullions are quite common, particularly in the Chokierian, Alportian, and Kinderscoutian shales, and some contain well-preserved goniatites, beautifully illustrated by F. Hodson. Many of the shales are pyritous and carbonaceous, some of them exceptionally so. In 1731, part of the cliff north of Ballybunion, County Kerry, cut in such shales, collapsed and ignited, probably through the heat given off by the oxidation of pyrite, and smouldered for some time. A contemporary account quoted by Charles Smith in his 'The Ancient and Present State of the County Kerry' (Dublin 1756) includes the following: 'The mixture of burnt clay, ashes and calcined stones is worth observing but the heat is so great and the sulphurous stench so strong that there is no waiting to be over curious in making remarks.'

173

The fauna of the Clare Shale Formation is dominated by goniatites, conodonts, and pectinoid bivalves. The goniatites were certainly nektonic and the conodonts, almost certainly, also were parts of free-swimming animals. The bivalves such as *Caneyella*, *Dunbarella*, and *Posidonia* are typical associates of goniatites in other Carboniferous basinal facies; but whether they were nektonic, epiplanktonic, or benthonic is open to question. If they were benthonic, they were adapted to a habitat which did not suit the diverse faunas of brachiopods, bryozoans, corals, echinoderms, and foraminifera which flourished in the shallow water carbonate areas that existed in Northern England and Scotland (Fig. 112) at that time. Probably the bottom of the Clare Shale sea was too deep or the substrate too muddy for a normal benthonic fauna. At most levels it is clear that infaunal organisms were also absent as there is little

Fig. 112. (a) Generalised palaeogeography of Britain and Ireland in Namurian times (partly after Ramsbottom 1969). (b) Generalised Namurian section from Ballycastle (A) to Galway (B) along dashed line.

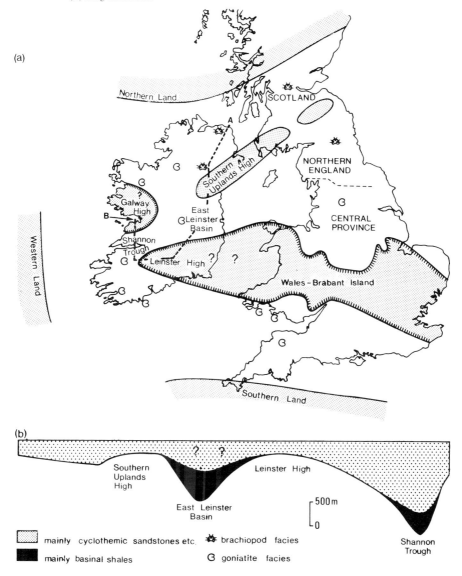

sign of bioturbation and the shales are delicately laminated. The sea floor, however, was colonised at various times by sponges whose spicules are common, particularly in siliceous platy shales and in Arnsbergian cherts, which have been called spongolites by G. C. Lewarne. Radiolaria at some horizons provide evidence of zooplankton and much of the carbon in the carbonaceous shales was probably derived from phytoplankton. Small flattened pieces of driftwood which floated out from the land, became waterlogged and sank, are quite common.

Fossils are not evenly distributed through the shales but occur in bands separated by barren beds. At least twenty such bands containing diagnostic goniatites have been found in the Clare Shale Formation which probably represents about half of Namurian time, or about 6 million years. Many of the bands are relatively thin and widespread (Fig. 113); the *Hudsonoceras proteus* band, for instance, is some 100 mm thick in Clare and has been found in the Central Province of England and as far east as the Ruhr district of Germany. According to W. H. C. Ramsbottom, it probably formed in less than 10,000 years. The reasons for the sudden appearance and disappearance of goniatites in Munster as in the rest of north-west Europe are not clear. However, it has been shown by Ramsbottom that in Derbyshire, in a facies comparable with the Clare Shale Formation, each faunal band may be made up of a sequence of differing faunal assemblages. In the ideal sequence, barren shales are followed by shales with bivalve spat, thin-shelled goniatites such as *Dimorphoceras*, pectinoid bivalves, and finally the thick-shelled goniatites which lend their names to the faunal bands. It has been suggested that these cycles indicate a change from low to normal salinity, which may be associated with eustatically controlled transgressions.

Thickness variations of the Clare Shale Formation are shown in Figs. 113a and 113b. Thin successions define the Galway and Leinster Highs; thicker successions occur in the Shannon trough and west of the nose of the Leinster High. The differences between the

STAGE	ZONE	SUBZONE
Yeadonian (G_1)	*G. cumbriense* (G_{1b}) *G. cancellatum* (G_{1a})	*G. crencellatum* *G. cancellatum* *G. branneroides*
Marsdenian (R_2)	*R. superbilingue* (R_{2c})	*G? sigma* *R. superbilingue*
	R. bilingue (R_{2b}) *R. gracile* (R_{2a})	*R. metabilingue* *R. bilingue*
	R. reticulatum (R_{1c})	*R. coreticulatum* *R. reticulatum*
Kinderscoutian (R_1)	*R. nodosum* (R_{1b})	*R. nodosum*
	R. circumplicatile (R_{1a})	*R. dubium* *R. todmordenense* *R. circumplicatile*
	Ht. prereticulatus (H_{2c})	*Ht. prereticulatus* *V. eostriolatus*
Alportian (H_2)	*H. undulatum* (H_{2b}) *Hd. proteus* (H_{2a})	
Chokierian (H_1)	*H. beyrichianum* (H_{1b}) *H. subglobosum* (H_{1a})	
Arnsbergian (E_2)	*N. nuculum* (E_{2c})	*N. nuculum* *Ct. stellarum*
	Ct. nitidus (E_{2b})	*Ct. nititoides* *Ct. nitidus* *Ct. edalensis*
	E. bisulcatum (E_{2a})	*E. bisulcatum* *C. cowlingense*
Pendleian (E_1)	*C. malhamense* (E_{1c}) *E. pseudobilingue* (E_{1b}) *C. leion* (E_{1a})	*E. hudsoni* *E. stubblefieldi* *E. tornquisti*

Table 13.

Stages, zones, and subzones of the Namurian (after Ramsbottom 1967). The generic names of the goniatites are abbreviated as follows:

Cravenoceras (C)

Cravenoceratoides (Ct)

Eumorphoceras (E)

Gastrioceras (G)

Homoceras (H)

Homoceratoides (Ht)

Hudsonoceras (Hd)

Nuculoceras (N)

Reticuloceras (R)

Vallites (V)

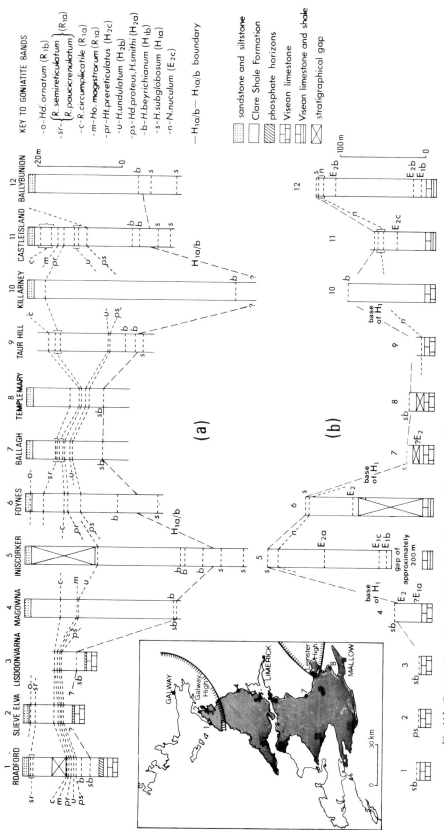

Fig. 113. Comparative sections of the Clare Shale Formation (Namurian outcrop stippled): (a) Chokierian (H₁) to Kinderscoutian (R₁) (b) Pendleian (E₁) and Arnsbergian (E₂): Ho − *Hodsonites*, other goniatite generic names abbreviated as in Table 13 (after Brennand 1965.

Hodson and Lewarne 1961. Morton 1965, Philcox 1961. Walsh 1967: Ballybunion section based on Kelk 1960. unpublished Ph.D thesis. University of Reading).

KEY TO GONIATITE BANDS

- -o − *Hd. ornatum* (R₁b)
- -sr − { *R. semireticulatum* / *R. paucicrenulatum* } (R₁a)
- -c − *R. circumplicatile* (R₁a)
- -m − *Ho. magistrorum* (R₁a)
- -pr − *Ht. prereticulatus* (H₂c)
- -u − *H. undulatum* (H₂b)
- -ps − *Hd. proteus, H. smithi* (H₂a)
- -b − *H. beyrichianum* (H₁b)
- -s − *H. subglobosum* (H₁a)
- -n − *N. nuculum* (E₂c)

— H₁a/b — H₁a/b boundary

- sandstone and siltstone
- Clare Shale Formation
- phosphate horizons
- Visean limestone
- Visean limestone and shale
- stratigraphical gap

successions in north-west Clare and the Shannon Estuary are particularly interesting. Close to the Shannon, the lowest goniatite band recorded is that of *Eumorphoceras pseudobilingue* (E1b) and it seems likely that there is a comfortable passage from Brigantian limestones and shales into Pendleian (E1) shales, as occurs at Ballybunion farther to the west. In contrast, around Slieve Elva in north Clare, the lowest goniatite horizon recorded is that of *Hudsonoceras proteus* (H2a) which occurs about 2·5 m above Dinantian bioclastic limestones; the same horizon occurs at least 180 m above the base of the Namurian section close to the Shannon. What is not clear is the nature of the apparent non-sequence in north Clare. Beds below the lowest diagnostic goniatite band on Slieve Elva and farther south around Lisdoonvarna and Roadford include phosphates which at Roadford were formerly commercially exploited. They occur as a thin veneer of pebbles welded to the top of the limestones and as thin laterally extensive lenses a short distance above the limestone. The phosphates consist of granular apatite and collophane, which together with pyrite and carbon are set in an apatite and carbonate cement; some of the apatite is in the form of fish remains and abundant conodonts. Such phosphates are known in other areas to be extremely condensed deposits and in County Clare they may represent the apparently missing parts of the Namurian. There is certainly little evidence that the top of the underlying limestones has undergone substantial subaerial erosion as would be expected if the apparent northward onlap of the Clare Shale Formation re-presented a transgression following a period of emergence.

South of the Shannon, the Clare Shale Formation thins and apparently disappears in very poorly exposed ground between Ballagh, County Limerick, and Templemary, County Cork. The supposed absence of Clare Shale in this area suggests a westerly extension of the Leinster High as shown in Figure 112.

The Clare Shale Formation is overlain by variously named sandstones and siltstones (Fig. 114) which occur earlier in the west (approximately H2a at Ballybunion and earlier than H2c at Loop Head) than in the east, where the highest shales are of high R1a age. Both at Foynes and near Slieve Elva the presence of 'Hudsonoceras' ornatum at or just above the top of the shales suggests that sandstones there enter near the base of R1b. The sandstones are petrographically greywackes, with bedding characters and other sedimentary structures typical of turbidites. The directions of transport deduced from abundant sole markings (flutes and tool marks) and ripples are generally from the west. A striking feature of these rocks is the abundance and scale of slumping, which is particularly well displayed along the coast of west Clare where it has been studied in great detail by W. D. Gill. There the lower Ross Sandstone Formation (Fig. 114), which consists of parallel-bedded turbiditic sandstones with subsidiary siltstones and shales, contains relatively few disturbed horizons. One of them, the Ross Slide (exposed around the Bridges of Ross north-east of Loop Head) is a laterally very extensive sheet about 6 m thick, which consists of thin upper

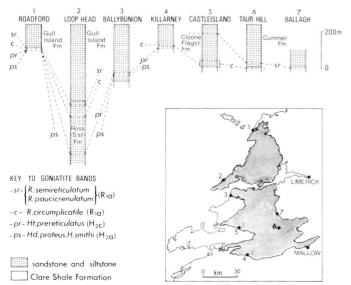

KEY TO GONIATITE BANDS

-sr- $\left\{ \begin{array}{l} \text{R. semireticulatum} \\ \text{R. paucicrenulatum} \end{array} \right\}$(R1a)

-c- R.circumplicatile (R1a)

-pr- Ht.prereticulatus (H2c)

-ps- Hd.proteus, H.smithi (H2a)

[::::] sandstone and siltstone
[ ] Clare Shale Formation

Fig. 114

Comparative sections of Alportian (H2) and Kinderscoutian (R1) turbidites of western Munster (Namurian outcrop stippled). (After Rider (1974) and sources acknowledged in explanation to Figure 113).

and lower layers of balled-up sandstone sandwiching a unit of black siltstones which have been intensively deformed by small-scale faults, and in places contain isolated rafts of sandstone. The upper surface of the sheet is covered by sand volcanoes, each one a cone (Fig. 115) formed of coarse siltstone and sandstone with a depressed crater and a central sandstone plug. The volcanoes are thought to have formed by the extrusion of sediment-laden water from a newly slumped body of sediment. The Gull Island Formation, which overlies the Ross Formation, is mainly formed of grey siltstones but contains, particularly in its lower part, turbiditic sandstones deposited in channels up to 6 metres deep and several hundred or more metres wide. The siltstones are extensively slumped, generally in sheets 3 to 5 metres thick. The slumps are internally folded into recumbent flow folds or are chaotic with no obvious structure. The most striking example is the Fisherstreet Slide which affects the lower beds (possibly up to 30 m thick) of the Gull Island Formation at Fisherstreet Bay (Fig. 116). The disturbed level can be followed for 4 km south-westwards along the coast. The direction of movement as in other such slumps in County Clare is towards the south, while the direction of transport of the turbiditic sandstones is from the west and south-west.

The beds above the Clare Shale Formation to the south of the Shannon are similar to those of County Clare in that they show an upward progression from sandstones to strongly slumped siltstones. The palaeoenvironmental interpretation of the Clare Shale Formation and the succeeding sandstones and siltstones is as follows. The sandstones were deposited as turbidites probably on a fan or fans related to a source to the west. The outer limit of turbidite deposition was around the mouth of the Shannon in early Alportian (H2a) times but had migrated eastwards to the eastern margin of the Namurian outcrop by the end of the early part of the Kinderscoutian (R1a). Beyond the margin of turbidite deposition the Clare Shale Formation was being deposited as deep-water muds. The slumped siltstones represent a shallower environment, possibly on the edge of a shelf or higher up on the submarine fan. The spatial distribution of the facies in the Kinderscoutian is shown in Figure 117.

The remainder of the Namurian throughout the outcrop belt consists of cyclothemic deposits, the subject of a detailed study by M. H. Rider (Fig. 118). These form the cliffs of west Clare (Fig. 4). A typical cyclothem is between 100 and 350 m thick and consists of a lower shale with a thin marine band at its base, a thick siltstone interval, and a thick upper interval containing and usually dominated by sandstones. The upper interval is very variable and may consist of thick massive sandstones with erosional bases; of laminated sandstones; or of a number of minor cyclothems, each coarsening upwards from a shale occasionally containing brachiopods, through siltstone to sandstone and sometimes culminating in a seat earth and thin coal (now anthracite). Each major cyclothem has been interpreted as the product of a prograding bird's foot delta, as diagramatically illustrated in Figure 119. The deltas were built by rivers flowing from between north-west and south-west. The laminated siltstones (pro-delta silts) and laminated sandstones (distributary mouth sands) are extensively disturbed. Slumping was related mainly to large scale syn-depositional (growth) faults affecting up to 60 m of sediment, which were aligned normal to the delta slope. Features associated with the fault planes include sand volcanoes, ball and pillow structures, and soft sediment folds.

Goniatites, which together with bivalves and rarer brachiopods, corals, and crinoids occur in the marine shales, show that cyclothemic deposition continued into the Westphalian, although Yeadonian and higher strata have been removed except in the Crataloe and Kanturk coalfield areas.

Very few Namurian outliers occur to the south of the main Munster outcrop belt. On Whiddy Island, in Bantry Bay, County Cork, Arnsbergian (E2b) goniatites occur in bullions in a black slate succession, overlain by sandstones. Probable Arnsbergian goniatite faunas also occur near Ballinhassig, south-west of Cork city, a locality which has yielded a considerable number of fish. Some extensive sections of probable Namurian sandstones occur around the Seven Heads, County Cork, but they have not yet been firmly dated.

To the east of the main Munster Namurian outcrop belt there are similar outliers to the south-east of Limerick (Rathjordan in Figure 118), to the north of the Slievenamuck range, and in the syncline between the Galty and Knockmealdown Mountains, east of Mitchelstown, County Cork. All of these outliers occur on the Leinster High and in none of them is there any representative of black shale similar to the Clare Shale Formation. In the Limerick basin, the succession probably corresponds to parts of two cyclothems; shales at the base have been shown by P. H. Shelford to rest on a pitted solution surface of Brigantian limestones or on oxidised basic volcanics, and are followed by siltstones, sandy shales, flagstones, and sandstones. The highest beds present are goniatite-bearing shales at the base of the overlying cyclothem, which contain *Reticuloceras bilingue* indicating a Marsdenian (R2b) age.

North of Slievenamuck, shales, siltstones, and sandstones (Fig. 118) rest unconformably upon a solution-pitted surface of upper Viséan cherty limestones; as yet, no marine fossils have been found in this succession.

Fig. 115

Sand volcano, Bridges of Ross, County Clare.

Fig. 116. Flat lying slum folds, Fisherstreet, County Clare.

Photographs by G. D. Sevastopulo

Further evidence of the Leinster High is found in the Leinster and Slieveardagh coalfields and scattered outliers in south County Tipperary. In the Slieveardagh area (Fig. 118), no marine fossils have been found in the 300 m of grey shales, siltstones, and sandstone below the *Gastrioceras cumbriense* horizon. Although the Namurian/limestone contact is not seen, there is little doubt that both there and in other south Tipperary outliers, black goniatite-bearing shales of Pendleian to Kinderscoutian age are absent.

In the Leinster coalfield there is evidence of the position of the northern flank of the Leinster High: the lowest Namurian beds are reported by W. E. Nevill to be of Marsdenian (R2) age in the south and Kinderscoutian (R1) near Carlow. Along the northern margin of the coalfield a thin succession of black shales contains goniatites of Arnsbergian (E2c) to Kinderscoutian (R1b) age. The Marsdenian and Yeadonian are represented by cyclothemic successions; the cycle beginning with the *Gastrioceras cancellatum* marine band passes up from shales through siltstones into sandstones containing, near their top, intervals of shale with non-marine bivalves. The sandstones are capped by the Rockafoil Coal, the lowest workable coal of the coalfield, which is overlain by the *Gastrioceras cumbriense* marine band. Some 20 m higher is the distinctive 'Fleck Rock', which contains a marine fauna including the goniatite *Gastrioceras subcrenatum*, whose first occurrence is correlated with the base of the Westphalian Series. Both in the upper Namurian and the lower Westphalian (see below) there is a change in the marine bands from north to south. The *Gastrioceras cumbriense* band in the north of the coalfield contains mainly goniatites; this is interpreted as reflecting deeper water conditions than in the south, where the fauna is dominated by the brachiopod *Martinia* and goniatites are rarer.

In the Leinster and Slieveardagh coalfields and also in the Limerick basin the Marsdenian and Yeadonian sediments were derived from the south-west. The Bregaun Flags (Fig. 120) of Slieveardagh are slumped down a north-easterly facing palaeo-slope; the slumps, described by W. E. Nevill, are associated with sand volcanoes.

To the north of the Leinster High is the East Leinster Basin; there, the Pendleian and Arnsbergian stages are very thick in comparison to the 30 m of shales resting on Dinantian limestones at the northern end of the coalfield. In the Summerhill area (Fig. 120) the base of the Pendleian lies within a basinal limestone and shale succession. Close above the boundary there are turbiditic greywackes. Outcrop is very poor but possibly as much as 600 m of combined Pendleian and Arnsbergian rocks are represented. A thin succession of black shales with ironstone bullions contains many of the goniatite bands from *Homoceras beyrichianum* (H1b) to *Reticuloceras circumplicatile* (R1a). The highest unit, the Moynalvy Sandstone, is of unknown stratigraphical position.

In north County Dublin (Fig. 120) and south of Navan, County Meath, as in Summerhill, the base of the Pendleian is within a succession of basinal shales, limestones, and thin sandstones. The Balrickard Sandstone Formation is probably of Pendleian (E1b) age and is succeeded by shales and siltstones which nowhere are younger than Arnsbergian.

The Kingscourt area, County Cavan, described by J. S. Jackson (Fig. 120), provides a complete Namurian succession which is very thin in comparison with those of the Shannon Trough and the East Leinster Basin (Fig. 112). The Pendleian Ardagh Shale, dark shales with clay-ironstone bands and goniatites, is conformable on Dinantian shales in the south of the area, but is cut out and overlapped to the north, where the Ardagh Sandstone rests directly on Dinantian limestones. Farther north, the Ardagh Sandstone is also cut out and the overlying Arnsbergian shallow-water, pebbly, Carrickleck Sandstone

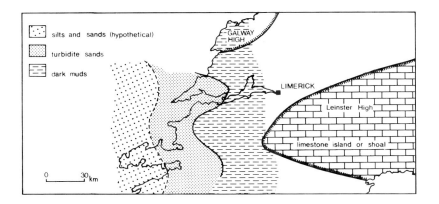

Fig. 117

Facies distribution in western Munster at the horizon of *R. circumplicatile* (R_{1a}).

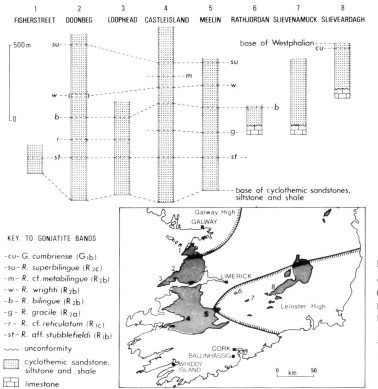

KEY TO GONIATITE BANDS

-cu- *G. cumbriense* (G₁b)
-su- *R. superbilingue* (R₂c)
-m- *R.* cf. *metabilingue* (R₂b)
-w- *R. wrighti* (R₂b)
-b- *R. bilingue* (R₂b)
-g- *R. gracile* (R₂a)
-r- *R.* cf. *reticulatum* (R₁c)
-st- *R.* aff. *stubblefieldi* (R₁b)

〰 unconformity

⬚ cyclothemic sandstone, siltstone and shale

⊞ limestone

Fig. 118

Comparative sections of Kinderscoutian (R₁) to Yeadonian (G₁) cyclothemic deposits in Munster (Namurian and Westphalian outcrop stippled). (After Nevill 1957; Shelford 1963, 1967; and sources acknowledged in explanation to Figure 113).

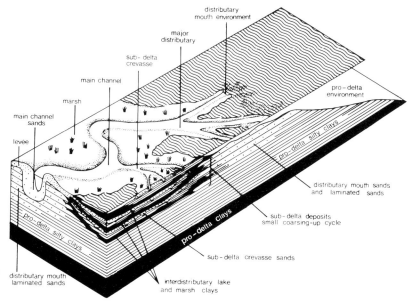

Fig. 119

Block diagram illustrating the production of a sequence of sediments similar to a County Clare Namurian cyclothem by a prograding bird's food delta (redrawn from Rider 1974).

comes to rest on the limestones. This progressive northwards overlap, which in conjunction with northerly thinning results in attenuation of the Namurian succession from about 600 m in the south to less than 350 m in the north, defines the southern margin of the Southern Uplands High. The Carrickleck Sandstone is overlain by a shale containing *Cravenoceratoides nitidus* (E2b) but above this level,

up to the marine band containing *Reticuloceras reticulatum* and *Vallites striolatum* (R1c), no diagnostic faunas have been found. The strata concerned, the Barley Hill Grits and Rathe Sandstone, are shallow-water sandstones and siltstones with some thin coals. Levels, which possibly correspond to goniatite bands in the more basinal areas, there only contain *Lingula* and plant remains. The Marsdenian

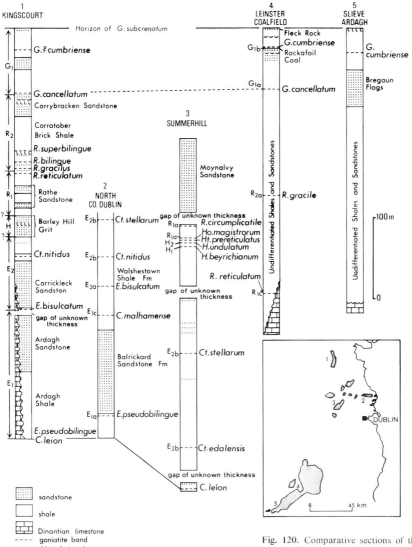

	sandstone
	shale
	Dinantian limestone
- - -	goniatite band
ʟʟʟʟ	*Lingula* band
◡◡◡	non-marine bivalve band
∿∿	unconformity

Fig. 120. Comparative sections of the Namurian in eastern Ireland (Namurian and Westphalian outcrop stippled). (After Jackson 1965; Nevill 1957; north County Dublin section modified from Smyth 1950; provisional section for the Leinster Coalfield kindly provided by Dr W. E. Nevill, University College, Cork).

and Yeadonian are represented by a generally cyclo-themic succession, in which the marine portion of the cyclothem contains goniatites and the highest part in some cases includes a seat-earth and a thin coal.

Some of the 'Yoredale' rocks and all of the 'Coal Measures' shown in the region of Lough Allen (the Connaught coalfield) on the Geological Map of Ireland are Namurian in age (Fig. 121). Smaller related outliers occur at Slieve Carna, west of Kilta-magh, County Mayo (and about 15 km east of Castle-bar) and at Doagh, west of Derrygonelly, County Fermanagh. In none of them are the strata younger than Arnsbergian. Slieve Anierin which lies in the south-east of the Connaught coalfield provides ex-cellent sections. The passage from Dinantian to Namurian occurs in shales containing bivalves and goniatites (The 'Yoredale Shales' of the Geological Survey, which are not like the 'Yoredale series' of Yorkshire). Between the fossiliferous shales and also higher in the succession are barren shales with con-spicuous bands of clay-ironstone, which were once used as iron ores. The lower part of the Arnsbergian is also developed in goniatite-bearing shales, but above the horizon of *Eumorphoceras bisculcatum* (E2a) there are some 60 m of sandstones, the 'Mill-stone Grit' of the Geological Survey, which contain coal horizons. These deltaic sandstones form the well-marked cliff near the summits of Slieve Anierin, Cuilcagh, and other hills in the Connaught coalfield. Above the sandstones on Slieve Anierin are more shales which become sandy towards the highest ex-

posed beds. They contain horizons with thick-shelled goniatites which indicate an E2b age, several levels with only the thin-shelled goniatite *Anthracoceras*, and one horizon with a prolific benthonic fauna including productoid brachiopods and trilobites, as well as goniatites. The successions in the northern part of the Connaught coalfield and the Doagh out-lier, described by A. Brandon, are thicker than in the south and at any particular horizon tend to be more arenaceous and less calcareous. The faunas differ also, containing more benthonic elements in the north and more diverse goniatite faunas in the south. These differing facies are related to the proximity of any section to the northerly sediment source.

The outlier of Slieve Carna, County Mayo, is made up of Pendleian and Arnsbergian shales and an Arns-bergian sandstone. The Arnsbergian strata are re-ported to overlap the Pendleian shales to the north-west to rest on Dinantian limestones, possibly defining the north-eastern flank of the Galway High.

Around Dungannon, County Tyrone (Fig. 121), Namurian rocks are poorly exposed; most informa-tion about the succession summarised by R. Fowler and J. A. Robbie has been gained from boreholes, some of them drilled to investigate the several coal seams which were formerly worked. The Dinantian/Namurian boundary probably occurs within the Rossmore Mudstones, a sequence of dark mudstones grading up into shallow-water, burrowed, laminated siltstones and fine sandstones, but diagnostic fossils are scarce. The overlying 'Millstone Grit' consists of

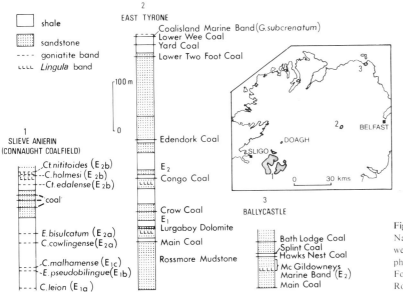

Fig. 121. Comparative sections of the Namurian in northern and north-western Ireland (Namurian and West-phalian outcrop stippled). (After Fowler and Robbie 1961; Wilson and Robbie 1966; Yates 1962).

shales with marine fossils, sandstones which are commonly pebble-bearing, seat-earths, and a number of coals. The mudstones are commonly calcareous but there is only one well-marked limestone, the Lurgaboy Dolomite, which is a useful marker in the Dungannon area and has also been found in a bore-hole at Magilligan, some 75 km to the north. The faunas of the upper part of the Rossmore Mudstones and the 'Millstone Grit' include bivalves, gastropods, and brachiopods. Goniatites are very rare. The only biostratigraphically useful fossils which have been found are an early form of *Tylonautilus nodiferus*, believed to be of Pendleian age, in the upper part of the Rossmore Mudstones and just above the Lurgaboy Dolomite; the typical form of *Tylonautilus nodiferus*, thought to be indicative of the Arnsbergian, from just above the Congo Coal; a gastropod, *Hesperiella loudoni*, also thought to indicate an Arnsbergian age from 40 m above the Congo Coal; and *Gastrioceras subcrenatum*, the lowest Westphalian goniatite, in the Coalisland Marine Band. Whether Namurian beds higher than the Arnsbergian are present is open to question, but comparisons with Scotland and Northern England suggest that the whole Namurian succession is represented. The Dungannon area, with its lack of goniatites and well-developed benthonic fauna, was influenced by its proximity to the northerly sediment source.

Highly arenaceous Namurian is preserved in the Ballycastle coalfield (Fig. 121). The base of the Namurian here is conventionally placed at the Main Coal, which is correlated with a similarly named coal in the Machrihanish Coalfield, across the North Channel in Kintyre, Scotland. The only fossil of biostratigraphical significance is *Schellwienella rotundata* from McGildowney's Marine Band, which is thought to indicate an Arnsbergian age.

Westphalian Series

The base of the Westphalian is taken at a horizon corresponding to the base of the marine band containing *Gastrioceras subcrenatum*. This boundary does not mark a major change of sedimentary regime in Ireland, although the cyclothemic sequence of mudstones, sandstones, seat-earths, and coals which continued from the Namurian shows progressively less marine influence upwards through the Westphalian. There has been little sedimentological investigation of the Irish Coal Measures but their general character suggests that they accumulated in low lying paralic environments which, particularly early in the Westphalian, were periodically transformed into shallow seas through widespread, probably eustatic, rises of sea level. The faunas of the marine bands formed during these incursions were varied, their composition being related to their proximity to the contemporary shore lines. The inshore environments are characterised by the trace fossil *Planolites* and *Lingula*, whilst the offshore and probably slightly deeper, fully marine mudstones contain stratigraphically important goniatites and pectinoid bivalves. Intermediate faunas contain articulate brachiopods. The non-marine strata contain plant material and bivalves as well as rarer arthropods, amphibians, and fish.

The Westphalian is subdivided into Westphalian A, B, C, and D; the base of Westphalian B corresponds to the marine horizon characterized by *Anthracoceratites vanderbeckei* and that of Westphalian C to the horizon with '*Anthracoceras*' *aegiranum*. The Westphalian D subdivision is recognised by its floras and non-marine bivalve faunas.

Correlation of the Irish Westphalian successions has been based on the identification of specific marine bands and the comparison of non-marine bivalve assemblages. It has recently been reviewed by R. M. C. Eagar. In Britain and elsewhere, plant-spores also provide useful biostratigraphical information, but no palynological studies have been made of Irish material.

The base of the Westphalian has been identified in all the coalfields except Kanturk (Fig. 122). In Leinster, the basal marine band includes the lithologically distinctive Fleck Rock, a grey argillaceous siltstone with black shale flecks. In the northern part of the coalfield goniatites including *G. subcrenatum* are common, but farther south the faunas are dominated by the brachiopod *Martinia* and in the Slieve Ardagh coalfields only *Lingula* is known to occur. A similar north-south change from offshore to inshore faunas occurs within the Namurian *Gastrioceras cumbriense* horizon (see above page 180), and both probably reflect the effect of the Leinster High. *G. subcrenatum* with pectinoid bivalves occurs in the Crataloe coalfield, but at Kanturk no goniatites have been found and the base of the Westphalian has been tentatively equated with the lower of two horizons containing *Planolites opthalmoides*. In the Kingscourt outlier, the Westphalian has been proved in borings in which occur dark shales yielding *G. subcrenatum*, pectinoid bivalves, and productoids. A similar association occurs in the Coalisland Marine Band.

The second widespread transgression in the Westphalian is at the horizon of *Gastrioceras listeri*, which is represented in the Leinster, Slieveardagh, and Crataloe coalfields by goniatites and pectinoid bivalve-bearing shales. It is tentatively identified with a *Planolites* band in the Kanturk coalfield and more certainly with brachiopod horizons containing *Lingula* and *Orbiculoidea* in the Kingscourt outlier and *Lingula* and productoids in the Coalisland coalfield. In the Leinster, Slieve Ardagh, and Crataloe coalfields, the cycle which started with the *G. listeri* marine band contains the thick Clay-Gall Sandstone, a feldspathic sandstone which contains in its lower part pebbles of mudstone (clay-galls) derived from the underlying strata. In the northern part of the Leinster coalfield the sandstone lies well above the *G. listeri* marine band but farther south it cuts down into rocks of the *G. subcrenatum* cycle. It is present in the north of the Slieve Ardagh coalfield but absent in the southeast. No detailed studies have been made of the sedimentology of the sandstone; the inclination of foresets in cross-stratified units suggests that the depositing currents flowed towards the north or north-east, and, although marine bivalves and productoids are recorded from near its base in Leinster, it is likely that the bulk of the unit is of non-marine origin.

The succession between Ward's Seam and the Double Fireclays of the Leinster coalfield shows evidence of fluctuating changes in the depositional environment with horizons rich in non-marine bivalves of the *Carbonicola lenisulcata* Zone, interspersed with marine bands. Of these, the lowest, just above Ward's Seam, contains *Lingula* and is correlated with a horizon containing marine gastropods in the Crataloe coalfield, while the remainder contain *Planolites*, and estheriid conchostracans, and equate

with an interval of the Slieve Ardagh succession whose faunas are not known.

The base of the *Carbonicola communis* Zone in the Leinster coalfield is taken just above the Fairy Mount Marine Band, which lies between the Double Fireclays and contain goniatites and a chonetid brachiopod; *communis* Zone bivalves occur just above Pat Mahers Seam of Slieve Ardagh but the highest faunas so far obtained from the structurally complex Kanturk coalfield are attributed to the *lenisulcata* Zone. In the Coalisland area, the *lenisulcata/communis* zonal boundary lies somewhere between the bivalve bands above the Monkey Coal and those below the Shining Coal.

The *communis* Zone of the Leinster coalfield includes the famous Jarrow Coal Seam. Shales above this coal in the Jarrow colliery contained a diverse fauna of vertebrates including eight genera of amphibians and several fish, described by T. H. Huxley and E. P. Wright, together with numerous plants including *Neuropteris* and *Sphenophyllum*, and the small limulid *Belinurus*, which is also recorded from shales above Ward's Seam in the Bilboa colliery.

Little is known about the faunas from the highest parts of the Coalisland and Slieve Ardagh successions but bivalves indicating a horizon high in the *communis* Zone have recently been found above the Stony Coal of the Leinster coalfield. There is no indication

Fig. 122. Comparative sections of the Westphalian of the Irish Coalfields and the Kingscourt outlier. (Compiled from Eager 1974).

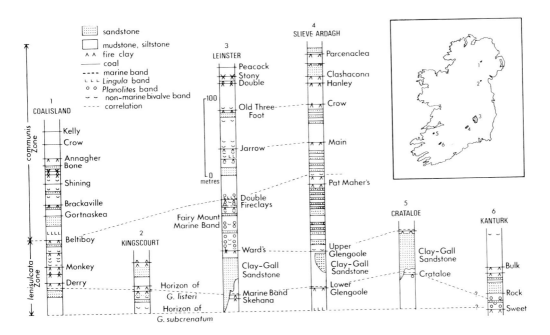

of any strata of the younger *Anthraconaia modiolaris* non-marine bivalve zone which spans the Westphalian A/B boundary.

It is interesting to speculate on the former extent of the Irish Coal Measures. The now isolated coalfields were almost certainly part of a continuous region of deposition which would have embraced the present Namurian outcrop and probably much of that of the Dinantian as well. Paradoxically, the areas in which Coal Measures might be expected to have been thickest (the Shannon trough and east Leinster basin) now only contain the Crataloe coalfield, while the Leinster and Slieve Ardagh coalfield and the Kingscourt region are situated on or close to Namurian and probably Westphalian highs. By comparison with Britain it is most probable that sedimentation in Ireland continued into Westphalian D and possibly into the Stephanian. The erosion of these measures in the Kingscourt and Coalisland areas was probably largely pre-Upper Permian in age.

BIBLIOGRAPHY

BRENNAND, T. P. 1965 The Upper Carboniferous (Namurian) stratigraphy north-east of Castleisland, Co. Kerry, Ireland. *Proc. R. Ir. Acad.*, **64B**, 41–63.

EAGAR, R. M. C. 1975 Neuere Arbeiten über das Westfal in Irland. *Zbl. Geol. Palaont.*, 1 (for 1974), 291–308.

FOWLER, A. & ROBBIE, J. A. 1961 Geology of the country around Dungannon. *Mem. geol. Surv. Nth. Ire.*, pp. 274.

GILL, W. D. & KUENEN, P. H. 1958 Sand volcanoes on slumps in the Carboniferous of County Clare, Ireland. *Q. Jl. geol. Soc. Lond.*, 113 (for 1957), 441–460.

HODSON, F. & LEWARNE, G. C. 1961 A mid-Carboniferous (Namurian) basin in parts of the Counties of Limerick and Clare, Ireland. *Q. Jl. geol. Soc. Lond.*, 117, 307–333.

JACKSON, J. S. 1965 The Upper Carboniferous (Namurian and Westphalian) of Kingscourt, Ireland. *Scient. Proc. R. Dubl. Soc. Ser. A*, 2, 131–152.

MORTON, W. H. 1965 The Carboniferous stratigraphy of the area north-west of Newmarket, Co. Cork, Ireland. *Scient. Proc. R. Dubl. Soc. Ser. A*, 2, 47–65.

NEVILL, W. E. 1957 Sand volcanoes, sheet slumps and stratigraphy of part of the Slieveardagh Coalfield, County Tipperary. *Scient. Proc. R. Dubl. Soc.*, 27, 313–324.

PHILCOX, M. E. 1961 Namurian shales near Buttevant, north Co. Cork. *Scient. Proc. R. Dubl. Soc. Ser. A*, 1, 205–209.

RAMSBOTTOM, W. H. C. 1969 The Namurian of Britain. *C. R. 6me Cong. int. Strat. Geol. Carb.*, Sheffield 1967, 1, 219–232.

RAMSBOTTOM, W. H. C., CALVER, M. A., EAGAR, R. M. C., HODSON, F., HOLLIDAY, D. W., STUBBLEFIELD, C. J., & WILSON, R. B. 1978 A correlation of Silesian rocks in the British Isles. *Geol. Soc. Lond. Spec. Rep.*, 10, pp. 81.

RIDER, M. H. 1974 The Namurian of west County Clare. *Proc. R. Ir. Acad.*, **74B**, 125–143.

SHELFORD, P. H. 1963 The structure and relationship of the Namurian outcrop between Duntryleague, Co. Limerick and Dromlin, Co. Tipperary. *Proc. R. Ir. Acad.*, **62B**, 255–266.

SHELFORD, P. H.   1967 The Namurian and upper Viséan of the Limerick volcanic basin, Eire. *Proc. Geol. Ass.*, **78**, 121–136.

SMYTH, L. B.   1949 The Carboniferous System in North County Dublin. *Q. Jl. geol. Soc. Lond.*, **105**, 295–326.

WALSH, P. T.   1967 Notes on the Namurian stratigraphy north of Killarney, Co. Kerry. *Ir. Nat. J.*, **15**, 254–258.

WILSON, H. E. & ROBBIE, J. A.   1966 Geology of the country around Ballycastle. *Mem. geol. Surv. Nth. Ire.*, pp. 370.

YATES, P. J.   1962 The palaeontology of the Namurian rocks of Slieve Anierin, Co. Leitrim, Eire. *Palaeontology*, **5**, 355–443.

11

HERCYNIAN STRUCTURES

G. D. Sevastopulo

The Palaeozoic stratigraphical record in Ireland contains a major break in the Lower and Middle Devonian (Chapter 8) which marks the final uplift and subsequent erosion of the Caledonian mountain chain. Upper Devonian and Carboniferous sediments accumulated above the folded and eroded Caledonian basement in a relatively quiescent tectonic environment. Although there was considerable differential downwarping and uplift, controlled, at least in part, by active faulting, there is little evidence for the occurrence of regionally synchronous episodes of deformation between the deposition of the oldest exposed strata in south-west County Cork (late Middle Devonian or early Upper Devonian) and the youngest Carboniferous strata preserved in the Leinster Coalfield (Westphalian A). The major structures affecting the outcrop patterns of the Upper Palaeozoic rocks were formed after early Westphalian times and mainly before the Upper Permian.

The geological map of Ireland shows clearly that the style of deformation of the Upper Palaeozoic rocks varies from north to south, with broad gentle folds in the north and generally tighter folds (associated with a regionally developed cleavage) in the south. A similar north-south change of tectonic style is evident in Britain. The less deformed Carboniferous is seen in northern England and from there it may be traced in the subsurface through the coal basins of the southern North Sea into the Netherlands, northern Belgium, northern Germany, and southern Denmark. More strongly deformed Upper Palaeozoic rocks are met in South Wales and south-west England and in mainland Europe, where they crop out within the large Palaeozoic upland areas of France, Belgium, Germany, Czechoslovakia, Poland, and Spain, such as the Ardennes, Rheinisches Schiefergebirge, Massif Central, and Iberian Meseta, and also within the Alpine fold belt.

The considerable duplication and complexity of terminology applied to this late Palaeozoic fold belt has resulted, in part, from its extent, crossing as it does several national frontiers, but also is a record of its importance as a foundry for theories of regional tectonics and orogenesis, especially in the nineteenth and first half of the twentieth century. Three terms in particular, have been applied to the Irish, and other, parts of the fold belt. Two of them have their origins in the monumental study by Suess entitled 'The face of the earth' (*Der Antlitz der Erde*) in which the present outcrops were depicted as the remnants of two arcuate mountain ranges, a western or Armorican range stretching from Dingle Bay to near Douai in Belgium with its highest elevation originally over the Massif Armoricain of Brittany, and a Variscan range extending eastwards from Aachen, with its inner zone identified in Bavaria in the former territory of the Varisci.

The term Variscan has become entrenched in the literature, and as well as being applied to the Variscan arc as originally delimited by Suess, it has assumed an extended meaning as descriptive of the whole fold belt and its orogenesis. In this usage, it is synonomous with Hercynian, as that term is now generally understood. Hercynian, (a name derived from the Harz Mountains) has been favoured by writers in French and has been adopted in a number of recent English language texts; it is used in preference to Variscan or Armorican in this account.

As originally demonstrated by W. D. Gill, it is possible to delimit three zones in Ireland, in each of which different tectonic styles are dominant (Fig. 123). The boundaries between the zones should not be understood as being precise, but rather as arbitrarily imposed on a gradational tectonic change from south to north.

The most southerly zone, corresponding with the

western end of the outer zone of Suess' Armorican arc, is identified to the south of a line drawn from Dungarvan to Dingle Bay. The dominant features of this zone are large-scale synclinoria and anticlinoria whose axes trend approximately east-north-east in the south and west, but swing to lie approximately east-west in the north-east. This structural grain is clearly expressed in the topography; the upland areas consist of Old Red Sandstone whilst the valleys, and the elongate bays of the Atlantic coast, correspond with complex synclines cored by Carboniferous limestone in the north and latest Devonian and Carboniferous mudstones and sandstones in the south.

The major folds have amplitudes and wavelengths of several kilometres. Many of them can be traced for tens of kilometres along strike and some were given individual names by the primary surveyors and later workers (see, for instance, Fig. 125). Other folds die out along strike or occur in trains with an *en echelon* arrangement. The profiles of the major folds are varied. Most of them are either symmetrical or have the northward younging limb steeper than the south-

Fig. 123. Sketch map of Hercynian structures in Ireland compiled from published sources. The Upper Carboniferous shown in the north includes some Dinantian. Anticlinal and synclinal axes have not been drawn where the structure is shown by the outcrop pattern. Faulting is known to be much more extensive in the Midlands than shown.

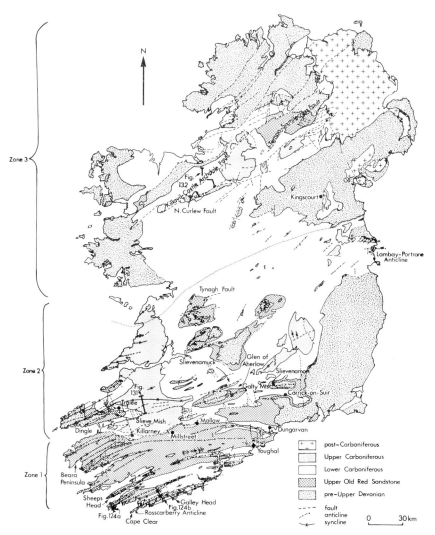

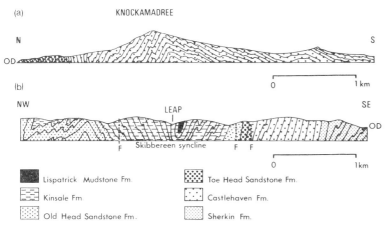

(a) KNOCKAMADREE

N   S

OD

0   1 km

(b)

NW   LEAP   SE

OD

Skibbereen syncline   F   F

0   1 km

Lispatrick Mudstone Fm.   Toe Head Sandstone Fm.

Kinsale Fm.   Castlehaven Fm.

Old Head Sandstone Fm.   Sherkin Fm.

Fig. 124

a) Profile across Mizen Head, County Cork, illustrating the structural style (redrawn from Gill 1962).

b) Profile across the Skibbereen syncline at Leap, County Cork (redrawn from Reilly and Graham 1972).

For location of both sections see Figure 123.

ward younging limb (Figs. 124 and 127). However, along the south coast of County Cork, T. A. Reilly and J. R. Graham recorded a number of major folds such as the Skibbereen syncline (Fig. 124) with northerly dipping axial planes.

Superimposed on the major folds are a variety of minor folds which are characteristic features of exposures within the region. There is a surprising lack of detailed information about the minor folding – the application of modern techniques of structural analysis here would seem to offer a fertile area for future research. However, examples may be drawn from some areas investigated over the last two decades.

Throughout the zone, the minor folds are not uniformly distributed, either as regards style, scale, or frequency, amongst different major folds or across the two limbs of the same major fold. For example, P. T. Walsh has shown that in the area west of Killarney (Figs. 125 and 126), the northward younging limbs of the major structures accommodate more minor folds than those of the southward younging limbs which are usually homoclinal. Probably the most commonly occurring minor folds are asymmetrical with limbs of markedly different lengths. They have wavelengths up to tens of metres and may have third order folds developed upon their flanks. J. G. Capewell has demonstrated the segregation of particular minor fold-styles in zones which may be traced along strike in an area around Sneem, County Kerry (Fig. 127). On the northern flank of the Kilcrohane Anticline broad symmetrical folds are developed. The hinge zone occupied by the Lower (Valentia) Slate Formation contains a large number of symmetrical upright folds with wavelengths of the order of tens of metres and similar amplitudes. The southern flank of the anticline is mainly homoclinal but towards the hinge region of the Rossdohan syncline it becomes plicated into almost

symmetrical flexures of small wavelengths. Farther south towards the core of the Kenmare syncline, the folds become asymmetrical, with steep southward younging limbs, and in the most south-easterly zone, isoclinal folds with north-westerly dipping axial planes are developed. Elsewhere south of Dingle and Dungarvan, intense folding also tends to develop within the cores of those major synclines which contain the change from massive and thick bedded sandstones to the lithologically more heterogeneous and thinner bedded marginal marine and marine strata.

There is considerable variation in the plunge of major and minor folds throughout the region, which may be illustrated by reference to the Iveragh peninsula and adjoining areas. Some folds, for example, the Currane/Mullaghanattin syncline (Fig. 125), maintain a persistent direction of plunge along their length, (in the example quoted, 30°/40° to the west-south-west on the Iveragh peninsula and 15°/20° south-west of Killarney). More common are folds with changes of plunge along their length; the Inny/Derrynafeana syncline (Fig. 125), for example, has an east-north-easterly plunge of 20° around Ballinskelligs; some 30 km inland along strike, the plunge is reversed and remains at a low angle to the west-south-west up to a depression near the Gap of Dunloe, where it once again reverses. The two limbs of the Kilcrohane anticline at its western end exhibit opposing plunges; similar situations have been described on the Beara peninsula and on the north limb of the Rosscarbery anticline in south-west County Cork (Fig. 123). The opposing plunges have been explained as being due to strike faulting (along the hinge zone in the case of the Kilcrohane anticline), in which the main displacement across the fault plane was rotational or 'scissor-like'.

One aspect of fold plunge which has provoked comment is best illustrated in West Cork. There,

regional mapping of lithological boundaries suggests
that the plunges of the Rosscarberry and Skibbereen
synclines are not more than 6° and 3° to the east respectively, whereas measured bedding/cleavage inter-
sections indicate plunges predominantly to the west.
A similar situation occurs in the region south-west of
Killarney where the measured fold plunges are far
greater than suggested by the outcrop pattern; an
additional and explanatory factor may be that normal
cross faults offset the effect of plunge.

Cleavage is a characteristic feature of the southern
zone (Fig. 128). All gradations between a coarse fracture cleavage and a penetrative cleavage occur, the
latter producing slates of commercial grade, once
exploited in the quarries on Valentia Island (page 136)
and at various places in West Cork. The cleavage fans
across the hinge zones of the major folds but is
generally steeply dipping and axial planar to them; it
is often not axial planar to the minor folds. Usually
only one cleavage is obvious but a number of examples are known where two are developed. The main
cleavage surfaces are often not planar, due either to
cleavage refraction between differing lithologies, or
less commonly to small scale folding, some of which

is related to late faulting. The cleavage surfaces are
also deformed by very abundant kink bands (Fig.
129). The most common type strike north-south and
are near vertical; almost all of these show a dextral
sense of rotation. Conjugate sets have been reported
less frequently.

Little is known about the amount and orientation
of strain within zone 1 although flattening of corn-
stones, conglomeratic pebbles and fossils can be
observed in many places (and see Fig. 90). Boudinage
is widely developed and K. Coe has shown that the
most common boudins lie in the plane of bedding with
their long axes parallel to the dip.

The metamorphic grade is very low and many of
the more pelitic lithologies yield plant miospores.
Locally, there has been growth of chlorite. The low
metamorphic grade links Ireland with other regions
on the northern margin of the fold belt. Some of the
Hercynian regions farther south are characterised by
extensive granite emplacement, migmatization and
higher grade metamorphism.

That the history of deformation was episodic and
protracted has been shown through studies of the
minor intrusions of the Beara peninsula, County

Fig. 125. Map of the Iveragh peninsula (Co. Kerry) showing the major structural features.
AB, CD, EF are lines of section illustrated in Figure 126. The stratigraphical nomenclature of
the Atlantic coast has been applied to the whole peninsula, following Capewell 1975. (Based on
Capewell 1975, Walsh 1968, and unpublished maps by R. T. R. Wingfield).

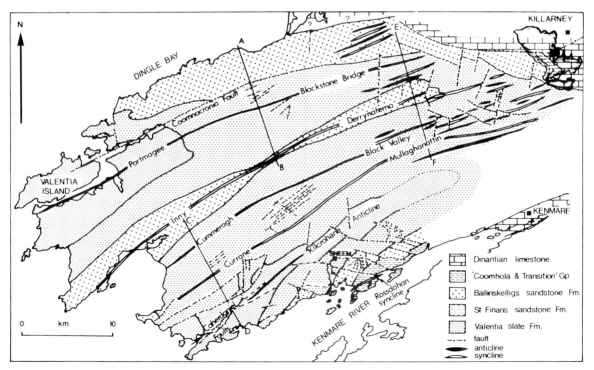

Cork (Fig. 123) by K. Coe and E. B. Selwood. The earliest intrusions were diorite sills which were folded during the main phase of folding. Younger dioritic sheet-like intrusions and intrusive tuffs clearly post-date the main folding; some of the intrusive tuffs contain xenoliths of cleaved country rock in which the cleavage (probably associated with the main phase of deformation) is discordant with a cleavage in the tuff matrix, which must have been post-folding in age. It has been suggested that the second cleavage was formed at the same time as the boudinage mentioned above.

Faulting is much more important and frequent than most published maps of the southern zone indicate. The lack of recent systematic mapping in the inland areas, coupled with the difficulties of establishing the sense and amount of fault-displacement, hinder the recognition of a regional pattern; however, interpretation of aerial photographs and satellite imagery promises to reveal a more complete picture than is available at present.

Some indication of the variety of fault trends and types, likely to be found elsewhere in the zone, emerges from recent mapping of the Iveragh peninsula (Fig. 125). In the west, most of the major faults trend along the east-north-easterly strike. The Coomna-cronia Fault is a southerly dipping high angle reverse fault with as much as a kilometre displacement. South of the Inny valley, there are a large number of strike faults with significant displacements. The Caherdaniel Fault Zone is one of these; it consists of a plexus of faults which bring opposing fold plunges into juxta-position probably by scissor-like movements across the fault planes. The downthrow is to the north and is greatest in the west where it may exceed 5 km. Farther to the east around Sneem (Fig. 127) regularly spaced approximately east-south-easterly trending faults dominate the pattern. They have long, steep, sinuous fault planes and have been interpreted as having dextral wrench displacements (with probably some additional dip-slip movement), ranging from hundreds of metres to over two kilometres. Although

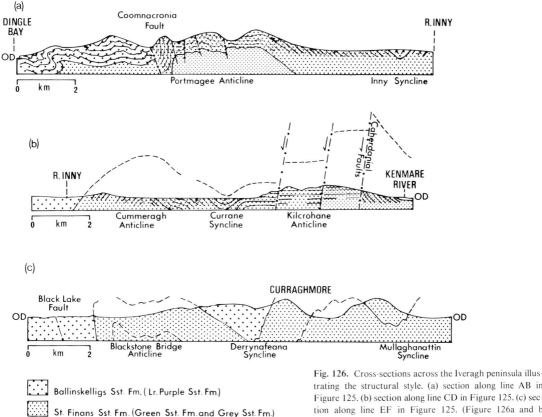

Fig. 126. Cross-sections across the Iveragh peninsula illustrating the structural style. (a) section along line AB in Figure 125. (b) section along line CD in Figure 125. (c) section along line EF in Figure 125. (Figure 126a and b redrawn from Capewell 1975, Figure 126c from Walsh 1968).

they have produced cleavage drag, they surprisingly do not shift the zones of minor folds mentioned above (page 191). The other dominant set of fractures in the Sneem area trends north-south, but appears to involve generally small displacements. In the area west of Killarney, faults trending east-south-east probably combine wrench and normal displacement to produce net northerly downthrows of up to several kilometres. North-south faults have lesser throws and may also combine wrench and normal displacements.

Some of the fault trends evident in the Iveragh peninsula may be discerned elsewhere in the southern zone. K. Coe and E. B. Selwood described an intersecting network of vertical faults on Sheep's Head (Fig. 123) which trend slightly east of north and south of east; both sets were interpreted as having a wrench displacement. East-west dextral wrench faults have been reported from the Allihies region of the Beara peninsula and from near Glandore, County Cork. In the latter area, T. A. Reilly and J. R. Graham have shown that the Glandore–Rosscarbery fault has a dextral horizontal displacement of the order of two kilometres, and that the latest faulting postdated the regional cleavage. Between Cape Clear and Galley Head, other faults recognised trend approximately north-west, north, north-north-east to north-east, and

along the regional strike. Farther east, and particularly between Youghal and Dungarvan (Fig. 123), faults trending approximately normal to the axial traces of major folds appear to be dominant according to published maps. However, it is now known that strike faults, which are usually difficult to detect, are of considerable importance around Cork Harbour, and it is likely that they are similarly important elsewhere.

The northern boundary of the southern zone has assumed particular significance in writings on Irish geology, where it has been called the Variscan, Armorican, or Hercynian Front or Thrust Front. The implication of these terms is that the boundary should be regarded as the outer margin of the fold belt; some authors would go further and suggest that it marks the site of important thrust faults similar to the Faille du Midi in Belgium over which the fold belt is thought to have been tectonically transported northwards onto the foreland. The putative front in Ireland is certainly an impressive topographical divide (page 137), separating as it does the Old Red Sandstone mountains of the south from the low lying Carboniferous country to the north, but whether it everywhere is a significant structural feature is open to question.

At its western end close to Dingle Bay (Fig. 125),

Fig. 127. Map and section of the Sneem area, County Kerry. For location see Figure 125. (Redrawn from Capewell 1957, Figures 2 and 3, using the original stratigraphical terminology).

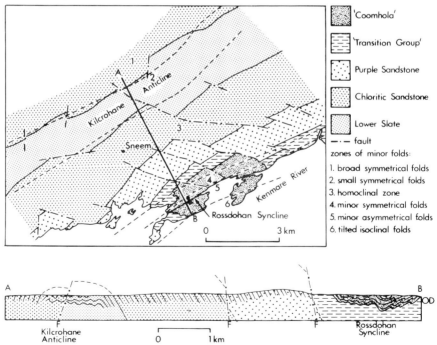

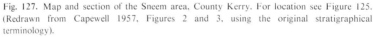

Fig. 128

Cleavage cutting calcareous mudstones of the Court-macsherry Formation, Fountainstown, County Cork.

Fig. 129

Dextral north-trending kink-band in calcareous mud-stones of the Courtmacsherry Formation, Fountains-town, County Cork.

Photographs by G. D. Sevastopulo

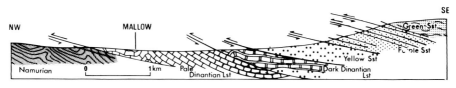

Fig. 130. Cross-section at Mallow, County Cork showing thrusting. See Figure 123 for location. (Redrawn from Gill 1962).

P. T. Walsh has shown that no fault is required to explain the outcrop relationships of Old Red Sandstone and limestone. However, south of Killarney, the northern scarp of Torc Mountain is related to a major east-west fault through Muckross Lake which throws Carboniferous Limestone against sandstones perhaps as much as three kilometres lower in the stratigraphy. The fault plane is vertical and there is evidence of some wrench displacement. Dr R. T. R. Wingfield, who has kindly made available the unpublished results of his research in the Killarney area, recognised a number of southerly dipping thrusts which trend east-west across Lough Leane. On the eastern side of the Lough, they are within the limestones but to the west they probably bring Old Red Sandstone northward over the Carboniferous. Farther east there is clearly a major fault separating beds low in the Old Red Sandstone around Lough Guitane (8 km south-east of Killarney) from the low ground floored by limestone to the north. Between Headford, some seven km east of Killarney, and Millstreet (Fig. 123), no limestone is exposed and published maps show Namurian in fault contact with Old Red Sandstone, which forms the high ground to the south. At Millstreet, there is some evidence of thrusting or reverse faulting. The boundary between Old Red Sandstone and limestone trends eastwards to Mallow where a series of southerly dipping thrusts have been reported (Fig. 130). From there to Dungarvan (Fig. 123) there is little evidence that the Old Red Sandstone/limestone contact is a thrust.

In spite of the obviously large fault displacements around Killarney, there are few reasons for regarding the northern boundary of the southern zone as unique. Significant thrusting, cleavage, and asymmetrical folds with steep northward younging limbs occur at considerable distances to the north of it, and it does not coincide with a major lithological facies or thickness change.

Zone 2 encompasses a transition from the generally close folding associated with cleavage of zone 1, to the gentle folding of zone 3; the placing of its northern boundary is particularly arbitrary.

In the south of the zone, the structural grain is clearly shown by the elongation of Old Red Sandstone inliers. Three of these, the approximately east-north-east trending Slieve Mish and Galty anticlines and the east-west Slievenamon anticline (Fig. 123), are approximately aligned (although their individual axial traces are en echelon). Their structure and that of the country to the south shows many features in common with zone 1. Cleavage is fairly widespread in the more pelitic units, and strongly flattened limestones occur as far north as the Carrick-on-Suir syncline and Tralee, County Kerry. Also, although rather little is known about the profile of the major folds, it appears that most of the asymmetrical examples (for instance the Slieve Mish anticline) have southerly dipping axial planes. Second order folds are commonly developed. Their style is strongly controlled by lithology and there is almost always marked disharmony between those in the Carboniferous Limestone and those in the overlying Namurian shales and sandstones. This has been particularly well demonstrated by T. P. Brennand in the Castleisland area (Fig. 131), where gentle folds in the limestone of the northern limb of the

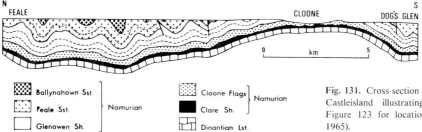

Ballynahown Sst. ⎱
Feale Sst.   ⎰ Namurian
Glenowen Sh.

Cloone Flags ⎱
Clare Sh.   ⎰ Namurian
Dinantian Lst.

Fig. 131. Cross-section through Namurian strata near Castleisland illustrating disharmonic folding. See Figure 123 for location. (Redrawn from Brennand 1965).

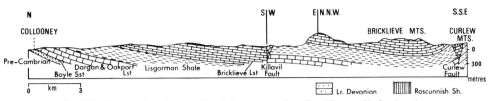

Fig. 132. Cross-section through the Ballymote syncline. See Figure 123 for location. (Redrawn from Dixon 1972).

Slieve Mish anticline pass upward into much tighter concentric folds with high angle reverse faults higher in the Namurian.

Fairly intensive faulting occurs within the southern part of zone 2. Most important in terms of displacement are the strike faults, a number of which are known to be thrusts or high angle reverse faults. These are best documented north of the Galty Mountains where P. H. Shelford has shown that the Old Red Sandstone of Slievenamuck is thrust northwards over the Namurian; a probably related reverse fault brings Silurian into contact with Dinantian limestones along the south side of the Glen of Aherlow (Fig. 123). Comparable faults are reported in north County Cork

and M. E. Philcox has suggested that the single thrust or reverse fault between Killarney and Mallow is replaced by a wider zone of thrusting to the east. Most of the other faults recognised trend between north-north-west and north-north-east and are thought to have normal or sinistral wrench displacements.

Farther north in zone 2, the folding becomes generally more gentle, with axial traces trending between east-north-east and north-east. Most of the major faults mapped trend between east and north-east and many of them have been traced for considerable distances. They appear to be normal faults with throws of hundreds of metres but some are known to have a complex history of movement. Faults trending

Fig. 133. Folded Posidonomya Limestones, Loughshinny, County Dublin, viewed from the east.
Photograph by G. D. Sevastopulo

between north-west and north-north-west are also common. Few studies have been made of jointing but the dominant set seem to be vertical and trend north-south.

In the Dublin region, and to a lesser extent in the Boyne Valley, the intensity of deformation is anomalously high. The structures are well displayed along the coast between Rush and Skerries (Fig. 133). At Rush, on the northern limb of the Lambay–Portrane anticline (see page 60), the lithologically homogeneous Rush Slates are strongly cleaved and deformed by numerous dextral kink bands. Towards the core of the Loughshinny syncline interbedded limestones and shales (the Cyathaxonia Beds and particularly the Posidonomya Limestones) are strongly folded, the most spectacular examples being the overturned chevron folds with southerly dipping axial planes in Loughshinny Bay.

In zone 3, the structural pattern is dominated by numerous long, approximately north-east trending faults. Attempts have been made to link some of them with major fractures in Scotland [for example, the Killavil–Castle Archdale Fault (Fig. 123) with the Highland Boundary Fault], but true continuity and precise identity is, perhaps, unlikely. Many of the faults bring into contact rocks stratigraphically separated by hundred of metres; it has been suggested that some (for example, the Killavil and Tempo–Six Mile Cross Faults) have considerable wrench displacements but this is difficult to prove. There is good evidence that some of the approximately north-easterly trending faults in both zones 2 and 3 [for instance, the North Curlew and Tynagh Faults (Fig. 123)] were active during the Dinantian; a number of them may well have been reactivated Caledonian structures. Folding throughout zone 3 is gentle (Fig. 132) and dips in excess of 30° are rare except along the postulated courses of some of the faults.

Through much of zones 2 and 3 there is a striking parallelism between the trends of Hercynian and Caledonian structures; only in the east of zone 2, such as on Slievenamon or along the coast north of Dungarvan, is there a clear divergence, with Caledonian structures trending between north-east and east-north-east, and Hercynian cleavage striking east-west.

Direct evidence of the age of Hercynian deformation in Ireland is limited. In the north-east, tilted and faulted Dinantian strata are overlain by Permian and Trias. The most complete section is at Kingscourt where Permian is inferred to occur unconformably above early Westphalian. However, in Britain, Coal Measures sedimentation continued into the late Westphalian or early Stephanian; the Hercynian granites of south-west England, which postdate much of the regional deformation yield isotopic dates around 290 m.y. which suggest that much of the folding occurred in the late Carboniferous.

Viewed in a regional context, Ireland presents a probably fairly typical transect across the northern margin of the Hercynian belt. Notable features are the low metamorphic grade, the lack of granite emplacement, and the gradual change of deformational intensity from south to north which prevents the precise delimitation of the northern boundary of the fold belt.

BIBLIOGRAPHY

CAPEWELL, J. G.	1957	The stratigraphy and structure of the country around Sneem, Co. Kerry. *Proc. R. Ir. Acad.*, **58B**, 167–183.
CAPEWELL, J. G.	1975	The Old Red Sandstone Group of Iveragh, Co. Kerry. *Proc. R. Ir. Acad.*, **75B**, 155–171.
COE, K.	1959	Boudinage structure in West Cork, Ireland. *Geol. Mag.*, **96**, 191–200.
COE, K.	1969	The geology of the minor intrusions of West Cork, Ireland. *Proc. Geol. Ass.*, **80**, 441–457.
COE, K. & SELWOOD, E. B.	1963	The stratigraphy and structure of part of the Beara Peninsula, Co. Cork. *Proc. R. Ir. Acad.*, **63B**, 33–59.
DIXON, O. A.	1972	Lower Carboniferous rocks between the Curlew and Ox Mountains, Northwestern Ireland. *Jl. geol. Soc. Lond.*, **128**, 71–101.
GILL, W. D.	1962	The Variscan fold belt in Ireland. *In* Coe, K. (Ed.). *Some aspects of the Variscan fold belt.* Manchester University Press, 49–64.

NAYLOR, D.   1978 A structural section across the Variscan fold belt, south-
                                 west Ireland. *J. Earth Sci. R. Dubl. Soc.*, **1**, 63–70.

PHILCOX, M. E.   1964 Compartment deformation near Buttevant, County Cork,
                                 Ireland, and its relation to the Variscan thrust front.
                                 Scient. Proc. R. Dubl. Soc. Ser. A, **2**, 1–11.

REILLY, T. A. &   1972 The historical and geological setting of the Glandore
    GRAHAM, J. R.   mines, southwest County Cork. *Geol. Surv. Ireland. Bull.*,
                                 1, 253–265.

SHELFORD, P. H.   1963 The structure and relationship of the Namurian outcrop
                                 between Duntryleague, Co. Limerick and Dromlin, Co.
                                 Tipperary. *Proc. R. Ir. Acad.*, **62B**, 255–266.

WALSH, P. T.   1968 The Old Red Sandstone west of Killarney, Co. Kerry,
                                 Ireland. *Proc. R. Ir. Acad.*, **66B**, 9–26.

12

PERMIAN AND MESOZOIC

H. E. Wilson

Unlike those of the earlier Systems the Permian, Triassic, Jurassic, and Cretaceous rocks, with a few exceptions, are confined to the north-eastern corner of Ulster where they have been protected from erosion by the Tertiary volcanic rocks of the Antrim plateau. Rocks of all four Systems appear around the edges of the plateau and their coastal outcrops, in particular, have made them conspicuous to observers from the earliest days of geology.

The restricted outcrops of these formations make difficult any palaeogeographical reconstructions but some general trends are clear. The end of the Carbon-iferous Period, marked by earth movements and general elevation of the land, left all of Ireland above sea level in the early Permian, and the succeeding eras saw a series of marine incursions from the east in Upper Permian, Rhaetic, Liassic, and Upper Cretaceous times. Each of these seems to have been more extensive than its predecessors, culminating in the Senonian transgression which may have covered all of Ireland.

In the north-east a ridge of Dalradian rocks (Fig. 134) lay just north of the Highland Boundary Fault and this was a positive feature during the whole of the Mesozoic. To the north-west and south-east of the ridge subsiding basins accumulated great thicknesses of Triassic, Liassic, and Cretaceous rocks, while over the ridge sedimentation was thin or absent. This ridge still appears as the inlier of Dalradian rocks at Torr Head in north-east Antrim and runs south-westwards towards the Sperrin Mountains.

Permo-Trias

Though the 'New Red Sandstone' was recorded by earlier workers, the first identification of Permian rocks in Ireland was by W. King in 1853, who described Permian fossils from Cultra and Ardtrea. The sketchy knowledge of the Permian provided by the small exposures at these locations has now been extended by the results obtained from boreholes. Except for the characteristic fauna of the Magnesian Limestone the beds are virtually devoid of macro-fossils and only with recent developments in paly-nology has any useful chronology emerged.

Permo-Triassic rocks underlie most of the Tertiary lava outcrop in Counties Antrim and Londonderry, reaching great thicknesses in sedimentary basins north and south of the Highland Border Ridge, and thinning out against the Longford–Down massif to the south. A tongue stretching south through the Dundonald Gap to the Strangford Basin and an isolated outlier in the Kingscourt area suggest that deposition may have extended south over wide areas beyond the present outcrop.

The Hercynian earth movements left in the north of Ireland a landscape riven by downthrown graben which were limited by steep fault scarps. In an arid climate weathering of the exposed rock surfaces pro-duced a regolith of angular fragments in a com-minuted matrix which locally, as piedmont screes, reached very considerable thicknesses. Such angular breccias are known to be over 300 m thick in the Strangford Basin and approach this thickness under Belfast. Wind-blown sands with rounded millet-seed quartz grains formed dunes over and around the breccias. These thick deposits are known only from boreholes. In the only exposure, on the foreshore at Cultra [J 412 809], the basal breccia is only 1·5 m thick. The age of these various deposits is unknown but may be Lower Permian.

An incursion of the Bakevellia Sea in Upper Per-mian (Thuringian) times transgressed the low desert areas from the east and formed conglomerates with rounded pebbles on the shores to the west and south-west. This sea had little or no direct connection across the Pennine area with the Zechstein Sea which covered Durham and east Yorkshire and extended across the North Sea to northern Germany, but appears to have been fed by straits to the north-west and, possibly the south-west, from a western ocean of which no direct evidence remains. In it the Magnesian Limestone was deposited in the northern cuvette, while to the south thick beds of gypsum were formed in the Kingscourt area in shallow coastal lagoons or 'sabkha' flats – a Lower Gypsum 20 to 35 m thick, and an Upper Gypsum 6 to 10 m thick interbedded with red, grey, and purple mudstones and clays, some with reduction spots (Fig. 135).

As time went on the shallowing seas in the whole basin were replaced by lagoonal conditions and beds of anhydrite together with mudstones and siltstones, often calcareous and with shallow-water desiccation breccias and gypsum veins, were laid down.

Palynological evidence shows that the boundary

between the Permian and Trias falls in this part of the succession, but there was no break in deposition and there is now no mappable boundary.

The onset of fluviatile conditions caused a transition from argillaceous to sandy sediments and the succeeding group of mainly arenaceous rocks, with plentiful intercalations of muddy and silty material, indicates deposition in conditions of intermittent floods, with current bedding, and aridity with desiccation breccias. These Sherwood Sandstones are usually about 300 m thick and overlap the Permian and Carboniferous to extend as thinning fringes on the Dalradian rocks in the west and over the Highland Border Ridge. They are even thicker in the downwarped sedimentary basins which have been detected by geophysical means in the Larne and North Antrim areas.

Whether the marine conditions in which the Waterstones were laid down in England reached the Ulster basin is not clear, but the fluviatile conditions in which the Sherwood Sandstone Group was deposited

Fig. 134. (a) Triassic palaeogeography in Sherwood Sandstone Group (lower Scythian) times.
           (b) Triassic palaeogeography in Mercia Mudstone Group (Anisian) times (both after Audley
           Charles 1970).

gave place to lagoonal or lacustrine environments in which the succeeding Mercia Mudstone Group was laid down. Periodic inundation by brine from the North Sea Basin gave deposits of evaporites, usually in the form of thin veins of gypsum. In the South Antrim Basin, where downwarping north of the Southern Uplands Fault gave a great thickness of sediments, thick halites were deposited (Fig. 134).

The South Antrim Salt Field is known to underlie a triangular area between Carrickfergus and Larne, but knowledge of the evaporite beds is confined to boreholes and shaft sections in the Carrickfergus and Redhall areas and a single deep borehole at Larne. Even in the restricted area around Carrickfergus it is difficult to correlate individual beds and no correlation is possible between this district and Larne; but though the halite deposits are doubtless present throughout the field it is probable that individual beds are lenticular and discontinuous.

The full thickness of the halite succession in the Carrickfergus–Redhall areas is unknown as boreholes and shafts never penetrated farther than the uppermost beds of salt – some 30 m or so – but it is clear that there is a general thickening of the whole succession to the east, and at Larne the total thickness of halite is some 400 m in 900 m of Mercia Mudstone Group.

The group has been divided on the basis of lithological variations in two deep boreholes into six formations (Fig. 135), most of which cannot be recognised in surface outcrop. The only distinctive formation is the uppermost, the Collin Glen Formation, formerly known as the 'Tea Green Marls'. Usually about 10 m thick, these beds are pale green in colour and indicate a change in depositional conditions at the end of Mercia Mudstone times, foreshadowing the marine transgression of the Rhaetian. Fish remains have been found in this formation in other parts of the British Isles.

There is a sharp unconformity at the base of the Rhaetic, which is of a shale-limestone facies with a restricted marine fauna.

Only two formations in the whole of the Permo–Trias have a useful macrofauna, the Magnesian Limestone and the Rhaetic, but spores and pollen have been found from many levels throughout the succession.

Magnesian Limestone is seen at outcrop in two areas, at Grange in County Tyrone where it is about 20 m thick, and on the foreshore at Cultra, where it is only 8·3 m. It is known also from bores in Tyrone and in the Belfast area. The limestone is a true dolomite and is moderately fossiliferous. The fossil assemblages from all known occurrences are notable for the predominance of the bivalve *Bakevellia* (*B.*) *binneyi* which must have been a particularly adaptable

species as it occurs where no other fossils are known. Other bivalves – *Schizodus*, *Permophorus*, *Liebea* – and rare gastropods and bryozoa are found and early collections from Cultra record *Horridonia horrida*, though the probable correctness of this cannot now be confirmed. In the Zechstein marine sequence of north-eastern England four main evaporite cycles can be distinguished, EZ1–EZ4. Though it is impossible to equate these precisely with the evaporite cycles of the Bakevellia Sea the faunal distribution suggests that the Magnesian Limestone in Ulster may be correlated with the carbonate phase of EZ1 or, possibly, EZ1 and EZ2.

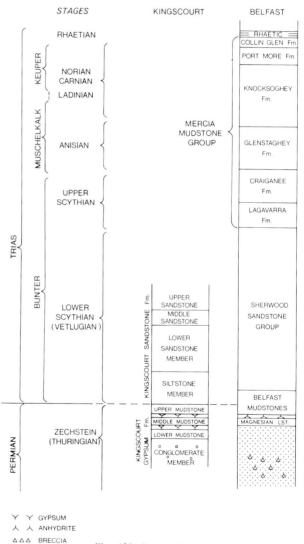

Fig. 135. Comparative sections in the Permo-Triassic rocks of Belfast and Kingscourt.

In the Kingscourt outlier macrofossils are absent but the argillaceous beds have yielded foraminifera, acritarchs, other chitinoid remains, and, most usefully, spores and pollen grains. These show that the Kingscourt Gypsum Formation is of Zechstein (Thuringian) age and that the boundary between Permian and Trias (Kingscourt Sandstone Formation) lies in a dominantly argillaceous group of beds, the lower part of which is Permian while the upper, yielding a *Lundbladispora* assemblage, is of Scythian age. To date no spores have been recovered from the Belfast Mudstone Group, which overlies the Magnesian Limestone and is in turn overlain by the Sherwood Sandstone of the Lagan Valley, but it may be conjectured that the Permian-Triassic boundary lies within these beds.

The only macrofossil from the Trias (except the Rhaetian Stage) is the phyllopod *Euestheria minuta* which occurs in the Sherwood Sandstone Group in County Tyrone. Palynological material from Kingscourt and from the Langford Lodge borehole near Lough Neagh shows that the lower arenaceous part of the succession is of lower and middle Scythian age while the Mercia Mudstone Group ranges from upper Scythian to the Norian Stage and is the equivalent of the upper Bunter, Muschelkalk, and Keuper of the German succession (Fig. 135).

In the Kingscourt assemblages the Scythian material is notable for the dominance of caveate spores, articularly species of *Lundbladispora*, while at Langford Lodge *L. nejburgii* is among the extensive assemblages of Scythian age found in the lowest 80 m of the Mercia Mudstone and in the Sherwood Sandstone.

Rhaetian and Lias

The occurrence of Liassic rocks in Ulster was first noted by Sampson in 1802 and by the remarkable trio of Dr Berger, Dr Buckland, and Mr Conybeare, during their travels around the Antrim Coast in 1816. The formations in the South Antrim area were described by Tate in 1864. They were recorded elsewhere by the Geological Survey in the 1880's but have until recently been the subject of little comment. In Tate's time the Rhaetic was considered to be part of the Jurassic and though it is now regarded as the uppermost formation of the Trias it is convenient to consider these formations together as they are conformable and no intraformational discontinuity is known.

The end of Triassic times was marked by a change from largely arid conditions with temporary lakes, to coastal lagoonal conditions with the incoming of a marine fauna, and finally to the transgression of the sea over much of England, the Irish Sea basin, and the Hebridean basin. The deposits in these shallow seas were dark shales and mudstones with some thin limestones and sandstones. The onset of true marine conditions in Liassic times led to the development of mudstones with thin limestones, ironstone ribs, and nodules, while the restricted and stunted fauna of the Rhaetic gave way to the abundant fauna of the Lias.

The Rhaetic and Liassic beds were probably laid down over a wide area in northern Ireland and western Scotland, but they were subject to considerable pre-Cretaceous erosion and are now present only in relatively localised areas where they have been preserved from Tertiary erosion by the basalt carapace of the Antrim plateau. The Rhaetic is best known from the Larne area and from a borehole in North Antrim. Other exposures are scattered and temporary as the plateau edges around which they appear are greatly affected by landslipping.

At Larne, 13·7 m of lower Rhaetic shales with *Rhaetavicula contorta* and *Protocardia rhaetica*, and 6·9 m of upper Rhaetic beds with *Eotrapezium concentricum*, *E. menkei*, *Meleagrinella fallax*, *Modiolus hillanoides*, *Protocardia philippiana*, *P. rhaetica*, and *Pteromya tatei* were recorded in a borehole; but faulted exposures on the foreshore at Waterloo |D 409 036| show only about 14 m of dark shales and mudstones with thin sandstone ribs near the base and thin limestones at the top. The overlying grey calcareous mudstones in the borehole contain no diagnostic fossils and are probably of pre-*planorbis* age, but from about 5 m above the Rhaetic the mudstones have an ammonite fauna including *Psiloceras planorbis* and, at higher levels, *P. (Caloceras) intermedium*, *P. (C.) leptoptychum*, and *P. (C.) johnstoni*, indicating the *planorbis* Zone of the Hettangian. Foreshore exposures, though much disturbed by faulting, include *Alsatites liasicus*, *Schlotheimia angulata*, and possibly *Arietites bucklandi* Zones. The total thickness of Liassic rocks here is over 100 m.

Elsewhere in south-east Antrim (Fig. 136) Rhaetic and Liassic rocks are exposed only in scattered and incomplete sections. The well-known exposures at Collin Glen, near Belfast |J 270 719| are now partly obscured and only limited sections of lower Rhaetic and *liasicus* Zone beds are seen, while the sections at Woodburn, Cloghfin, and Barney's Point are small and obscure. North of Larne exposures of landslip Liassic material are abundant but clear sections are non-existent. There is evidence of the presence of Lias as far as Red Bay but no sign of Rhaetic material is seen north of Straidkelly Point.

North of the Highland Border Ridge the Rhaetic appears in much the same form as to the south, but Liassic rocks reach much greater thicknesses. There are limited surface exposures at Portnakillew, White

Park Bay, Portrush, and in streams at Tircreven [C 702 325], Tircorran [C 696 280], and The Lynn [C 709 279]; but our most detailed knowledge comes from boreholes at Port More and Magilligan.

At Port More [D 068 435] a massive Tertiary sill intruded between the two formations may have assimilated part of each. The Rhaetic beds are only 4 m thick and contain *Rhaetavicula contorta*. They are ascribed to the lower Rhaetic. The Lias is almost 250 m thick ranging from the *Arnioceras semicostatum* Zone up to the *Tragophylloceras ibex* Zone. If the lowest zones were present they must have been assimilated by the sill.

In the Magilligan borehole the upper part of the Lias is cut out by a massive sill and though 90 m of Liassic beds are known, only *planorbis* Zone has been recognised. The Rhaetic is 7·3 m thick. The beds in Tircreven Burn, which is topographically above the Magilligan area, have *semicostatum* Zone fossils.

Though never reaching outcrop, Rhaetic and Liassic beds were found at depth in the Mire House bore, east of Dungannon. Nine metres of upper Rhaetic Mudstones underlie 130 m of shales and thin limestones which range from pre-*planorbis* to *angulata* Zone in age.

At Portrush the peninsula on which the town is built is formed by a massive Tertiary sill. This intrusion was emplaced, like that in the Port More Borehole, into the Lias beds and has metamorphosed the mudstones above it – those below are not exposed – for some tens of metres from the contact into a hard fine-grained hornfels. This rock is dark and bears a superficial resemblance to fine-grained basalt, but it contains recognisable ammonites of *raricostatum* Zone age and other fossils (Fig. 190). During the controversies between the Vulcanists, who believed that basalts were volcanic in origin, and the Neptunists, who considered that they were crystalline deposits formed, like limestone, in the sea, the 'Portrush Rock' was advanced by the latter as evidence of the marine origin of 'basalt' with fossils preserved in it. The name of the tiny fishing village, as it then was, was known throughout the scientific world (see also page 303).

No Jurassic rocks more recent in age than the Lower Lias are known at outcrop in Ireland, but shale blocks with Middle Lias fossils have been recorded from the drift in North Antrim, and ammonites of Middle and Upper Lias age have been found in the Cretaceous (Senonian) conglomerates of Murlough Bay. Middle and Upper Lias shales are known from the Inner Hebrides and no doubt beds of this age were extensively deposited throughout the Hebridean basin. It seems improbable that the drift blocks could have travelled far and it is likely that beds of Middle Lias age may underlie the Cretaceous rocks on Rathlin Island and crop out beneath the North Channel and Rathlin Sound.

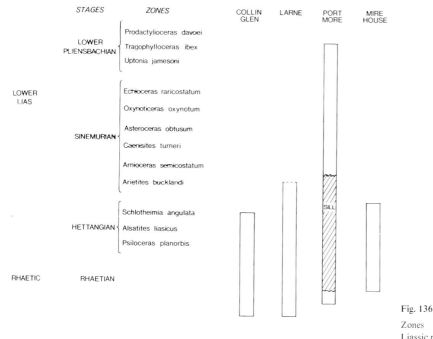

Fig. 136

Zones and local ranges of the Liassic rocks (not to scale).

Above: 'Elephant Rock', Sliddery Cove, near Portrush. Marine erosion in White Limestone, with rows of flint nodules.

Fig. 137. Cretaceous White Limestone of Northern Ireland.

Photographs Geological Survey of Northern Ireland

Below: Knocknadona Quarry, near Lisburn. Irregular basalt dykes cutting White Limestone and overlying Antrim Lava Group (Tertiary) basalt flow.

Cretaceous

The late Jurassic and early Cretaceous seem to have been times of erosion and of little or no deposition in Ireland – certainly there are no remaining rocks of these ages – but the Upper Cretaceous marks the inundation, probably of the whole area, by the Chalk sea and the deposition of the very characteristic sediments which mark this period throughout the whole of Western Europe – the Greensands and the Chalk or White Limestone.

The remarkable appearance of the White Limestone (Fig. 137) and the overlying black basalt lavas on the Antrim Coast was the subject of comment by the earliest geological observers in the area, Whitehurst and Hamilton in 1786, the former equating the limestone with the Chalk of southern England. Sampson in 1814 and Conybeare and Berger in 1816 noted the underlying greensands, and the beds were described by Portlock in 1843 and Bryce in 1853, before Tate in 1864 made the first comprehensive study of the succession.

Like the underlying Triassic and Jurassic rocks the Cretaceous in Ulster is confined to a peripheral outcrop round the lava plateau, but the former widespread distribution of the system is indicated by the occurrence of Chalk in a late-Cretaceous swallow hole in County Kerry and on the continental shelf off the south and west coasts of Ireland (Fig. 138 and see Chapter 18).

The Cretaceous rocks of Antrim range in age from Cenomanian to Maestrichtian. A far from uniform succession and numerous breaks in deposition indicate unstable conditions with sedimentation interrupted by frequent periods of uplift and erosion.

The rocks are of two main sedimentary facies: glauconitic clastics of the Hibernian Greensand Formation and pelagic limestone and flint of the White Limestone Formation. The former covers a considerable time span.

In the early Cenomanian the sea transgressed the southern part of the area and deposited a group of Lower Cenomanian Greensands. The earliest deposits were of the Glauconite Sands, deposits of grains of dark green glauconite in a marl matrix, with locally a thin basal bed of pebbles and phosphatised fossils. The bivalve *Exogyra obliquata* is common. These dark green beds are followed by the Yellow Sandstones and Grey Marls, a largely calcareous group of argillaceous sandstones and mudstones with local doggers of muddy limestone and occasional cherty concretions, and a fauna of poorly preserved echinoids and small bivalves including the characteristic *Arcostrea colubrina* and *Neithea* spp.

A sharp disconformity is followed by the Glauconitic Sandstones, now known only at Collin Glen and Island Magee. These are a group of quartzose sandstones with abundant glauconite grains and plentiful fossils, notably *Exogyra columba*. They are overlain at Collin Glen only, by the Quartzose Sands, sparsely glauconitic in their lower part but pale and siliceous above. These are practically unfossiliferous save for some possibly Turonian foraminifera.

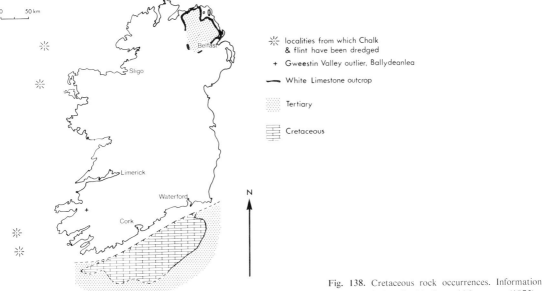

Fig. 138. Cretaceous rock occurrences. Information for the Celtic Sea after Naylor and Mounteney (1975).

A major unconformity, indicating a period of non-deposition and widespread erosion, follows this formation. The succeeding deposits rest unconformably on beds which range from the Quartzose Sands west of Belfast through the Yellow Sandstones at Belfast and Woodburn to (possibly) the Glauconite Sands at Glenarm. The Cenomanian beds are preserved only in restricted areas – in the hills above Belfast, east of the Groganstown Fault; in South Antrim from Woodburn to Glenarm; and a possible relic at Tircreven in eastern Londonderry. At their maximum these beds are about 22 m thick.

The major break in deposition was followed in Senonian, or possibly late Turonian, times by a series of transgressions in which three principal groups of sediments were deposited – glauconitic greensands, pebble conglomerates, and the White Limestone.

The Senonian Greensands are best known from the Island Magee area, but outcrop extends from Whitehead to Garron Point in eastern Antrim. In the southern part of this outcrop the succession begins with glauconitic sands and sandstone, soft and largely unbedded, with layers of *Inoceramus* fragments and other fossils which include reworked material from the Cenomanian Greensands. Chalk infillings in some of the fossils suggest that chalk facies sedimentation began earlier than the remaining White Limestone would indicate, but that the beds then deposited were removed by contemporaneous erosion. The lower part of the glauconitic beds is in the Zone of *Micraster cortestudinarium* and they range up into the *M. coranguinum* Zone (Fig. 139). Though the Lower Cretaceous beds are divided into biozones by the ammonites occurring in them, these become scarce in the Upper Cretaceous and the zone fossils are echinoids and, in the uppermost beds, belemnites.

Above the glauconitic sandstones the sediment changes to a hard glauconitic limestone with irregular partings and abundant sponge remains, preserved as phosphatic pseudomorphs which range from small fragments to complete specimens, all of detrital origin. The sponges are all Hexactinellida and form one of the earliest developments of a general Senonian sponge fauna found from Ireland to Russia. These Cloghfin Sponge Beds are well exposed at Cloghfin, Hillsport, Portmuck, Waterloo, and Ballygalley. Northwards they become inconspicuous and beyond Garron Point consist only of occasional sponges in the glauconitic top of a thin basal conglomerate. The sponge beds appear to begin in the *coranguinum* Zone and extend into the *Uintacrinus socialis* Zone.

In the north-west, exposures around the Benevenagh Plateau show glauconitic greensands which may include *coranguinum* Zone at the bottom and range up through *socialis*, *Marsupites testudinarius*, and *Offaster pilula* Zones.

From Glenballyeamon near Cushendall to Murlough Bay on the north coast and from Keady Mountain to Magherafelt in the west, the Cretaceous transgression was affected, as was the deposition of many earlier formations, by the Highland Border Ridge across which Cretaceous rocks transgress on to the Dalradian basement. In the west the whole Cretaceous succession is cut out but in the north-east the White Limestone, though locally very thin, is always present and is underlain by a bed of conglomerate commonly less than a metre thick. This conglomerate contains predominantly Dalradian rock type pebbles, sparse sandstones of Triassic and possibly Cretaceous age, and rare derived Liassic fossils, in a chalky matrix with quartz and glauconite grains. The conglomerate sometimes consists of two layers with an erosion surface between and differing clasts, as at the east end of Murlough Bay. The top of the conglomerate throughout is typically eroded and stromatolitic and the bed cannot be considered to be a basal facies to the White Limestone. Locally it contains a restricted fauna – *Orbirhynchia*, *Exogyra*, *Pleuretomaria*, *Neithea*, etc. – and appears to be Senonian in age.

White Limestone

The most widespread sediment of the Upper Cretaceous succession in western Europe is the Chalk, and, though unique in some respects, the White Limestone of Antrim is part of this remarkable body of rock which persists from Ireland to the Caucasus. The Chalk is almost entirely organic in origin with only 1–2% clay and silt throughout most of the succession. The conditions of its deposition must have involved very low and arid coastlands around the Chalk sea. The origin of the Chalk was long uncertain, with only relatively large organic remains being discernible in a very fine grained matrix. The advent of the electron microscope proved this matrix to be of organic rather than chemical origin and it is now known that the main constituents of the rock are coccoliths, with smaller proportions of foraminifera, molluscan and echinoderm debris, and *Oligostegina* spheres. Coccoliths are microscopic calcareous discs which develop within the cell of minute unicellular algae, the Coccolithophoridea, modern types of which live a marine planktonic existence. On sinking to the bottom after the death of the organisms the discs form a coccolith ooze on the sea floor in which burrowing animals lived and on which others moved.

At times of interrupted sedimentation the surface of the ooze became indurated and mineralized to form a feature known as a hardground. Most of these display conspicuous green glauconitic staining and, locally, skins of brownish calcium phosphate. In

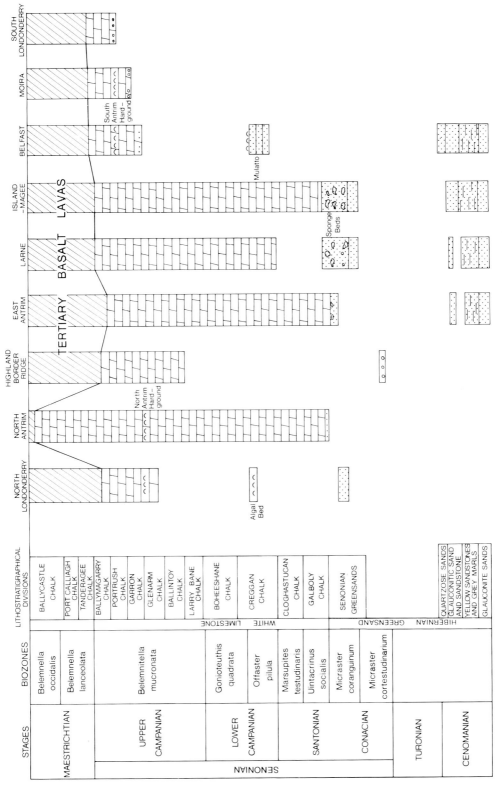

Fig. 139. Zones and local ranges of the Cretaceous rocks (not to scale).

contrast to the soft ooze the hardgrounds offered a firm surface for bottom-living animals, and they are accompanied by a fauna different from that in the normal Chalk, though this is often in the form of rolled and glauconitised specimens. The formation of hardgrounds is usually attributed to shallowing in water perhaps 50 m deep, while the depth in which the ooze was formed was probably 300 m or more. Extreme shallowing, up to 20 m or so, allowed physical erosion of the sediments and the development of algal stromatolitic growths on the erosion surfaces.

Normal compaction of the sediments produced a soft porous limestone of the type common in England and France, but the Antrim White Limestone is a hard, compact, and non-porous rock, comparable in strength to a normal crystalline limestone. The intergranular cavities are filled with diagenetic calcite and recent work suggests that the hardening was due to a combination of hydrothermal alteration and compaction by loading during the eruption of the Tertiary lavas in this area.

Flint is present throughout the White Limestone, usually as rows of nodules (Fig. 137), rarely as tabular sheets, and, at one horizon only, as giant barrel-shaped 'paramoudras', up to a metre long, and large horizontal rolls. It consists of cryptocrystalline silica, so fine grained as to present a homogeneous appearance. It breaks with a conchoidal or shell-like fracture and varies in colour from pale grey to almost black. The nodules were doubtless formed as accretions while the chalk was soft, sometimes in the form of burrow-fillings; but the tabular flints locally transect bedding planes and are apparently secondary, probably deposited by percolating silica-rich groundwaters.

The macrofossils are divisible into free-swimming nekton – belemnites, ammonites, and fish – and bottom-dwelling benthos – notably echinoids, asteroids, bivalves, and sponges. A burrowing fauna is detected only by its burrows, ascribed to annelid worms (*Chondrites*), crustaceans (*Thalassinoides*, apparently a burrowing prawn), and some echinoids. These burrows are rarely recognisable in the Antrim White Limestone, though common in softer chalks, but some dark streaking in the Limestone is probably burrow traces.

The belemnites were squid-like free-swimming predators, and some of the ammonites were free-swimming plankton feeders, though others may have been bottom scavengers. The fishes included sharks, holosteans, teleosts, and skate. The asteroids and most echinoids were surface movers, though some of the latter may have lived in shallow burrows. Some of the bivalves (*Plagiostoma*, *Aequipecten*) also moved about, but most of these, like the Hexactinellid

sponges, were sessile, either embedded in the mud by spines, attached to hardground surfaces or to other anchorages, or simply immobile because of size, like the large Inoceramids. The siliceous sponges, whose roots grew into the sediment, were doubtless important substrates for the articulate brachiopods (*Gibbithyris*, *Terebratulina*, *Cretirhynchia*, *Orbirhynchia*) and other encrusting organisms.

The White Limestone succession has been divided lithostratigraphically into thirteen members (Fig. 139) distinguished primarily by the type of flint and delimited by bedding planes which are often erosion surfaces. In no one area are all these members exposed together and the uppermost members are only very locally preserved as post-Cretaceous erosion has removed much of the succession in many places.

The thickest and most complete successions occur in two main depositional basins lying north-west and south-east of the Highland Border Ridge. Towards the margin of the basins the successions are condensed and non-sequences develop, but taken as a whole the post-Santonian succession is one of the most complete in Northern Europe. The greatest known thickness of the White Limestone is 91 m in North Antrim though an anomalous 150 m is recorded from an old borehole in Tyrone.

The oldest White Limestone deposits in both basins are of *socialis* Zone age in White Park Bay, Carnlough, and at Hillsport in Island Magee, and with succeeding *testudinarius* and *pilula* Zones form the lowest three members in the East Antrim basin. The lowest beds are cream in colour and contaminated with glauconite grains and the whole is notable for the abundance of *Inoceramus* shell fragments, which appear in the rock as small rectangles of crystalline calcite.

In the North Antrim Basin the three zones seem to be present throughout – in fact in White Park Bay the basal conglomerate of rolled coprolites and sparse glauconite may be of *coranguinum* age. The succession is, however, interrupted by a number of minor erosion surfaces with green glauconitised pebbles and terminated by a well-marked erosion surface – the Terminal *Pilula* Pebble Bed, with rolled and glauconitised pebbles, mainly Hexactinellid sponges but including echinoids and *Gonioteuthis*. The upper part of the *pilula* Zone is missing.

In the East Antrim Basin the sequence is attenuated in the area around Larne where the lowest beds are of *pilula* Zone age and this area appears to have been one of uplift throughout the Santonian. The maximum limestone development of the *socialis* and *pilula* Zones in both basins passes laterally into sandy glauconitic and stromatolitic limestones as at Belfast where these beds were the 'Mulatto' of earlier writers, and at Tircreven Burn above Magilligan, where this marginal facies includes the succeeding *Gonioteuthis quadrata* Zone.

The succeeding Boheeshane Chalk of *quadrata* and lowest *Belemnitella mucronata* Zones is present in the main basins only and is overstepped on to the Highland Border Ridge and the areas to the west by *mucronata* Chalk, marking the period of maximum subsidence throughout the area. The lowest full member of the *mucronata* Zone is the Larry Bane Chalk, a distinctive double unit (lower part about 2·5 m and upper 5 m), which, with well-marked erosion surfaces above, between, and below, is an easily recognised marker horizon throughout the whole of County Antrim. This member oversteps the Highland Border Ridge except for a small area east of Cushendall.

The Ballintoy Chalk is marked by large pachydiscid ammonites which can be seen at Ballintoy and in the quarry in Glenballyeamon, and the Glenarm Chalk by two conspicuous hardgrounds in North Antrim. The area of uplift and attenuation at Larne persisted during this time and local disconformities and erosion planes abound. The Ballintoy Chalk is absent in Londonderry where the Glenarm Member is attenuated and has several non-sequences. The succeeding Garron Chalk is marked by the occurrence of giant flints, exceptionally in the form of rolls up to 4·5 m long, and is the earliest member in much of the area west of Belfast, where it rests directly on Triassic rocks with only a thin basal glauconitic pebble bed. The Portrush Chalk above it was the lowest bed in southern County Londonderry and around Limestone Lodge near Lisburn. It has many non-sequences and the 'Green Beds' or 'South Antrim Hard-Grounds' of the Moira area are within this member. The uppermost Senonian Chalk, the Ballymagarry Chalk, occurs extensively in North Antrim and locally in the Moira area, south Derry and on Keady Mountain. In East Antrim, however, pre-basalt erosion has removed these beds except very locally at Garron Point.

White Limestone of Maestrichtian age occurs mainly on the north coast, though small thicknesses of beds with an *Echinocorys* fauna of typical Tanderagee Chalk aspect are known in the Magheralin and Ballysillan (Belfast) areas and in south Derry. The best exposures of Maestrichtian Chalk are on the cliffs west of Ballycastle Harbour.

How long Cretaceous sedimentation persisted in Antrim is not known – late Cretaceous or early Tertiary erosion has removed any trace of post-Maestrichtian beds if they ever existed. Early Tertiary tuffaceous deposits containing Maestrichtian microfossils are known from near Ballycastle Harbour and from White Park Bay.

Three hundred kilometres south of the Antrim occurrences Cretaceous rocks have been found at Ballydeanlea in the Gweestin Valley near Killarney. The Chalk appears as matrix in a breccia of Namurian shale which forms a pocket in surrounding unbrecciated Carboniferous rocks, and flint nodules also enclose shale fragments. Foraminiferal evidence indicates a Senonian age for the Chalk and the mode of occurrence shows that the deposit was formed by submarine subsidence, probably collapse of a cavern in the underlying Carboniferous Limestone, which mixed unconsolidated Cretaceous sediment with brecciated shale from the sea floor.

Dredged samples from the ocean floor west of Kerry and west of Connemara have long been known to include Cretaceous flints and Chalk. Cretaceous and later rocks are also now well known off the south coast (Fig. 138 and see Chapter 18). It seems probable that the Senonian transgression extended over much, if not all, of present-day Ireland and far beyond.

BIBLIOGRAPHY

AUDLEY-CHARLES, M. G.　1970　Stratigraphical correlation of the Triassic rocks of the British Isles. Triassic palaeogeography of the British Isles. *Q. Jl. geol. Soc. Lond.*, **126**, 19–89.

FLETCHER, T. P.　1977　Lithostratigraphy of the chalk (Ulster White Limestone). in Northern Ireland .*Rep. Inst. Geol. Sci.* No. **77/24**, pp. 33.

HANCOCK, J. M.　1961　The Cretaceous System in Northern Ireland. *Q. Jl. geol. Soc. Lond.*, **117**, 11–36.

HAWKES, J. R. & WILSON, H. E.　1975　The Portrush Sill, County Antrim, Northern Ireland. *Bull. geol. Surv. Gt. Br.*, **51**, 1–20.

IVIMEY-COOK, H. C.　1975　The stratigraphy of the Rhaetic and Lower Jurassic in east Antrim. *Bull. geol. Surv. Gt. Br.*, **50**, 51–69.

MANNING, P. I.,   1970 Geology of Belfast and the Lagan Valley. *Mem. geol. Surv.*
    ROBBIE, J. A., &   *Nth. Ire.*, pp. 242.
    WILSON, H. E.

MANNING, P. I. &   1975 The stratigraphy of the Larne Borehole, County Antrim.
    WILSON, H. E.   *Bull. geol. Surv. Gt. Br.*, **50**, 1–36.

PATTISON, J.   1970 A review of the marine fossils from the Upper Permian
                                rocks of Northern Ireland and north-west England. *Bull.*
                                geol. Surv. Gt. Br., **32**, 123–165.

RAWSON, P. F., CURRY, D., 1978 A correlation of Cretaceous rocks in the British Isles.
    DILLEY, F. C.,   *Geol. Soc. Lond. Spec. Rep.*, **9**, pp. 70.
    HANCOCK, J. M.,
    KENNEDY, W. J.,
    NEALE, J. W.,
    WOOD, C. J., &
    WORSSAM, B. C.

REID, R. E. H.   1958 Remarks on the Upper Cretaceous Hexactinellida of
                                County Antrim: Part 1. *Ir. Nat. J.*, **12**, 236–243.

REID, R. E. H.   1971 The Cretaceous rocks of north-eastern Ireland. *Ir. Nat. J.*,
                                17, 105–129.

REID, R. E. H.   1973 The Chalk Sea. *Ir. Nat. J.*, **17**, 357–375.

REYNOLDS, D. L.   1928 The petrography of the Triassic sandstone of north-east
                                Ireland. *Geol. Mag.*, **65**, 448–473.

SMITH, D. B.,   1974 A correlation of Permian rocks in the British Isles. *Geol.*
    BRUNSTROM, R. G. W.,   *Soc. Lond. Spec. Rep.*, **5**, pp. 45.
    MANNING, P. I.,
    SIMPSON, S., &
    SHOTTON, F. W.

VISSCHER, H.   1971 The Permian and Triassic of the Kingscourt Outlier, Ire-
                                land. *Geol. Surv. Ire. Spec. Paper*, **1**, pp. 114.

WALSH, P. T.   1966 Cretaceous outliers in south-west Ireland and their impli-
                                cations for Cretaceous palaeogeography. *Q. Jl. geol. Soc.*
                                Lond., **122**, 63–84.

WILSON, H. E.   1972 *Regional geology of Northern Ireland*. Ministry of Com-
                                merce, Geol. Surv. Northern Ireland. Belfast, H.M.
                                Stationery Office, pp. 115.

WILSON, H. E. &   1978 Geology of the Causeway Coast. *Mem. geol. Surv. Nth.*
    MANNING, P. I.   *Ire.*, pp. 172.

WILSON, H. E. &   1966 Geology of the country around Ballycastle. *Mem. geol.*
    ROBBIE, J. A.   *Surv. Nth. Ire.*, pp. 370.

13

TERTIARY IGNEOUS ACTIVITY

J. Preston

Widespread emergence of the northern continents from the Cretaceous seas foreshadowed a volcanic episode which dominated the geological record of the Tertiary period in Ireland. Both the siting and the timing of this igneous activity were closely linked to the growth of the North Atlantic Ocean.

Siting

Doming and rifting accompanied the extension of the Atlantic Ocean some 53 to 65 million years ago, and old and new crustal fractures tapped sources of basaltic magma which had collected in the upper mantle and poured out floods of basaltic lava to build plateaux and shield volcanoes over a broad region either side of the main rift – a region known as the Thulean Volcanic Province.

Earlier, abortive spreading axes between Europe and Greenland may have initiated rifts between England and Ireland or between the Porcupine Bank (Chapter 18) and the Rockall microcontinent, but beyond a few seamounts – possible submarine volcanoes and some intercalated tuffs of Mesozoic and Cretaceous age – no earlier phases of volcanism have been observed.

The main rift between Greenland and northern Europe and the continued separation of the two continental plates brought new crust to the ocean floor and opened rift-parallel fractures in the newly freed plate edges. Dyke swarms, feeding surface extrusives, follow these north-east to south-west fissures in Greenland and the Faeroes.

One set of fractures, however, could not completely relieve the tensional stress imposed by doming; rift-normal fractures along north-west to south-east lines would have been a necessary complementary structure

and dyke swarms now follow such fissures across the north European plate.

One such zone passing through St Kilda and Bororey (some rift-parallel dykes are found here), the Outer Hebrides, Mull, south-western Scotland and north-eastern England is matched by one, some 200 km to the south, which connects Rockall, Donegal, Slieve Gullion, Anglesey, North Wales, and the English Midlands. These linear dyke swarms contain many local centres of volcanic activity and swing into an east-west trend at their eastern extremities. Two hundred kilometres farther south occur two of the more southerly outposts of Tertiary volcanism in the British Isles – the Doon Hill Plug of County Galway and the granitic-basic dyke complex of Lundy Island. The positions of these rift-parallel and rift-normal swarms at the onset of rifting are illustrated in Figure 140.

Many local volcanic centres follow other alignments; and older fractures, possible lineament structures in the upper mantle or lower crust, must be invoked to explain the full pattern of Thulean volcanism. Richey, long ago, commented on the north-south alignment of Tertiary intrusive centres from Skye to the Mournes and this line now takes in hidden centres, such as the Blackstones Bank off Islay, and can be extended south to Lundy Island and north beyond the Faeroes to Jan Mayen. Before rifting occurred, it may have intersected the east coast of Greenland.

Another north-south lineament may underlie the west coast of Ireland in line with hidden centres off north-western Donegal and with St Kilda. Complementary east-west lineaments are not so well marked; explosive vents follow the faulted north coast of County Antrim, and in Counties Mayo and Sligo the linear dyke swarms have an east-west trend.

Local and often intense activity high lighted weak

spots through the crust. Magma collecting below
north-south lineaments exploited their intersection
with major faults, or feeding along the north-west to
south-east fissures found easy access into well-jointed,
and readily-melted, acid plutons. The deep sedimentary basins of late Palaeozoic and Mesozoic
rocks, rich in oxidizing water and carbon dioxide,
probably influenced the chemistry and differentiation
of the rising magma more than the rocks of the crystalline basement.

Timing

Radiometric age dates offer, as yet, the only stratigraphical correlation across the Thulean Volcanic

Province. Though subject to error in consequence of
hydrothermal alterations, they show a remarkable
synchronism of rifting, initial plate movement, crustal
foundering, and volcanism over the North Atlantic
region (Figs. 140 and 141). The period of 15 million
years from 65–50 m.y. is comparable with the life of
other volcanic provinces and the sequence of activity
follows a well-established order at most localities.
Flood basalts, 62–58 m.y., anticipate the central volcanoes, 59–53 m.y., whereas hypabyssal intrusions
are associated with every phase of eruption. Mac-
Intyre has confirmed the Tertiary age of many olivine
dolerite plugs and dykes in Counties Donegal, Sligo,
Mayo, and Galway and has added to the list of
Tertiary intrusions the arfvedsonitic (alkali-amphi-
bole) rhyolite dykes of County Donegal and the

Fig. 140. Thulean Volcanic Province prior to rifting 60 m.y. (after Bott and Watts 1971).
Isobaths in fathoms. Black areas – early Tertiary volcanics. Figures – age in m.y. Dyke trends
sketched in and the pattern of north-south lineaments and north-west to south-east fracture
zones superimposed.

Killala and Inishcrone gabbros at Killala Bay.

No migration of volcanism across the Thulean Province can be interpreted from the age distribution shown in Figure 141. Geological evidence only demonstrates minor shifts of centralized activity along individual crustal fractures.

R. L. Wilson, using palaeomagnetic data, has made more detailed comment on the building of the Antrim Basalt Plateau. This may have taken less than 1 m.y. for the entire thickness and may belong to one magnetic epoch.

Pre-volcanic conditions

Late Cretaceous times (Chapter 12) saw the maximum transgression of the Chalk seas over Ireland. Then, many of the Caledonoid trending land ridges were finally submerged, only to be reaccentuated by early Tertiary uplift. Gentle undulations across the

north-eastern corner of Ireland may have controlled both the erosion of the emergent Chalk and the distribution of the first basaltic lavas. Neville George has argued that the Midland Valley (of Scotland) showed only the faintest surface expression across Ireland, and little appears to be known of the role played by the Longford–Down massif. Cretaceous rocks if deposited as they were to the south and west, must have been completely removed before the onset of volcanism. Over Donegal, the present-day drainage pattern originated on a gently, southerly, inclined surface which may have been the emergent Cretaceous surface or the basalt plateau itself.

Foundering of the north European plate edge followed the initial rifting. The coast of Ireland may well have been defined at this time. The Irish Sea basin was most probably in existence and normal faults, down-throwing to the west, redefined the north-south lineament which separated England from Ireland and the mainland of Scotland from the Outer

Fig. 141. Tertiary volcanic rocks of Ireland. Isopachytes of the Basalt Plateau in metres (after Tomkeieff 1964). D.G. – Newry Granodiorite. *Insets*: Slemish Plug – reconstruction of firepit and lava lake; Maddygalla feeder dyke – with associated lava flow (black) and tephra deposits (triangles); Killala Gabbro – marginal dolerites enclose 2 units of layered and laminated gabbro; central complexes of Slieve Gullion, Carlingford, and the Mournes.

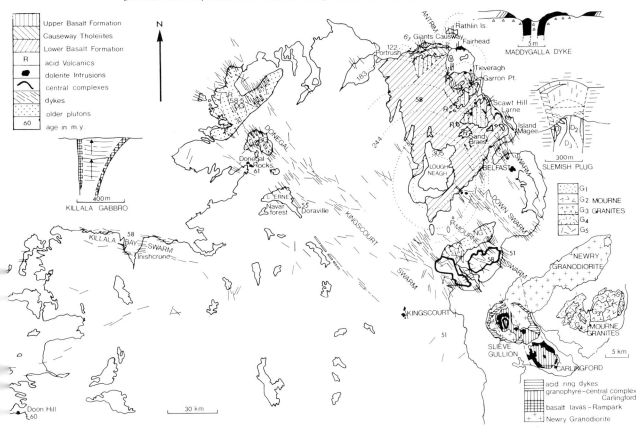

Hebrides and the Atlantic Shelf. G. P. L. Walker accounts for the soda-rich gmelinite zone along the east Antrim coast by seepage of sea-water into the hot pile of basalt lavas.

Subaerial erosion left its mark on this emergent surface. The differentially eroded Chalk, pock-marked by solution hollows 15 m deep, and covered by a patchy residual deposit of 'clay with flints' supported a scant flora. A warm arid climate and a low water table must have resulted in desert conditions over low relief terrain.

Over such a surface quiet effusions of basaltic lava rapidly filled the hollows and buried the landscape.

Sub-aerial volcanism

Tomkeieff, Patterson, and Walker have made the largest contribution to this facet of Tertiary geology.

Lavas are virtually confined to north-eastern Ireland (Fig. 141), though outliers extend almost as far south as the central volcanoes of Slieve Gullion and Carlingford.

Open fissures, trending north-north-west, fed lava fountains and lava flows; locally, as in North Antrim, an initial explosive phase covered the ground with tephra (volcanic ash). Very few examples of feeder and flow are now exposed; the best example, though of minor importance, occurs at Maddygalla on the south-east coast of Rathlin (Fig. 141 inset). Here the associated pyroclastic rocks may be the highly vesiculated product of fountaining lava. Other examples of spatter ramparts around lava fountains may be examined on Island Magee.

Lower Basalt Formation

Feeders such as have been mentioned, now preserved as members of a north-north-westerly (Antrim) linear dyke swarm, must have poured out great floods of primitive olivine tholeiitic basalts to build the lowermost formation of the basalt plateau – the Lower Basalt Formation. This tholeiitic magma, poorer in alkalies and richer in silica than alkali basalt gave rise to even more silica-rich differentiation products. In the vicinity of their source, the lavas were possibly of *pahoehoe* (ropy lava) type. Sequences of thin flows with ropy surfaces are exposed in the cliff sections of Island Magee. Typically, however, the flows are 5–10 m thick with an oxidized and scoriaceous top more characteristic of an *aa* (scoriaceous lava) type. Flows of unusual thickness, such as that at Cave Hill, Belfast, or those with a distinctive petrography may be traced for some 10 km. In general, correlations of flows between exposures are difficult to make and recourse must be made to their palaeomagnetic properties.

R. L. Wilson's contribution to the stratigraphy of the Antrim lava pile is of the greatest value and must, eventually, be extended in its scope. Groups of flows extruded at short time intervals have the same palaeomagnetic declination and dip and can be traced round the edge of the Garron Plateau. Flow group succeeds flow group after a longer interval during which time any flows extruded inherited a palaeomagnetic field unrelated to the groups above or below. Rates of eruption at recent volcanoes and the secular variation of the earth's magnetic field point to interflow intervals of 100–200 years for each group and intergroup intervals of 10,000–20,000 years.

No single set of fissures could have built the whole plateau; each set must have erupted a lens-shaped pile of flows along its length. Other fissures would have extended the plateau laterally with only an occasional flow overlapping the first group until, at a much later date, a new group directly succeeded the first to initiate a new level.

Many basalt plateaux develop a synclinal structure above the fissure system. In Antrim, subsidence of this nature is centred over Lough Neagh, a sedimentary basin since Carboniferous times, where the Lower Basalt Formation reaches its maximum thickness of 531 m (Fig. 141). Aeromagnetic maps indicate an extension of the County Down dyke swarm into this area, but surface exposure is poor and lava may have streamed into the Lough Neagh depression from fissure and conduit feeders in the Antrim dyke swarm.

Fountaining lava would produce large volumes of wind-borne, oxidized, basaltic tephra; vesicular lava fragments, glass shards, Pele's hair (natural glass wool) would drift downwind to cover the neighbouring lava surfaces with 'red bole' and filter into every open joint and cavity. Glassy dusts of this kind would have readily hydrated and leached to form clayey soils and yet remained in sharp contact with the oxidized top of a flow which they appear to replace by veining.

Very little crystallization modified the rising magma. Olivine, and to a lesser extent plagioclase, are the commonest phenocrystal phases and removal of early formed olivine was the principal control of differentiation. Olivine-rich rocks are found in volcanic plugs and among the flows; the complementary fractions appeared as mugearites and quartz trachytes towards the close of this first eruptive phase. The basalts themselves show considerable variation in Figure 143.

Interbasaltic Formation

The first cycle of magmatic activity must have established one or more central volcanoes. Certainly the long period of quietude which followed was interrupted, locally, by effusions of more fractionated lavas.

In Antrim, the Causeway Tholeiites (Middle Lavas) rest on an eroded and *in situ* weathered surface of earlier flows. Similar lateritic soils isolate them from the succeeding cycle of activity. Seven, possibly nine, very thick flows (up to 30 m) are still preserved and can be traced from Portrush to Ballycastle and as far north as Rathlin (Fig. 141). The 3-tiered, columnar structure so beautifully displayed at the Giant's Causeway (Figs 142 and 191), is characteristic of deep ponded lava, and some topographical feature, other than the river valley buried under the first flow, must have contained the lava streams. The source of the Causeway Tholeiites is hidden; a few dykes of the same quartz tholeiitic composition traverse the Causeway cliffs as apparent members of the linear swarm but the mineralogy and petrochemistry (Figs 143 and 144) indicate either a lower pressure fractionation process in some high-level magma chamber or decompression melting of depleted mantle. If a central volcano existed then ponding may have occurred be-

Fig. 142. The Interbasaltic Formation in cliff section at Port Moon and Dunseverick, east of Benbane Head, County Antrim. In the foreground the first two flows of the Causeway Tholeiite Member are exposed in precipitous cliffs above the thinner and darker coloured flows of the Lower Basalt Formation. Scree covers the interbasaltic laterite and lithomarge (Port na Spaniagh Member) between. The three-tiered structure of the first tholeiitic basalt is clearly visible. A southerly dip brings in higher flows towards Dunseverick.
Aerofilms photograph

tween its flanks and the slopes of a highland ridge to the south; if fissures tapped a deeper source then copious floods of lava ensued.

In mid-Antrim some 60 m of rhyolite, obsidian, and volcanic tuffs at Sandy Braes show a slight doming around a central vent filled with welded tuffs. Many other outcrops of rhyolite, quartz porphyry, and acid tuffs, some now entirely altered to bauxite, occur at isolated localities farther afield (Fig. 141) and may be related at depth to some common intrusive complex.

Weathering under a sub-tropical climate rotted the plateau surface to a depth of 15 m. A little of this laterite and the vegetative cover above were reworked into stream deposits. The time involved is open to speculation. All the lavas of Lower and Upper Formations show reversed magnetization and unless the Interbasaltic Formation hides a normal magnetic epoch its duration must have been relatively short.

Upper Basalt Formation

A second cycle of fissure eruptions flooded the area anew; the parental magma to the Upper Basalt Formation was of more primitive composition, poorer in incompatible elements than that of the first cycle, and possibly derived from a deeper source (Fig. 144). Lyle's Ni–MgO variation diagram (Fig. 143) shows two well-defined groups of flows less affected by processes of differentiation than the earlier lavas.

At least one of the first olivine tholeiitic basalt flows chilled under water ponded on the lateritic soils, for

above Milltown on the Garron Plateau the Inter-basaltic laterite is succeeded by a pillow lava/hyaloclastite (fragmented basaltic glass) deposit 5 m thick.

Olivine and possibly plagioclase fractionation again controlled the differentiation process, but the late magmatic fractions have long since been eroded from the top of the volcanic pile. The successive flows are mostly of *aa* type, somewhat thicker and so more viscous than those of the Lower Basalt Formation. Fewer red boles occur between the flows. On Agnew's Hill, West of Larne, one bright red bole marks a change from dark-coloured, coarse-grained olivine basalts to lighter-coloured, finer-grained, olivine porphyritic and even picritic basalts above. This group can be traced north to the Garron Plateau and Trostan where conspicuous flow-banding, in convolute style, is a common feature.

Volcanic feeders

The elongate, almost dyke-like, plugs of Trosk, Craigcluggan, and Slemish are possible feeders to the final group of the Upper Basalt Formation; the last-named example is now filled with rocks which formed close to the contemporary Tertiary surface. Well-oxidized and gas-drilled masses of older lava are preserved in a fossil lava lake whose circulation system is still defined by the pattern of xenolithic crusts. Such a pool could exist at depth within a fire pit. Walker's independent estimate of 300–600 m eroded from the Upper Basalt Formation is not in conflict with this picture.

Other plugs lack the chilled selvedge of simple intrusions. Tilley's now classical interpretation of the Scawt Hill plug can be restated for dolerite-limestone contacts at Carneal and Ballycraigy in Antrim, for the Blind Rock and Doonan Rocks in County Donegal, and for the Inishcrone Gabbro at Killala Bay.

Where 'hydrostatic' pressure failed to lift magma to the surface or where a standing column of magma

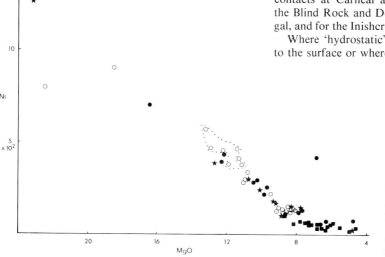

Fig. 143

Ni-MgO diagram for the Antrim basalts after Lyle (personal communication). Solid circles – Lower Basalt Formation. Squares-Causeway Theoleiites. Open circles – Upper Basalt Formation, uppermost chrysophyric group enclosed by dotted line. Stars – dykes and plugs. Compositional variation indicates olivine fractionation.

leaked away through the conduit wall, olivine dolerite sills invaded the sedimentary basins as at Scrabo, Fairhead (Fig. 145), or Portrush.

The Fairhead Sill also demonstrates the controlling fractionation process. Glomeroporphyritic olivines often encased in plagioclase crystals accumulated near the base of the intrusion whereas olivine-free gabbro pegmatite abounds as veins, lenses, and schliers under the porcellanized roof of Carboniferous shale.

Farther west in Ireland only the possible feeders of surface eruptions remain. Plugs, dykes, and a few sills mark the track of the Kingscourt–Donegal linear swarm across the Old Red Sandstone and Carboniferous rocks of Fermanagh. Many of the intrusions indicate a repeated use of the same conduit or fissure. The Doraville Dyke has its olivine-rich, flow-banded margins scoured by later pulses; columnar growths of olivine and plagioclase line other internal contacts. In the Doonan Rocks intrusion, delicate dendrites of pyroxene, some 0·2 m long, grew in quiescent, supercooled magma from a later pulse. At Navar Forest, multiple dykes follow an anastomosing system of fractures; phreato-magmatic explosions shattered the thin septa of country rock and choked the rising magma with sandstone xenoliths. Phreatic activity in the porous, water-bearing sediments oxidized the primitive melt and accentuated the trend to tholeiitic compositions.

Killala Gabbro

Around Killala Bay a more complex suite of igneous rocks invaded the Carboniferous sediments along east-west trending fissures. A giant gabbro dyke, over 400 m wide and of funnel-shaped cross-section, contains within steeply flow-banded dolerite margins a core of laminated gabbros and anorthosites which by their trace element variation exhibit two cycles of layering (Fig. 146). The differentiation process culminated in an alkali facies, preserved as an aegerine, arfvedsonite, reibeckite, alkali feldspar, and quartz assemblage lining the cavities of an unusual drusy monzodiorite. Across Killala Bay the gabbro frays out into several feeder dykes. A later basic swarm of flash injections can be traced for 60–70 km along this North Mayo–Sligo coast.

Central volcanoes

Whether or not the intrusions already referred to brought lava to the land surface remains uncertain. Some evidence, however, points to the establishment of centralised activity. A high-level magma chamber appears essential to the growth of an intrusive complex and elsewhere in the British Isles these were sited at depths of 4–5 km below the present surface. Older granite plutons make an ideal site for crustal magma reservoirs and the Kingscourt–Donegal dyke swarm increases markedly in its intensity as it crosses the Donegal and Barnesmore Granites and the Newry Granodiorite (Fig. 141).

There are many local examples where the country rock is partially or completely melted against a Tertiary intrusion. This occurred most readily where rock of a minimum melting composition was completely engulfed in basic magma. Rafts of feldspathic Triassic sandstone were partially melted to tridymite quartzite in the Scrabo Sill or between parts of the bifurcating Waterfoot Dyke. In both examples the same rock at an external contact is barely metamorphosed. At Tieveragh, Old Red Sandstone arkose is now a vitric buchite in consequence of total fusion against the magma column. At the limiting depth where magma can survive cooling between successive injections, such rock types would readily melt in the

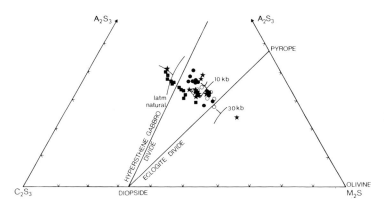

Fig. 144

Antrim basalts plotted in CMAS tetrahedron of O'Hara (projection from MS onto plane C_2S-A_2S_3-M_2S after Lyle (personal communication). Symbols as for Figure 143. Causeway Tholeiite plots close to 1 atmos. cotectic in natural system.

narrow septa between dykes. A spongy network of acid, basic, and hybrid magma would gradually coalesce into a larger volume where further melting would corrode the roof or the undersides of subsiding blocks.

The Donegal Granite is too shallow a pluton to support such a centre, though melting at dyke contacts occurs on a small scale. The Barnesmore

Granite, on geophysical evidence, extends to a depth of 4 km and here a few acid dykes accompany the basic swarm, their flow structures pointing to a source directly below. The Newry Granodiorite is apparently subjacent and its south-western end co-incides almost exactly with the ring fault which bounds an intrusive complex.

Fig. 145. The Fairhead sill (viewed from the north-west), a rudely columnar jointed dolerite intrusion, crops out in 1.9 km of unbroken precipitious cliff around Benmore or Fair Head (194 m O.D.). Westwards the main sill fingers out into Carboniferous sandstones at Farra-gandhu (foreground). Scree covers most of the underlying Carboniferous strata – volcanic tuffs and basalt lavas. Lough Doo and Lough na Cranagh fill glacially eroded hollows in the roof zone of the sill; north-south lineations on the dip slope mark small faults. Beyond the headland a small slipped mass of the dolerite forms Drumnakill Point. Cretaceous chalk resting on Triassic and Dalradian rocks overlooks the slipped ground above Murlough Bay.

Aerofilms photograph

Slieve Gullian Volcano

The Slieve Gullion complex was probably a large shield volcano with a summit caldera similar to that of Mull. The earliest intrusion of porphyritic felsite followed the southern perimeter of the caldera, its mineralogy and texture the consequence of explosive degassing as vents were drilled through the overburden. Fragments of Newry Granodiorite and Silurian slates fill these vents which here and there contain isolated masses of basalt and trachyte, the only remnants of the shield itself.

A later porphyritic granophyre invaded the same ring fault around the northern and eastern sectors and congealed under a more impervious roof, a sequence of events noted by Richey for the Ardnamurchan volcano.

The Central Complex postdates the two ring-dykes. Reynolds' 'actualistic interpretation' is one of successive flows, pillow lavas, tuffs and agglomerates burying the caldera floor. The acid rocks were derived from the older pluton, and a ramifying network of acid veins of similar origin penetrated the volcanic pile as incandescent tuffs, and no doubt helped to recrystallise it into rocks of gabbroic and granophyric aspect. Bailey and McCallien regarded the Complex

as essentially intrusive, a relationship borne out by recent subsurface exploration. The peripheral Lislea Granophyre is probably ring-dyke in form and may well have been continuous with the higher level acid layers of the Complex. It appears to post-date a 'layered' sequence of granophyre and gabbro (the successive flows of Reynolds) whose contacts represent every gradation from liquid-liquid to liquid-solid conditions. The chilled basic magma was repeatedly disrupted by violent degassing of the mobile acid melt.

Carlingford Volcano

The intense intrusive activity within the Slieve Gullion caldera eventually migrated along the linear fissure system, breaching the bounding ring-dyke at Anglesey Mountain and Clermont Carn and establishing another intrusive centre at Carlingford. Le Bas' recent studies detail the subsequent activity which may well have overlapped in time with that of Slieve Gullion.

Carboniferous limestones, domed by volcanic pressures over a Silurian basement, are covered at Rampark by 100 m of basalt with intercalated hawaiite flows. Early alkali gabbro plugs penetrate this fragment of the volcanic superstructure and a later gabbro lopolith or possibly the laccolithic top of a ring-dyke,

Fig. 146. Trace element data for the Killala giant dyke (supplied by ASARCO) plotted against depth in Borehole 6 as measured along the length of the inclined hole. Cu and Ni contents, apart from high concentration in the contact zone, decrease with height through the lower gabbros and succeeding monzonitic rocks; above 94 m high values are again seen in the gabbros of a succeeding layered series.

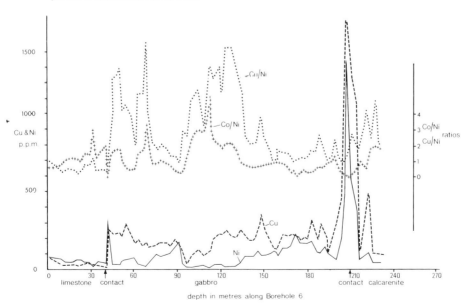

fed by four pulses of magma, exploited the basalt-Silurian uncomformity. Cryptic layering modified each pulse of high-alumina basaltic magma. Explosive vents at Slievenaglogh contain fragments of an early granophyre; a later granophyre, a ring-dyke with a laccolithic top, crystallised under increasing water-vapour pressure until a reduction in gas tension allowed a more rapid solidification. High pressures below the complex drove magma up swarms of cone-sheet, radial dyke, and linear dyke fractures.

Mourne Granites

A high gravity anomaly underlies the Slieve Gullion and Carlingford centres and extends eastwards into Mourne Country where the deepest level of intrusive activity is now exposed. No new surface features of volcanism have been found. Basic xenoliths of cumulate gabbros in early dykes support the geophysical evidence for a large mass of basic rock at depth. Richey and Emeleus have given us the structural picture of the five Mourne Granites emplaced by repeated and asymmetrical subsidence on outward dipping ring faults. The Silurian roof to the laccolithic tops of these ring-dykes remained unbroken. Slight eccentricity among the Eastern Granites (G1, G2, and G3) foreshadowed a westerly migration of the centre of subsidence when the Western Granites (G4 and G5) were intruded. Drilling in G3 has since revealed a subsurface contact with a sixth granitic member of this ring complex.

The origin of the acid melt remains one of the outstanding problems of Tertiary igneous activity. It is difficult to envisage a complete absence of crustal melting at a high-level magma chamber. The repeated and often simultaneous appearance of two contrasting magmas, the one basaltic and the other granitic in composition, has prompted the view that the first is parental and mantle-derived whereas the second is a product of complete or partial melting (anatexis) of crustal rocks.

Some aphyric rocks do occur in the suites of hypabyssal intrusions at Carlingford and the Mournes which are intermediate in composition and lend some credence to the alternative hypothesis of fractional crystallisation.

Meigan and Gamble have now determined major and trace elements for these Tertiary intermediate and acid rocks of Ireland and the results (Fig. 147) make a convincing case for fractionation. Among the Mourne Granites and Antrim Rhyolites occur rocks which are greatly enriched in rubidium and depleted in strontium and barium. The trend of differentiation is almost continuous from basic compositions, and the relative volumes of parental and late fractionates are not in conflict with the theoretical estimates. Possibly the two processes go hand in hand, and given time to equilibrate with basic magma, an anatexic melt itself fractionates and becomes indistinguishable from its entirely fractionated counterpart.

Waning stages

The central volcanoes probably outlived the fissure eruptions (see age dates on Figure 141) but for a long period following their extinction hot plumes of groundwater must have broken the surface above most intrusions as hot springs and geysers. The high thermal gradient allowed groundwater to leach the volcanic rocks, preferentially attacking olivine, plagioclase, and any glass. The leached material was redeposited in all rock cavities as zeolite, clay mineral, serpentine, carbonate, or silica. According to Walker this assemblage of amygdaloidal minerals reflects the temperature zoning of the volcanic pile, the hydrothermal process post-dating the tilting and fracturing of the rocks as the crust readjusted itself to the added burden of volcanic material. Sporadic outbursts of volcanism probably persisted into late Tertiary times.

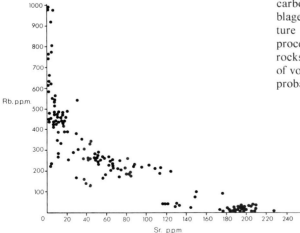

Fig. 147

Rb-Sr variation diagram for ring dyke and central complex rocks of Slieve Gullion, Mourne Granites, and Antrim Rhyolites, after Meighan and Gamble (personal communication).

BIBLIOGRAPHY

BAILEY, E. B. & McCALLIEN, W. J.   1956   Composite minor intrusions, and the Slieve Gullion Complex, Ireland. *Lpool Manchr Geol. J.*, **1**, 466–501.

CAMERON, I. B. & SABINE, P. A.   1969   The Tertiary welded-tuff vent agglomerate and associated rocks at Sandy Braes, Co. Antrim. *Rep. Inst. Geol. Sci.* No. **69/6**, pp. 15.

ELWELL, R. W. D.   1958   Granophyre and hybrid pipes in a dolerite layer of Slieve Gullion. *J. Geol.*, **66**, 57–71.

EMELEUS, C. H.   1955   The granites of the Western Mourne Mountains, County Down. *Scient. Proc. R. Dubl. Soc.*, *N. S.*, **27**, 35–50.

EMELEUS, C. H.   1962   The Porphyritic Felsite of the Tertiary Ring Complex of Slieve Gullion, Co. Armagh. *Proc. R. Ir. Acad.*, **62B**, 55–76.

GAMBLE, J. A., OLD, R. A., & PRESTON, J.   1976   Subsurface exploration in the Tertiary Central Complex of gabbro and granophyre at Slieve Gullion, Co. Armagh, Northern Ireland. *Rep. Inst. Geol. Sci.* No. **76/8**, pp. 17.

LE BAS, M. J.   1960   The Petrology of the Layered Basic Rocks of the Carlingford Complex, Co. Louth. *Trans. R. Soc. Edinb.*, **64**, 169–200.

LE BAS, M. J.   1967   On the origin of the Tertiary granophyres of the Carlingford Complex, Ireland. *Proc. R. Ir. Acad.*, **65B**, 325–338.

MACINTYRE, R. M., McMENAMIN, T., & PRESTON, J.   1975   K-Ar results from Western Ireland and their bearing on the timing and siting of Thulean magmatism. *Scott. J. Geol.*, **11**, 227–249.

MEIGHAN, I. G.   1979   The acid igneous rocks of the British Tertiary Province. *Bull. geol. Surv. Gt. Br.*, **70**, 10–22.

OLD, R. A.   1975   The age and field relationships of the Tardree Tertiary Rhyolite Complex, County Antrim, Northern Ireland. *Bull. geol. Surv. Gt. Br.*, **51**, 21–40.

PATTERSON, E. M.   1957   The Tertiary dolerite plugs of north-east Ireland. A survey of their geology and geochemistry. *Trans. R. Soc. Edinb.*, **63**, 317–331.

PRESTON, J.   1963   The dolerite plug at Slemish, Co. Antrim, Ireland. *Lpool Manchr geol. J.*, **3**, 301–314.

PRESTON, J.   1967   A Tertiary feeder dyke in County Fermanagh, Northern Ireland. *Scient. Proc. R. Dubl. Soc. Ser. A*, **3**, 1–16.

REYNOLDS, D. L.   1951   The geology of Slieve Gullion, Foughill, and Carrickarnan: an Actualistic Interpretation of a Tertiary gabbro-granophyre complex. *Trans. R. Soc. Edinb.*, **62**, 85–143.

TILLEY, C. E. & HARWOOD, H. F.   1931   The dolerite-chalk contact of Scawt Hill, Co. Antrim. The production of basic alkali-rocks by the assimilation of limestone by basaltic magma. *Mineralog. Mag.*, **22**, 439–468.

TOMKEIEFF, S. I.   1940   The basalt lavas of the Giant's Causeway district of Northern Ireland. *Bull. volcan. Ser. 2*, **6**, 89–143.

TOMKEIEFF, S. I. & MARSHALL, C. E.   1935   The Mourne dyke swarm. *Q. Jl. geol. Soc. Lond.*, **91**, 251–292.

WALKER, G. P. L.   1959   Some observations on the Antrim basalts and associated dolerite intrusions. *Proc. Geol. Ass.*, **70**, 179–205.

14

GEOPHYSICAL EVIDENCE

T. Murphy

Geologically Ireland is often considered to be part of a single block along with Scotland, England, and Wales, separated by a shallow sea from continental Europe. The geophysical evidence, however, indicates that it must be considered a distinct unit with perhaps only a few links.

This separateness is well brought out from a study of earthquakes. It is quite remarkable that, although instrument recordings go back nearly one hundred years, very few earthquake epicentres have been detected in the country or on the adjacent continental shelf. This is in strong contrast to Great Britain where earthquakes are frequently recorded. A few cause physical damage while many more are detected by seismometers.

The most recent earthquake felt in Ireland occurred at 0357 on December 26th, 1979, the epicentre being near Carlisle. The magnitude was about 5 and it was felt in County Down and County Antrim.

This absence of seismic activity indicates that Ireland and the adjacent shelf act as a stable block and no further movement of much consequence is taking place along the major faults.

Explosion seismology, in which the seismic wave pattern from timed explosions is recorded at various locations and the results analysed, is at a preliminary stage in Ireland, so that very simple models only can at present be constructed. It seems that the crust under Ireland is 25–30 km thick and the velocity of seismic waves within it fairly constant at about 6·3 km per second. There is a hint that a layer 5 km thick with a lower velocity occurs at a depth of 10 km. This has been interpreted as a primordial granite layer overlain by a metasedimentary layer.

At a depth of about 30 km the seismic velocity shows a marked increase of about 15 per cent. This is brought about by a change either in chemical composition or phase of the rocks and has been taken as

representing the crust-mantle boundary of the earth. Insufficient seismic experimental work has yet been carried out to ascertain whether this boundary is at a constant depth throughout Ireland and the adjacent seas.

This relatively simple picture of the deep structural setting of Ireland on a global scale is borne out by the results of a gravity survey illustrated in Figure 148. This contoured map of the Bouguer Anomaly represents the departure of the measured gravity at sea level from a theoretical value based on the shape of the earth derived from geodetic measurements. The range of the anomaly is from −25 to +70 mGal with the mean areal value close to zero, which indicates that this part of the world is in isostatic equilibrium and hence there is no great tendency for the country to rise or sink vis-à-vis sea level.

The variations in gravity shown on Figure 148 are caused by variations in density of parts of the crust at varying depth but mainly within 10 km of the surface; below this level the density of the crust tends to uniformity.

The outstanding features are: first, the general alignment of the contours in a north-east to south-west direction and, secondly, the location of high values near the coast. When compared with the geological map of Figure 2, certain correlations are immediately apparent such as the coincidence of low values over the granite areas of Connemara, Donegal, Leinster, and Down and over the Mesozoic basins in the north, and the high value over the Tertiary volcanic centre under the Carlingford peninsula.

The granite bodies mentioned have fairly uniform densities of about 2,650 kg per metre cube while the mean value for the surface rocks of Ireland is estimated to be 2,725. Although there seems no doubt about this correlation of low gravity areas with granite bodies, the mapped geological boundaries are

225

only partly in agreement with the gravity pattern. Thus the geophysical evidence points to the buried extension south-eastwards of the Connemara granites under the coast of Clare, and the continuation of the Leinster granites south-westwards with a western limit under the Devonian of the Killarney district. The suggestion once put forward that the Connemara and Leinster granites formed a chain separated by an east-west fault is not substantiated, nor is the view that the Newry Granite is connected with the Crossdoney pluton.

Detailed studies of the gravity anomalies over the granites have shown that even the large batholithic type are made up of separate bodies with diameters of the order of 10 km, and that some of the smaller plutons such as Crossdoney and Ardara are more akin to horizontal discs than vertical cylinders.

The Mesozoic basins of the north, with low density infills usually less than 2,300 kg per metre cube, are well defined having in general a north-east to south-west trend.

In Ireland it has been found that rocks of Lower Palaeozoic age and older, with a few exceptions, have densities which can be related fairly simply to the relative proportions of acidic and basic minerals they contain. The extremes are quarzites and granites (2,650) and gabbro (2,800). The Pre-Cambrian, containing great thicknesses of rocks of these types, gives great variations of gravity, particularly over steeply folded formations or where large faults bring

Fig. 148. Gravity anomaly map of Ireland (Bouguer Anomaly).

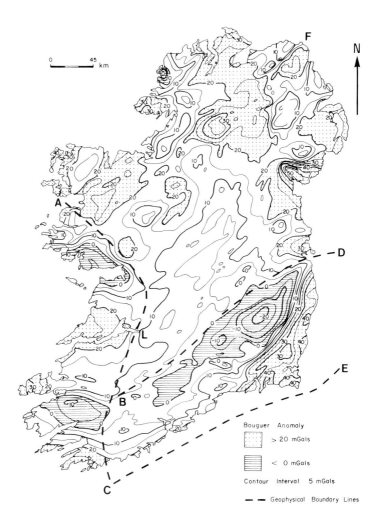

together masses of different densities. This is well seen in the north-west and south-east where the large variations in gravity can be used to delimit various formations and to indicate the lines of large discontinuities, some of which are faults.

The Ordovician, similarly containing basic materials such as pillow lavas as well as acidic extrusives and intrusives, is most probably the main contributor to the marked north-east to south-west pattern over central Ireland. It is thought to have a density greater than the succeeding Silurian, Devonian, and Carboniferous strata and hence where basins of these rocks occur in the Ordovician a relatively lower gravity results. Thus the central plain is thought to consist of a

series of basins and swells within the Ordovician strata which are thinly covered by Silurian and Devonian rocks. It is anticipated that the positions of maximum basin development within the succeeding Carboniferous are largely controlled by the topography of the Ordovician basement structure. This simplification is known to be incomplete in some areas but can be looked on as a fair working hypothesis.

Silurian formations have a more uniform density about 2,730 differing little from the main mass of the Devonian. The Carboniferous containing a high proportion of limestone of density 2,700 is marginally less dense. Within any formation there are minor developments of lighter rocks exemplified by porous

Fig. 149. A magnetic anomaly map of Ireland (after Riddihough).

Magnetic Anomaly

> 100 gamma

< 0 gamma

Contour Interval 50 gamma

sandstones in the Devonian and shales in the Namurian but as these are usually quite thin, less than 300 m, they produce only local effects.

Magnetic survey coverage of the country is incomplete, some parts having been mapped by airborne and others by ground surveys (Fig. 149). The magnetic effect produced by rocks is related almost entirely to their magnetic content and varies from virtually zero in the sedimentary rocks to 2 per cent in the Tertiary intrusive basalts. Locally high concentrations are present in ore bodies and serpentinites, but the metamorphic rocks, although varying considerably, are in general not very magnetic.

The most notable features on the magnetic maps of Ireland are the intense effects due to the Tertiary basalts, and to a lesser extent to the Ordovician and Carboniferous basic volcanics, together with the quite characteristically large areas of low value with negligible magnetic relief associated with the sedimentary basins. Within the basins small changes in the magnetic field are very useful in ascertaining the depth and character of the underlying magnetic basement even though it may be only slightly more magnetic than the overlying sediments.

When combined, gravity and magnetic surveys are of great value for elucidation of the deep structure. Commencing in the north, the picture is somewhat as follows.

In the north the magnetic anomaly pattern is dominated by the effect of the basaltic sheets and when allowance is made for this it is similar to that of gravity. Both have a predominantly north-east to south-west trend but differ in detail as the causes which give rise to the changes in each are not the same. The magnetic map has a well-marked system of narrow north-west to south-east anomalies, mainly negative, produced by Tertiary volcanic dykes north of a line from Dublin to Sligo; but south of this they are very scarce and where they do occur it is with a different alignment. This sharp division of the Tertiary province, also apparent on the adjacent shelf, can be seen in the gravity map, where to the north areas of distinctly low values reflect graben structures filled with Mesozoic sediments absent in the southern part.

In this northern sector attempts have been made at various times to trace the continuation of the known large faults of Scotland, in particular the Highland Boundary Fault. Many well-marked discontinuities lined roughly north-east to south-west are evident on both the magnetic and gravity maps. These could be attributed to large faults but in general they do not coincide with the positions of major faults postulated on geological grounds. These geophysical features do not follow straight lines for any great distance and usually cannot be followed much farther than the Sligo to Dublin line. The largest and a somewhat typical one can be traced on both maps from Fair Head (F) up to the region of Sligo, but thereafter the prominent feature is different on each map.

Over the central part of the country, where the gravity picture exhibits considerable detail, the magnetic map on this scale shows only two large features, both positive and produced by variations in character of the crust at a depth of about 10 km. It would seem that, following the major movements of the Caledonian Orogeny, strike faults remained active permitting basinal structures to develop, and that these continued up to quite recent times.

On the west of the central region the sinuous line ABC (Fig. 148) marks a change of over 45° in the general north-east to south-west trend of the rest of the country. However, it is not persistent and the trend reverts back to its former direction, as can be seen on detailed gravity and magnetic maps of the sea around the Dingle and Iveragh peninsulas. The most marked change takes place from east to west at 'L' near Limerick, the gravity changing from low to high and the magnetic field from high to low.

In the western part of the country a Tertiary dyke system is evident on magnetic maps related to a probable volcanic centre situated at 53°N 11·5°W.

The line BD (Fig. 148) is a boundary line, the gentle basin and swell structure of the midlands dying out south-eastwards as the character of the underlying crust changes, possibly indicating an actual thinning.

The low gravity values west of BC are similar to those south-eastwards of the line BD and earlier it has been pointed out that the cause is probably a granite mass similar to the Leinster Granite. However the positions of the high values are on opposite sides of the lows and hence the possibility that the masses are continuous across the line BC is speculative. South and south-eastwards of the belt of low gravity anomalies and east of BC the trend is distinctly north-east to south-west, with only a mere recognition of the east-west folding of the Hercynian Orogeny so well known in the neighbourhood.

The highest values of gravity occur in the southeast over the Pre-Cambrian, but fall again abruptly on the line CE as the deep Mesozoic graben structures are reached. This latter line marks, for the most part, the position of a large normal fault (Fig. 138).

BIBLIOGRAPHY

DAVISON, C. 1924 *A History of British Earthquakes.* Cambridge University Press, pp. 416.

DUBLIN INSTITUTE ADVANCED STUDIES. 1974 Gravity Anomaly Map of Ireland. *Dubl. Inst. Adv. Stud. Geophys. Bull.*, 32.

GEOL. SURV. NORTHERN IRELAND. 1971 *Magnetic Anomaly map of Northern Ireland.*

MORRIS, P. 1973 Density, Magnetic and Resistivity Measurements on Irish Rocks. *Dubl. Inst. Adv. Stud. Geophys. Bull.*, 31, pp. 48.

YOUNG, D. G. G. 1974 The Donegal granite – a gravity analysis. *Proc. R. Ir. Acad.*, 74B, 63–73.

15

OTHER TERTIARY EVENTS

G. F. Mitchell

G. L. Davies has recently written about *The Enigma of the Irish Tertiary*, a title which in itself says nearly all there is to say. Of the events of the Palaeogene (Palaeocene, Eocene, Oligocene) we have perhaps a few clues; of the Neogene (Miocene, Pliocene) we have perhaps one glimpse.

W. A. Watts has attempted to draw together and evaluate the scrappy and dispersed information that exists about the flora of the Irish Tertiary. The Lower and Upper Basalt Formations of Antrim have already been described as separated by the Interbasaltic Formation (Fig. 142), which can be as much as 30 m in thickness. The Interbasaltic Formation is the result of the decomposition of the top of the Lower Basalt into laterite and bauxite, caused by subaerial weathering, probably under tropical or warm-temperate forested conditions. There are occasional lignites derived from lake-muds and peats which contained tree-stumps and logs. Among the gymnosperms *Pinus* (pine), *Cupressus* (cypress), and *Araucaria* (monkey-puzzle) are present, and there is a wealth of angiosperm leaf-debris, including *Alnus* (alder). Ferns are present, but herbs are poorly represented. Watts suggests a Palaeocene age, but it is perhaps safer not to go beyond Palaeogene. Throughout the Palaeogene there was an extensive Arcto–Tertiary forest flora in quite high latitudes, with much less regional differentiation than exists today, and the trees represented in the Interbasaltic Formation fall into place in this Arcto–Tertiary flora.

Today Lough Neagh lies in a basin of subsidence with faulted margins. In a boring at Washing Bay (for location see Fig. 150, No. 4) the Interbasaltic Formation lies at a depth of 500 m, with 140 m of Upper Basalt Formation resting on it, the top of the basalt having been weathered to a depth of 20 m. The Lough Neagh clays, which are 350 m thick, rest on

the weathered Upper Basalt Formation their sequence being:

0–270 m	Upper Clays and Shales, fossiliferous below 200 m
270–310 m	Middle Shales with plant macro-fossils and fresh-water mollusca
310–350 m	Lower Clays and Sands, with thick lignites.

The flora is very different from that of the Interbasaltic Formation, but must still be Palaeogene in age, as it bears little resemblance to that of the Miocene (Neogene) brown coals of Germany. *Sequoia* (redwood), *Taxodium* (swamp-cypress), *Engelhardtia*, *Eurya*, *Alnus*, *Ilex* (holly), *Nyssa*, '*Tilia*' (lime?), and '*Quercus*' (oak?) all show that the Arcto–Tertiary forests were still persisting.

In the vicinity of Cahir, County Tipperary, there are several deposits of 'pipe-clay'. The deposit at Ballymacadam (Fig. 150, No. 5), which is still sporadically exploited, is the best known. Here a rise in the local Carboniferous Limestone reaches a height of 100 m and has on its western side a hollow filled with residual siliceous clay, which has been proved by borings to a depth of more than 10 m. The clay contains pieces of lignite and has also a high content of pollen at some levels. In places brecciation is apparent; whether this is due to collapse of the deposit to lower levels or to frost action in the Quaternary is not clear. Winged gymnosperm grains and a '*Quercus*'-type predominate, and *Engelhardtia*, *Symplocos*, Ericaceae (heathers), and Palmae (palms) occur sparsely. The flora is of the same general character as that of the Lough Neagh clays, and probably overlaps in time with it.

Still another fossiliferous deposit has recently been

discovered by the Geological Survey at Hollymount (Fig. 150, No. 6), in the valley of the Barrow, north of the town of Carlow. The countryside is of Carboniferous Limestone at a height of about 70 m. The limestone is pierced by solution-pipes, and a boring in such a pipe went to a depth of 75 m in fossiliferous

siliceous clays without reaching solid rock. At some horizons the clays are bright red in colour, and are impregnated with haematite and pyrite; at others they contain pollen, seeds, leaves, and wood. Preliminary examination of the pollen suggests an affinity with the Brassington flora of Derbyshire, which is regarded as

Fig. 150. Diagram to show difference in elevation of the various Tertiary deposits in Ireland. For details see text.

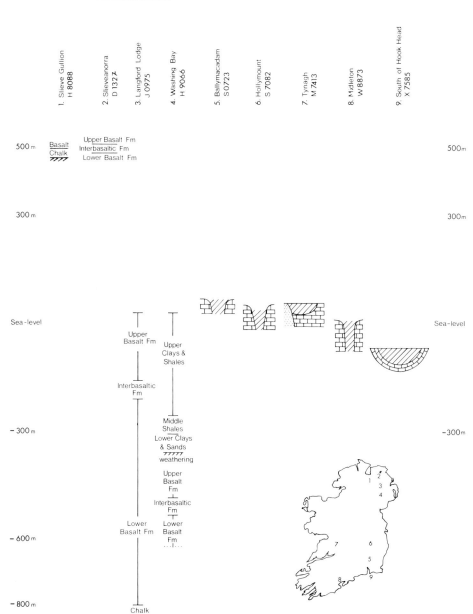

Neogene in age, because pollen-types characteristic of the Neogene are relatively more common than those of the Palaeogene.

As the Tertiary progressed, the two types of *Pinus* pollen, *sylvestris* (the modern Scots pine type) and *haploxylon* (the antique type), changed in their proportions. In the Palaeogene *haploxylon* is dominant; in the early Neogene (Miocene) the two types are about equal in frequency; in the later Neogene (Pliocene) *sylvestris* is dominant. *Symplocos*, now confined to the warmer parts of Asia, Australia, and America, had formerly a much wider range, being common in the Miocene and rare in the Pliocene. At Hollymount *haploxylon* and *Symplocos* pollen occur only sparingly, suggesting that the deposit may be as young as Pliocene. Of evergreen trees *Tsuga* (hemlock), *Sciadopitys*, and *Ilex*, and of deciduous trees *Alnus*, *Betula* (birch), *Carpinus* (hornbeam), *Corylus* (hazel), and *Salix* (willow) appear to have been present. Ericaceous pollen and fern spores were very common. The plant data suggest closed woodland, rich in variety of trees, growing when temperatures were slightly higher and seasonally more uniform than at present.

Our knowledge of the Irish Tertiary flora thus comes from three types of site: horizons of soil formation between lava flows, lake deposits, and fillings of solution hollows. No marine deposits have been examined (though see also Chapter 18). A few other localities should be mentioned. The upper part of the ore deposit at Tynagh, County Galway (Fig. 150, No. 7), is a deeply weathered residual mass which rests on Carboniferous Limestone with a karstic surface. During the excavation of the ore, mineralised wood attributed to *Cupressus* was discovered. The wood and the weathering products in which it was embedded are almost certainly of Tertiary age. Near Midleton in County Cork (Fig. 150, No. 8), solution hollows in Carboniferous Limestone descend to a depth of 100 m, or about 85 m below modern sea-level. Though the clays that fill the hollows are probably Tertiary, they have not yielded any fossils. Geophysical surveys have revealed rocks and structures, thought to be of Tertiary age, at a depth of about 80 m off the Waterford coast (Fig. 150, No. 9) and they are extensive in the Celtic Sea (Fig. 138). Tertiary deposits also lie in several basins which are concealed beneath the waters of the Irish Sea. These offshore areas are treated in Chapter 18.

Much has been written about the evolution of the Irish landscape in Tertiary time, and erosion surfaces, on which the modern river system developed, have been postulated. But, as G. L. Davies has suggested, the remarkable difference in elevation of the various Tertiary deposits in Ireland points to extensive tectonic activity, which has so far not been taken into account by those who have endeavoured to analyse the Irish river system, or who study the 'peneplanes' which seem to be present in the south-east of the country. Figure 150 has been prepared to emphasise this point in a schematic way.

Thus the sub-basaltic Chalk-surface varies in height from +500 m at Slieve Gullion (Fig. 150, No. 1) to −800 m in the Langford Lodge boring (Fig. 150, No. 3), a range of 1300 m. The prominent plant-bearing Interbasaltic Formation varies from +500 m at Slieveanorra (Fig. 150, No. 2) to −500 m in the Washing Bay boring, a range of 1000 m. In the Washing Bay boring the base of the Lough Neagh Clays lies at −350 m, while the deposit of Ballymacadam, which is broadly of the same age or perhaps a little older, lies at a height of +100 m, a range of 450 m.

The deposit at Hollymount, County Laois, which is probably substantially younger in time than that at Ballymacadam, is at a slightly lower level. The Hollymount deposit raises another question, that of the age and origin of the solution-pipes that frequently penetrate the Carboniferous Limestone to considerable depths, especially in the areas from which Namurian shales have been stripped off. Some of the associated solution must be of high antiquity because the deposit of Chalk at +90 m near Killarney (see page 211) lies in a hollow created by the downward collapse of Namurian shales overlying limestone in which solution cavities had developed. It is now clear that such solution-pipes are very much more common than has hitherto been thought. They are very well exposed in the big limestone quarry at Tullyallen, north of Drogheda, where they contain highly weathered unfossiliferous material. They are very common in the Midleton/Cloyne district, east of Cork city, where they contain residual siliceous clays which have been commercially exploited; they appear to extend to a depth of at least −80 m. Solution-pipes also occur in the Shannon Estuary and again go down far below sea-level. It is difficult to see how solution can proceed to such depths, and there must be envisaged either a Tertiary sea-level lower than that of today, or else tectonic movement since the pipes were formed. A pipe in limestone near Ballellin, County Carlow, at +30 m, about 2 km east of the limit of the Leinster Granite, is filled with quartz gravel and micaceous debris, and indicates a drainage pattern very different from that of today.

The deposit at Tynagh (see also page 282) raises a different question, that of the age of the Irish karst which has both an upland and a lowland component. The local limestone must have had a karstic topography before it was mantled with hydrated and oxidised ore, formed under weathering conditions almost certainly very different from those of today. The karstic surface of the Irish midlands, lying between

+60 and +120 m in height, may represent the end-product of a very long period of perhaps 40 million years — back to the opening of the Oligocene — of essentially karstic denudation and the removal of vast quantities of rock.

Estimates suggest that today in Ireland a limestone surface weathers downwards at a rate of 0·053 mm *per annum*. If this rate is projected backwards, it means that the surface would be lowered by over 50 m in one million years. Such a rate of destruction would be quite incompatible with the survival of the deposits at Ballymacadam and Hollymount. Thus possibly: (i) the current rate is higher than average, or (ii) the rate in the Tertiary was lower than average,

or (iii) there has been extensive tectonic movement in the Tertiary.

It is difficult to avoid the conclusion that the evolution of the modern landscape must have been influenced by Tertiary tectonic movements on a considerable scale throughout Ireland. These movements were accompanied, at least from the beginning of the Miocene, by a lowering of temperature, and this brought about the break-up of the warm temperate forests that had girdled the northern hemisphere in high latitudes, forests which to some extent survive as shadows of their former selves in the mountains of eastern North America and of China.

BIBLIOGRAPHY

BOULTER, M. C. 1971 A palynological study of two of the Neogene plant beds in Derbyshire. *Bull. Br. Mus. nat. Hist. (Geol.)*, 19, 359–410.

BOULTER, M. C. 1980 Irish Tertiary plant fossils in a European context. *J. Earth Sci. R. Dubl. Soc.*, 3, 1–11.

CURRY, D., ADAMS, C. G., BOULTER, M. C., DILLEY, F. C., EAMES, F. E., FUNNELL, B. M. & WELLS, M. K. 1978 A correlation of Tertiary rocks in the British Isles. *Geol. Soc. Lond. Spec. Rep.*, 12, pp. 72.

DAVIES, G. L. 1970 The Enigma of the Irish Tertiary. *In* Stephens, N. and Glasscock, R. E. (Eds.). *Irish Geographical Studies.* Queen's Univ. Belfast, Dep. Geogr., 1–16.

MITCHELL, G. F. 1976 *The Irish Landscape.* Collins, London, pp. 240.

MITCHELL, G. F. 1980 The search for Tertiary Ireland. *J. Earth Sci. R. Dubl. Soc.*, 3, 13–33.

WATTS, W. A. 1970 Tertiary and Interglacial Floras in Ireland. *In* Stephens, N. and Glasscock, R. E. (Eds.). *Irish Geographical Studies.* Queen's Univ. Belfast, Dep. Geogr., 17–33.

WILKINSON, G. C., BAZLEY, R. A. B. & BOULTER, M. C. 1980 The geology and palynology of the Oligocene Lough Neagh Clays, Northern Ireland. *Jl. geol. Soc. Lond.*, 137, 65–75.

WILLIAMS, P. W. 1970 Limestone morphology in Ireland. *In* Stephens, N. and Glasscock, R. E. (Eds.). *Irish Geographical Studies.* Queen's Univ. Belfast, Dep. Geogr., 105–124.

16

THE QUATERNARY – UNTIL 10,000 BP

G. F. Mitchell

In 1914 an Irish geologist, W. B. Wright, published his classic textbook, *The Quaternary Ice Age*, and this title sums up in four words the popular conception of the Quaternary – that it lasted for a considerable period, and that it was dominated by ice. Wright's title probably sprang from that of Geikie, *The Great Ice Age*, written at a time when geologists were still intoxicated by the realisation that the ice-polished rock-bosses and striated boulders that could be seen in many parts of north-western Europe were identical with those produced by modern ice in the Alps. The unconsolidated superficial deposits of 'drift', that up to that time had been thought to have been 'drifted' into position by a marine transgression, were now seen to have been deposited by melting ice. Studies of former glacial events thus originated in north-western Europe, and thinking based on what was to be seen in that region dominated Quaternary studies for a long time.

Recently there has been a swing away from the concept that great masses of ice were the chief feature of the Quaternary. The picture is becoming one of a period of cold that had its origin back in the Tertiary. In the Quaternary the cold intensified, but in the main it seems to have been a period of dry cold when freeze-thaw processes – often referred to as periglacial processes – were dominant, interspersed with shorter periods of two other types, in one of which meteorological conditions favoured the formation of ice, and in the other temperatures ameliorated sufficiently to allow woodland to re-establish itself. And thus there is in north-western Europe today the concept of 'cold stages' with frost action, in some of which ice-masses may have formed, alternating with 'warm stages', defined as giving temperatures sufficiently high for closed deciduous woodlands to establish themselves. As there is no reason to think that the climate of today is any more firmly established than that of

previous 'warm stages', here the view will be taken that the current so-called 'Postglacial' or Holocene is merely another 'warm stage', now named in Ireland the Littletonian Warm Stage (see *infra*) which will in all probability be succeeded in due course by yet another 'cold stage'.

Periglacial features

The various cold and warm stages of the Quaternary have left in north-western Europe – and in many other parts of the world – a wealth of features and deposits of glacial (Fig. 151), periglacial (Fig. 152), and temperate origin. In Ireland the features of glacial and temperate origin have been studied with ever-increasing intensity for more than one hundred years, but the study of periglacial features is still in relative infancy. The present moist oceanic climate is familiar and it is difficult to picture Ireland in the dry grip of perennial frost, which would give rise to a cold polar desert landscape.

In order that such a landscape with its periglacial features may develop, mean annual temperatures must be below $0°$ C, but the summer months must be warm enough for some seasonal thawing to take place, and at some times there must be oscillation of temperature backwards and forwards through the freezing-point of water.

With mean annual temperatures below $-5°$ C a layer of permanently frozen subsoil – permafrost – will develop. In Siberia today the permafrost may extend to a depth of 500 m; we do not know to what depth it formed in Ireland, but structures characteristic of it were formed in several cold stages. Marked contraction of the surface layer during the cold of winter caused tapering shrinkage-cracks to develop

Fig. 151

Glacial striae demonstrating approximately north-east to south-west direction of ice movement: locality northeast of Mullagh More. Burren, County Clare

Photograph by M. C. F. Proctor

Fig. 152

Involutions produced by shallow freeze-thaw processes, shore of Smerwick Harbour, Dingle Peninsula, County Kerry.

Photograph by G. F. Mitchell

and these became filled with wedge-shaped tongues of ice; if, when ice later melted, foreign materials filled up the former wedge, then an ice-wedge-cast was produced. In Ireland these are known from Tyrone to Kerry (see Table 14). Sometimes the shrinkage-cracks were arranged in polygonal form (Fig. 153) – just like the shrinkage-cracks in the basalt of the Giant's Causeway – and ice-wedge-polygons, whose patterns can still be traced today, were formed.

Where the grip of permafrost is not quite complete, some slight movement of ground-water may be possible in summer. If the water is concentrated at one point and it freezes in the following winter, then an upwardly expanded lens of ice, with a dome of earth and soil arched over it, will form an ice-mound or pingo (Fig. 154). When thawing begins, the cover of earth and soil slumps down to encircle the decaying ice-mound, so that the final melting of the ice leaves a residual central hollow. Fossil structures of this kind are very common in south-eastern Ireland (see Table 14).

If in summer the surface layers of the frozen ground thaw, while permafrost remains below, then water cannot drain away downwards and the surface layers become supersaturated and highly mobile, forming the so-called 'active layer'. If the slope of the ground exceeds 1°, the surface material will move downslope in an unsorted condition, forming when it eventually comes to rest a deposit of solifluction-earth or 'head'. Such deposits of head are common in Ireland. If the slope is less than 1°, gravity may not be able to draw the material away and, as water changes in density with changes in temperature near its freezing-point, movements analagous to convection-currents appear to develop in the active layer. Sorting takes place and in plan a net-like pattern may appear, with finer material in the interstices of the net and coarser material along the strands. In section irregular columns of stones arranged with their long axes vertical underlie the strands, while below the interstices finer material has the appearance of a basin-fill. Polygonally patterned ground, of origin quite different from that of ice-wedge-polygons, is thus formed. Such patterned ground can be seen from Donegal to Kerry (see Table 14). Less regular currents produce involutions i.e. churn the active layer in an irregular manner, and where the ground does slope slightly the sorted stones may be drawn out into stripes. Both involutions (Fig. 152) and stone-stripes are also common in Ireland.

The expansion and contraction of water near its freezing point is the chief source of kinetic energy – as opposed to the latent pull of gravity – for the creation of these structures and it may well be that the latitudinal position of Ireland enabled the number of freeze-thaw alternations to reach a high level.

Stratigraphy

It must at once be admitted that the complex stratigraphical sequences presented by glacial, periglacial, and temperate features in Ireland are far from being clearly understood and much controversy still surrounds their interpretation. Systematic botanists can be divided into 'lumpers' and 'splitters', and while there are few 'monoglacialists' left, Quaternary geologists can be divided into 'stretchers' and 'shrinkers'. I tend to follow a 'stretched' point of view, but in recent years in Ireland the voices of the 'shrinkers' have been becoming louder. This chapter will endeavour to tell a coherent story, but it must be remembered that other workers might assemble the same data into a very different account.

In terrestrial Quaternary studies the three methods of classical historical geology – lithostratigraphy, biostratigraphy, and chronostratigraphy – are all employed. Unfortunately glacial and periglacial deposits vary rapidly in facies both laterally and vertically and attempts to sort them out by simple studies of lithology and superposition soon run into severe difficulties. For the dating of the events of the past 50,000 years, the span of time over which C^{14} dating is possible, geochronometry has had some success; but beyond this limit – until palaeomagnetic studies are further developed – there are no dating techniques available to be of assistance.

In recent years study of sea-floor deposits has revealed a remarkable record of alternating warmth and cold, and part of the record has been dated by C^{14} and palaeomagnetic determinations. It is clear that great advances can be made if the terrestrial and the marine records can be correlated. But the number of fluctuations suggested by the marine record greatly exceeds the number so far established by terrestrial studies, and this type of correlation will be difficult and attended by controversy. Such correlation will not be attempted here.

On land biostratigraphical methods at first sight appear very promising and have been applied in Ireland to deposits of organic origin interstratified in glacial and periglacial deposits. But as these deposits, which derive in the main from warm rather than cold stages, are studied more closely it becomes clear that in each warm stage the vegetational development ran a rather similar course which can be presented in tabular form (Fig. 155).

If the vegetational cycle had repeated itself exactly in each warm stage, then study of the plant fossils in the organic deposits of a stage could not lead to the pin-pointing of the deposit as belonging to one particular warm stage rather than to any other. Fortunately there were some variations in different warm

Fig. 153

Fossil ice-wedge polygons, probably of Mid-landian age, Broomhill Point, County Wexford.
    Photograph J. K. St Joseph, Cambridge University Collection:

Fig. 154

Fossil pingos, Camaross, County Wexford.
    Photograph J. K. St Joseph, Cambridge University Collection:

stages and so detailed studies may reveal key characteristics by which the particular deposits of each may be identified.

Fossil assemblage zones, of which pollen assemblage zones will be much the most important, will be built up by study of the various deposits and the character and sequence of such zones may have great importance for stratigraphy.

Correlation

Under the auspices of the Geological Society of London an attempt has been made to correlate the deposits of the cold and the warm stages of the Quaternary throughout the British Isles. In East Anglia the complete sequence may be present, ranging from the upper limit of the Pliocene (at the top of the Boytonian horizon of the Coralline Crag) to the current warm stage. In East Anglia seven warm and seven cold stages have been recognised, but in Ireland the record is very much less complete. The last three cold and warm stages have been recognised (see Table 15), but before them there is only one tantalising glimpse.

Some years ago a sand-pit at Killincarrig, County Wicklow, excavated in outwash sands and gravels from relatively young ice that had moved down the basin of the Irish Sea, produced large numbers of Quaternary shells. The ice had presumably picked up a shelly gravel of considerable antiquity from the sea floor and had transported it without major disturbance to this locality, where it had been washed out of the melting ice. The shells were a group of northern forms, including *Neptunea antiqua*, *N. despecta*, and *Trophonopsis clathratus*, which closely resembles the fauna of the Little Oakley horizon of the Waltonian Red Crag, a cold stage at the base of the Quaternary in East Anglia. Thus sea water must have had access to the basin of the Irish Sea at the opening of the Quaternary.

The Gortian Warm Stage

In the Quaternary of Great Britain no site is more famous than the brick-pit at Hoxne in Suffolk. In 1797 its warm stage deposits yielded the first Palaeolithic hand-axes that were generally accepted as the work of man; in 1895 its plant fossils were first investigated by Clement Reid. Its botanical aspects, and in particular its palynology, were worked on by Professor Richard West in 1956, and its archaeological content and its palaeomagnetic record are being studied at present. The fir, *Abies*, is the tree of prime interest at Hoxne, and this is the key tree for the Hoxnian Warm Stage of the British Quaternary.

Over one hundred years ago, in 1865, the distin-

Table 14. Periglacial structures from different stages of the Quaternary in Ireland. The list is not comprehensive, but indicates the wide distribution of such features.

	ICE-WEDGE-CASTS	ICE-WEDGE-POLYGONS	PINGOS	SCREE, HEAD, SOLIFLUCTION-EARTH	POLYGONAL PATTERNS	INVOLUTIONS, ERECTED STONES
IN LATER PART OF MIDLANDIAN	Tyrone C 4817 Dublin O 0621 Wicklow T 1998	Galway M 3917 Wicklow S 9093	Waterford S 5903 Wexford S 8925 Wicklow T 2479 Cork W 9495 Kerry Q 9611	Dublin O 2020 Galway L 7246 Wexford T 0214	Tyrone C 7500	Tyrone C 6402
					Donegal C 3959	Cork W 9985
MIDLANDIAN s.l.	Wexford S 7319	Wexford S 7505 Wexford T 0907		Kerry Q 7714 Fermanagh H 3733 Donegal G 5578	Kerry Q 6811	Kerry Q 7714 Mayo L 7474
MUNSTERIAN	Kerry Q 7714			Kerry Q 7714 Wexford S 9604 D G 5387	Cork W 9966	

guished Irish geologist, George H. Kinahan, described a deposit of peat and mud below till in a stream valley near Gort (Fig. 158) in County Galway; remains of fir, spruce (*Picea*), and other plants not native in Ireland today were recorded. The deposits were re-examined by Professor Knud Jessen and the results of the pollen-studies indicate a vegetational development essentially similar to that at Hoxne and it was generally accepted that the deposits at Hoxne and Gort were formed during the same warm stage. Other Irish deposits which also contain *Abies* pollen and have thus been presumed to belong to the Gortian Warm Stage occur at Kildromin and Baggotstown in County Limerick, Burren and Derrynadivva in County Mayo, Kilbeg and Newtown in County Waterford, Ballykeerogemore in County Wexford, and Benburb in County Tyrone (Fig. 158).

It can be pictured that at the opening of this warm stage vegetation was scanty and sea-level was low. In the central part there were dense woodlands and sea-level was high, probably about 25 m above that of today. As climate worsened at the end of the stage the woodlands deteriorated and sea-level fell back.

At Gort the deposit shows at its base a stratigraphical change from fine sandy clay to muddy clay. In the sandy clay, pollen of herbs and of *Betula* (probably the dwarf form, *B. nana*) are common, indicating the immigration of the pioneer vegetation as the preceding cold stage came to an end. This level is labelled at the right margin of the schematic Gortian diagram (Fig. 156) by the letters IGWA (G= Gortian), meaning that here we have the pre-dawn of the Gortian Warm Stage in Ireland, with woodland still absent.

Below the sandy clay there was a gravel with local stones but without erratics. Beyond the evidence for cold indicated by the plant fossils, Gort provided no evidence for former glaciation. At Kildromin the

organic deposit was underlain first by stone-free laminated unfossiliferous clay, probably a glacial lake clay, and under that a stony clay with non-local stones, which was perhaps a till. At Baggotstown also a stone-free laminated unfossiliferous clay was underlain by a stony clay with erratics, which appeared to be a till. Thus these three sites indicated, admittedly on the evidence of very small samples recovered from the bottom of boreholes, that there had been cold conditions, and almost certainly ice-masses, in Ireland before the Gortian Warm Stage. But until deposits that can document this cold stage more clearly have been examined, no type-site can be designated, and the stage is tentatively described as a pre-Gortian Cold Stage.

Returning to the Gortian diagram (Fig. 156), there is then an upsurge in pollen of *Juniperus* as temperature rises sufficiently to allow this tree to spread widely and flower freely. This is the beginning of the expansion of the woodland and phase IGWB opens the Gortian Warm Period proper. The broad-leaved trees, *Quercus* (oak) and *Alnus* (alder) then appear, followed by *Corylus* (hazel) and *Fraxinus* (ash) and the evergreens, *Ilex* (holly) and *Taxus* (yew), and the climax-woodlands are established in phase IGWC. The climax-woods of this Gortian phase were very different from those of the current warm stage, the Littletonian (see *infra*). In these later woods *Quercus*, *Ulmus* (elm), and *Corylus* had much greater importance, while the role of *Taxus* was very much smaller.

Abies next appears in the diagram and, as it increases in quantity, is joined by *Picea*. Ericaceous pollen, among which that of *Rhododendron* is important, also appears in quantity. These developments follow the trend towards soil acidity, with its resulting encouragement of coniferous woodland and heath, that marks the opening of phase IGWD, when degradation is setting in. *Abies* and *Picea* did not establish

Fig. 155. Successive phases of woodland development in a warm stage. For further explanation see text.

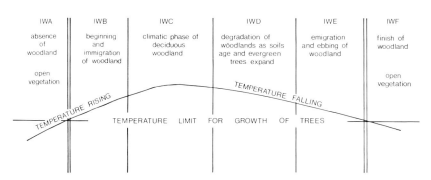

themselves in the Littletonian woodlands in Ireland, although today they are widely planted. *Rhododendron ponticum* is also here today, but only as a result of introduction in the eighteenth century. Once introduced it found ideal conditions on Ireland's acid soils, and has run like wildfire through woods and over upland bogs. It is a classic example of a tree that had a wider distribution in an earlier warm stage, was then driven by cold far back into Europe – it now centres to the south and west of the Black Sea, with a few outlying localities in Spain and Portugal – and has since been prevented by geographical barriers from returning to areas where it formerly grew and can again flourish after introduction by man. These later phases of the Gortian woodlands are not known in modern Ireland and the European woods that most

resemble them today are on the southern slopes of the Caucasus.

At Gort the diagram is truncated in this phase by overlying till. The upper part of the schematic diagram derives from the record at Kilbeg. Most of the trees ebb away, *Pinus* and *Betula* only surviving into phase IGWE, the final boreal phase. At the top *Betula* and *Pinus* disappear, *Juniperus* gets a final opportunity, and grasses and herbs extend. Here in IGWF the Gortian woodlands are finished and the tundras that mark the opening of the following cold stage are establishing themselves.

The vegetation of the Gortian Warm Phase can now be followed in some detail, because about 100 taxa of higher plants have been identified; of these about twenty are not native in Ireland today. The

Table 15. Table showing stages of the later Pleistocene in the British Isles.

BRITISH STAGES	IRISH STAGES	IMPORTANT SITES	NOTES
FLANDRIAN WARM	LITTLETONIAN WARM	Littleton, Tipperary	The record in the peat and underlying muds in a raised-bog at Littleton runs from 12,000 years ago to the present day.
———— 10,000 BP ————			
LATE		Nahanagan, Wicklow	A corrie moraine here records a short stadial or cold phase from 10,500 to 10,000 BP.
		Woodgrange, Down	The lacustrine deposits here record an interstadial or warm phase that lasted from about 14,000 to 10,500 BP.
		Armoy, Antrim Kells, Meath Ballylanders, Limerick	An end-moraine here marks the limit of a late advance of ice from Scotland. An end-moraine here marks the eastern limit of an ice-advance during which drumlins were formed. An end-moraine here probably marks the southern limit of a late advance of ice from the Midlands.
DEVENSIAN COLD - 26,000 BP - MIDDLE	MIDLANDIAN COLD	Derryvree, Fermanagh Castlepook, Cork Hollymount, Fermanagh	Silt with organic remains, resting on till, and covered by till which is moulded in drumlin form, has been dated to 30,500 BP. A femur of Woolly Mammoth (E. primigenius) from a cave here has been dated to 33,500 BP. Silt with organic remains, resting on till, and covered by till which is moulded in drumlin form, is older than 41,500 BP.
- 50,000 BP - EARLY		Hollymount, Fermanagh	The lower till here may be of Early Midlandian age.
———— 70,000 BP ————			
IPSWICHIAN WARM	LAST WARM		no suitable type site yet discovered.
WOLSTONIAN COLD	MUNSTERIAN COLD	Garryvoe, Cork Ballyvoyle, Waterford Ballycroneen, Cork Ballymakegoge, Kerry	Till deposited by ice moving eastwards from west Cork and Kerry rests on Ballycroneen till. Till deposited by ice moving south-eastwards from the Midlands rests on Ballycroneen till. Shelly calcareous till deposited by ice that had advanced down the basin of the Irish Sea has its western limit here. Peats and silts under head record the end of the Gortian woodlands, and the opening of cold stage. The deposits rest on a raised beach (Courtmacsherry Raised Beach).
HOXNIAN COLD	GORTIAN WARM	near Gort, Galway	A thick deposit of mud below till records the development of the Gortian woodlands. The mud passes down into muddy clay, which rests on sandy clay. The plant fossils show that the base of the muddy clay is the base of the warm stage.
ANGLIAN COLD	PRE-GORTIAN COLD	near Gort, Galway	The basal sandy clay belongs to this cold stage.

trees have already been referred to above. The heathers are another important group. These plants are present in a remarkable variety in Ireland today and many of them were also present in the Gortian Warm Stage; in addition two forms, *Erica ciliaris* and *E. scoparia*, were present in the Gortian, but are not here today. Before the Quaternary many plants which are still common in North America also grew in western Europe, including Ireland. The repeated climatic changes of the Quaternary thinned out the American types in Europe. Some present in the Gortian are no longer here; other still survive:

	Present in Gortian	Present today
Brasenia cf. *purpurea*	+	−
Eriocaulon septangulare	+	+
Naias flexilis	+	+
Nymphoides aquaticum	+	−

The final phases of the Gortian Warm Stage and the transition to the following cold conditions, can be seen in a coastal environment and brought into relationship with sea-level near Fenit, on the north shore of Tralee Bay in County Kerry. Here, as along much of the south coast of Ireland, a raised beach rests on a wave-cut rock platform a few metres above modern sea-level; the beach is buried by glacial and periglacial deposits.

This beach was first described by Wright and Muff as long ago as 1904 and its stratigraphical position has been a subject of controversy ever since. At first it was thought that the platform on which it rests was cut almost immediately before the beach was deposited on it, but it now appears that the platform is probably a composite feature of considerable age and that the beach gravels were trapped on its bench-like form at a very much later date. In the south of Ireland the beach is probably late Gortian in age. There is a substantial amount of evidence from England that, at the warmest part of this warm stage, sea-level was about 25 m above its present level. As temperature fell, and water began to be locked up in the growing ice-masses of the oncoming cold stage, not only was the level of the ocean lowered, but the temperature of its surface water also fell. In the vicinity of the British Isles, even before the sea had dropped down as far as its present level, surface waters were cold enough to transport debris-laden ice-floes, which often carried erratic boulders for long distances. Continuing fall in sea-level stranded such boulders among beach deposits on the shore-platform. In Ireland the type-site for this beach is at Courtmacsherry in County Cork.

This Courtmacsherry Raised Beach is well seen on the north shore of Tralee Bay and at Ballymakegoge, near Spa, the cliff-section (Fig. 157) at one point was as follows:

Fig. 156. Schematic pollen diagram to show phases of woodland development in the Gortian Warm Stage.

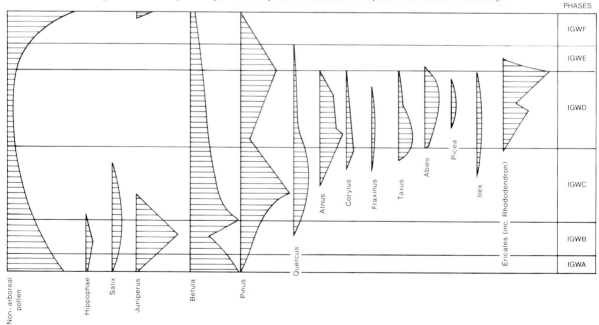

	Depth	Deposit	Description
SUCCEEDING COLD STAGE OR STAGES	0– 30 cm	*modern soil*	
	30–200 cm	*upper head*	Sand with angular shale fragments, also sandstone and silicified limestone; strongly cryoturbated with pockets of coarser shale descending to 175 cm.
	200–240 cm	*deposit with 'foreign erratics'*	Horizon of red sandstone boulders (many striated) up to 100 cm long.
	240–390 cm	*lower head*	Stratified loamy sand with angular shale fragments up to 10 cm, and also rounded sandstone pebbles up to 10 cm; penetrated by grey-stained cracks to 350 cm.
	390–410 cm		Finer layer rich in silt
	410–450 cm		as before
	450–467 cm	*peat-mud*	Laminated fine-grey peat-mud with some content of sand, interrupted by pale layers richer in sand and silt; the pollen-content suggested formation in phase IGWF.
	467–475 cm	*silt*	Grey stone-free sandy silt
	475–540 cm	*lower head*	Sand packed with small stones
	540–550 cm	*peaty silt*	Sandy silt with lenses of peat; the pollen-content suggested formation in phase IGWF.
	550–567 cm	*silt*	Silt with a content of pollen appropriate to phase IGWD
	567–570 cm	*peat-mud*	Peat-mud; the pollen-content suggested formation in phase IGWF.
GORTIAN WARM STAGE	570–605 cm	*peaty silt*	Silt with vegetable debris with a content of pollen appropriate to phase IGWD
	605–630 cm	*peat-mud*	Peat-mud; the pollen-content suggested formation in phase IGWE.
	630–650 cm	*silt-mud*	Brackish silt-mud, with macrofossils of *Chenopodiaceae*, *Triglochin maritima*, and sea-weed; pollen of *Plantago*, probably *maritima*; the general pollen-content suggested formation in phase IGWE.
	650–680 cm	*sand*	Sand, probably a beach sand, with small shale fragments at base (Courtmacsherry Raised Beach).
	at 680 cm	*shore-platform*	The surface of the shore-platform was at about mean sea-level

As the late Gortian sea dropped down to and below modern sea-level, beach-ridges of Courtmacsherry age were abandoned on the shore-platform and dune-slacks formed between the ridges. Peats and muds accumulated in the slacks, first a brackish silt-mud and then a freshwater peat-mud, both with a pollen content that indicates formation in phase IGWE. Frost-action then began to affect the soils on the slopes above the shore and peaty silt containing pollen from an earlier Gortian phase (IGWD, with *Abies* and *Rhododendron*) moved down the slope as a solifluction-earth. The deposits above this level had no pollen of juniper or pine, while sedge pollen had increased very considerably. Here the Gortian woodlands have finally disappeared and in phase IGWF, the succeeding cold stage, has begun. In Figure 157, illustrating this section, a 'golden spike' is shown at the transition. Sea-level continued to fall, and the organic deposits and early solifluction-flows were buried beneath massive deposits of head. At one stage the head deposits must have become anchored by permafrost, as they are penetrated at one horizon by intra-formational ice-wedge casts. The deposit at 200–240 cm was formerly thought to have been emplaced by primary deposition from ice of Munsterian age. But re-examination of the section suggests that it too has been moved by solifluction, and the emplacement of all the material above 390 cm could have taken place in one cold stage. Thus the lower head need not necessarily be of Munsterian age.

The Munsterian Cold Stage

In the Munsterian Cold Stage most of Ireland seems to have been buried by ice at one time or another, though some high ground in the south and west may have escaped being overridden (Fig. 158). Ice evidently first formed in the Midlands, because the stratigraphically lowest – and therefore perhaps the earliest – glacial deposit of this stage appears to be a till of inland Irish origin near Drogheda, whose erratics, fabric, and striae indicate movement from the west and north-west.

An immense ice-mass then formed in Scotland, and, as far as Ireland is concerned, it may have had a south-westerly component and certainly had a southerly component. At places in north-western Ireland, in both Donegal and Mayo, there is an early shelly till which may well have been deposited from ice that had its origin in Scotland; it was recorded long ago at Belderg in Mayo, and a Belderg Lobe is shown on the map (Fig. 158).

The southerly component poured down the basin of the Irish Sea, transporting as it went erratics of the microgranite of which Ailsa Craig is built up and large quantities of shelly calcareous mud from the sea-floor. It thrust south-eastwards deep into the Cheshire lowlands and beyond, and eastwards into the Bristol Channel, almost as far as Bristol itself. It continued along the face of the high cliffs of Devon and Cornwall and came to a halt against the northern members of the Scilly Islands group. On the Irish side of the basin the Scottish ice pushed westwards across the low coasts near Drogheda, Dublin, and Arklow.

It overrode the Carnsore promontory and continued along coastal Waterford and Cork as far as Ballycroneen Bay, just east of Cork Harbour, where the Ballycroneen Lobe of its shelly calcareous till has its western limit. Francis Synge would see the Ballycroneen Lobe as a floating ice-shelf of younger age. But floating ice-shelves cannot collect material from the underlying sea-bed, and such a suggestion will not explain how the till of the Ballycroneen Lobe at its western extremity (and particularly on the shores of Ballycotton Bay) is crammed with chalk and greensand which must have been collected from the chalk now known to lie a short distance offshore.

The main Munsterian ice-mass will have produced an immense isostatic depression of the earth's crust beneath it, so much so that, although sea-level had fallen considerably below its present level, an arctic fiord would have occupied the basin of the Irish Sea in front of the advancing ice. Near Drogheda, and now at a height of 35 m above sea-level, there is a series of glacio-marine deposits ranging from clays to bedded gravels and containing a cold-water marine fauna. These deposits, which are buried by the shelly calcareous till deposited by the advancing Scottish ice, contain ice-rafted erratics and give a clear demonstration that ice-rafting of blocks of rock did take place in the Irish Sea basin.

Ice of Irish origin then became more important. It is not known when this ice first formed, but it now invaded areas that had formerly been occupied by the Scottish ice. The Irish ice-centre was perhaps in the mountains of Connemara, because Galway granite was carried southwards, as far as Kerry and Cork, and Blacksod granite was carried north-

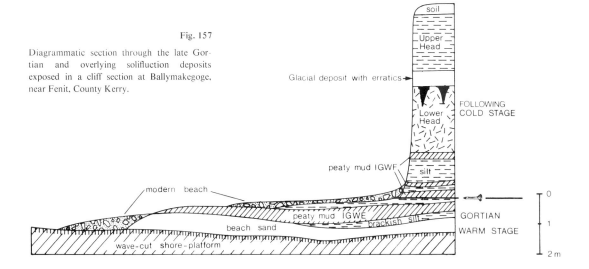

Fig. 157

Diagrammatic section through the late Gortian and overlying solifluction deposits exposed in a cliff section at Ballymakegoge, near Fenit, County Kerry.

westwards across the islands of Mayo by an Inishkea Lobe. To the south the ice reached the Dingle peninsula, depositing quantities of limestone debris and occasional boulders of Galway granite against its northern slopes. This was recorded over a hundred years ago by the Rev. A. B. Rowan and we may speak of a Finglas Lobe. The ice entered Smerwick Harbour and may have reached its southern limit in the sound between the Great Blasket and the mainland. To the south-south-east a lobe of the radiating ice reached as far as Midleton in County Cork, big gravel deposits north of the town at Knockakeen and elsewhere containing not only volcanic rocks from the Limerick area, but also occasional erratics of

Galway granite. Farther to the east a lobe pushed between the Galty Mountains and the Comeraghs and then expanded southwards down Waterford Harbour in a Ballyvoyle Lobe. It buried the Kilbeg Gortian deposit beneath its till, disturbed the corresponding deposit at Ballykeerogemore, and ploughed up other similar deposits, drawing them out into wisps and lenses, as at Newtown. As it reached the coast it stripped away much of the calcareous shelly till of the Ballcroneen Lobe. At Garrarus, on the Waterford coast, a layer of head is interposed between the Ballycroneen till below and the Ballyvoyle till above.

The ice that reached the Wexford coast still

Fig. 158. Map to show location of Gortian Warm Stage sites referred to in the text, and extent of ice-masses of Munsterian Cold Stage.

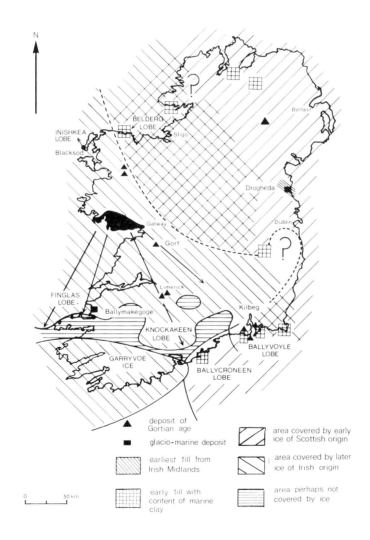

farther east had passed over outcrops of Leinster granite, and a till rich in Leinster granite occurs on the coast as far east as Kilmore Quay. There is evidence of movement of Leinster granite from the main mass of the Wicklow Mountains east towards the Irish Sea, but it is not clear whether the transporting ice had its origin in an independent ice-centre in the Wicklow Mountains, as Farrington thought, or whether this was Connemara ice pushing east over the top of the Wicklow Mountains. Connemara ice certainly reached an altitude of over 300 m on the western slopes of the Castlecomer plateau.

There was an independent ice-cap in the mountains of Kerry and west Cork, and ice advanced east along the synclinal valleys past the site of Cork city as far as Garryvoe, where its deposits rest on the till and outwash sands of the earlier Ballycroneen Lobe. As yet very little is known of the position in Donegal at this stage, but there are suggestions of the presence of a local ice-cap in the mountains there.

Thus, to summarise the Munsterian Cold Stage, the first ice-masses formed in the Midlands and there was a movement eastwards into the basin of the Irish Sea near Drogheda. As this ice withdrew the down-pressed area was invaded by a glacial fiord and this was then obliterated by ice advancing south from Scotland, and perhaps extending over Donegal and north Mayo also. From the Irish Sea proper the ice flowed on to reach its limit at Ballycroneen, just east of Cork Harbour. The flow from Scotland then weakened, and ice expanded from centres in the mountains of Kerry and west Cork, the mountains of Connemara, and perhaps in the mountains of Donegal also. Little is known about the retreat and dissolution of these final Munsterian ice-sheets.

The Ipswichian Warm Stage

Another warm stage followed and in England its deposits are well known, ranging from Devon to Durham. They are particularly common in East Anglia and a site near Ipswich has been chosen as the type-site, and gives its name to the Ipswichian Warm Stage. In north-western Europe corresponding deposits, both fresh-water and marine, are well known, and the stage is known as the Eemian Warm Stage.

In Ireland the position is quite the reverse, no deposit being known which can unequivocally be allotted to this stage. One would think that as this warm stage is younger than the Gortian Warm Stage, its deposits would have a better chance of survival than those from the older period and that the chances of discovery should be at least equal. But there are nine deposits thought to be Gortian, and only two that may be Ipswichian (Fig. 160), and Warren has recently bluntly stated that the Gortian deposits of Ireland do belong to the last interglacial. The reply is that *Abies* is the key tree of the later stages of the Hoxnian/Gortian Warm Stage, while *Carpinus* is the key tree of the later stages of the Ipswichian/Eemian Warm Stage. In north-western Europe no deposit of Ipswichian age contains substantial amounts of pollen of *Abies* but very many deposits of this age carry substantial amounts of *Carpinus* pollen. With two exceptions, to be noted below, all Irish warm stage deposits carry substantial amounts of *Abies* pollen, so, unless in the Ipswichian Stage the vegetation of Ireland was utterly different from the vegetation of north-western Europe, these deposits must equate with Hoxne in age. In the Littletonian Warm Stage the vegetation of Ireland has been markedly similar to that of north-western Europe, and it is difficult to conceive how it could have been completely out of step in the preceding warm stage. Deposits rich in *Carpinus* and attributed to the Ipswichian range from north-western France to north-western England, so it seems almost certain that such deposits will sooner or later be discovered in Ireland.

In the meantime some slender evidence is all that is available. At the interglacial site at Baggotstown, County Limerick, the stratigraphy was not fully elucidated, but can perhaps be presented as follows:

> 0–135 cm   till with limestone and igneous rocks (Midlandian?)
> 135–140 cm   white calcareous sandy mud (warm stage?)
> 140–500 cm   till with limestone and igneous rocks (Munsterian?)
> 500–675 cm   peats, silts, and muds (Gortian?)
> 675–875 cm   stone-free laminated clay
> below 875 cm   stony clay with erratics, apparently a till (pre-Gortian?)

The upper part of the organic sequence between 500 and 675 cm yielded pollen of *Abies* and *Rhododendron* and no pollen of *Carpinus*, and is regarded as being Gortian in age. The calcareous mud between 135 and 140 cm, though thin, was recorded at three separate points. It contained pollen of *Alnus* to a value of 50 per cent, pollen of *Pinus* to a value of 15 per cent, with lesser quantities of *Quercus*; *Corylus*, *Ilex*, *Taxus*, and *Juniperus*. It is unlikely to be a disturbed part of the lower sequence because its pollen spectrum cannot be matched in that sequence. The spectrum clearly derives from a temperate forest in its climax phase, and it here regarded as belonging to the 'missing' warm stage, between the Munsterian and the Midlandian Cold Stages, which should equate with the British Ipswichian. This site urgently requires more detailed investigation.

At Shortalstown, County Wexford, a polleniferous

temperate estuarine sand lies between an upper and a lower shelly calcareous till. In the opinion of the investigators the two tills were significantly different from one another and were separated by the estuarine sand. The lower till was regarded as Munsterian and the upper till as Midlandian in age, and the sand was attributed to the 'missing' warm stage between them. A short pollen-diagram was prepared (Fig. 159), which clearly derives from a temperate forest in its climax stage. The main criterion by which it can be separated from a Gortian diagram at a similar stage is the amount of *Ulmus* pollen present. Pollen of *Ulmus* is almost unknown from Gortian deposits, and no Gortian pollen-diagram shows such amounts of *Ulmus* pollen as are seen in the Shortalstown diagram. With two exceptions the other plants noted were of little special interest. One pollen grain of *Stratiotes aloides* was seen: this plant, which is thought to have been introduced to the modern Irish flora by man, was widely distributed in Europe in interglacial times. Of more interest was a seed of *Decodon* sp. This genus has one living species, *verticillatus*, which to-day grows on river margins in the central United States. Seeds of the genus are known in Europe from the Pliocene to the lower Pleistocene, but because of anatomical differences they are ascribed to a different extinct species, *globosus*. As only one specimen was found, it was not sectioned as would be necessary to determine the species. In Europe the occurrences of *Decodon* are earlier in the Quaternary, and the suggestion has been made that the Shortalstown specimen was derived from an older deposit. But no deposits from which it could have been derived are known in Ireland, and here it is regarded as an American plant which survived in Ireland into this warm stage. Careful search for its seeds should be made in Gortian deposits.

During this warm stage sea-level would have been high, and in England there is some evidence that at its maximum the Ipswichian sea-level was perhaps some 7·5 m above its present level. There are two possible beaches of this age in Ireland. One occurs at Cahore, County Wexford, where the modern tidal range is very small. Below a shelly calcareous till, probably of Midlandian age, there is a small unfossiliferous deposit about 1 m thick of well-rounded pebbles with horizontal axes, suggesting a beach. Most of the pebbles are of local stone, but there are some erratics. The deposit rests on angular head about 1 m thick, which in turn rests on solid rock. The deposit is about 3 m above spring-tide highwater mark.

The second beach is at Ballybunnion, County Kerry. Here the waves have cut a platform about 2·5 m above spring-tide highwater mark in contorted till of Munsterian age. Unfossiliferous beach gravels about 3 m thick rest on the platform, and are buried below 8 m of soliflucted till. As the region must have been isostatically depressed by the Munsterian ice, and the beach is without fossils, all one can say is that it is unlikely to be older than a major Munsterian ice-advance.

The Midlandian Cold Stage

There is now a considerable body of evidence which suggests that the last cold stage began about 70,000 years ago. During this cold stage much of the south of Ireland remained ice-free, but the Midlands were deeply buried and so the stage is called in Ireland the Midlandian. Here there can be found morainic deposits with undulating and irregular topography, kames, eskers, etc., all the features that develop when an ice-sheet disintegrates and survive in unmodified form, provided that they are not subjected to alteration by later frost action or by prolonged temperate weathering.

This topography of the Midlands – a topography

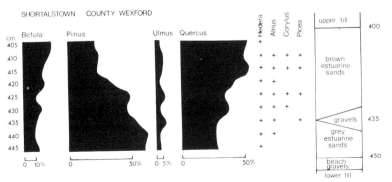

Fig. 159

Pollen diagram from warm stage deposit, possibly of Ipswichian age, at Shortalstown, County Wexford.

that is often described as 'fresh' or 'young' – is very much rarer in the south of Ireland, where the landscape is typically much smoother and without minor undulations, a topography that is described as 'old'. A line can be drawn between the two landscapes, essentially the line of the South Irish End-Moraine of Charlesworth, with 'older drift' to the south and 'younger drift' to the north. When first deposited the Munsterian glacial materials of the south were probably just as irregular in form as those of the Midlands today, but they were exposed first to temperate weathering during the Ipswichian Warm Stage and then to freeze-thaw and other periglacial processes during the Midlandian Cold Stage. Deep frost churning took place where the ground was relatively flat, while on slopes there was downhill movement of head.

Thus south of the Charlesworth line there is 'older' smoother Munsterian topography, where sections show erected stones, convolutions, and head; whereas north of the line the Midlandian topography is 'younger' and irregular and periglacial disturbances are not seen in sections.

Though the cold stage is taken as beginning about 70,000 years ago, there is considerable controversy as to when large ice-masses started to form in north-western Europe. One school would hold that large ice-masses only formed about twenty thousand years ago. The other considers that, although ice did form about twenty thousand years ago, it had also formed much earlier in the last cold stage, as in North America.

Two deposits in the drumlin landscape of County Fermanagh are of importance here. At Derryvree in the course of road improvements it was decided to straighten a road that ran round a drumlin by making a cutting through it. In the course of these operations a thin layer of detritus-mud and moss-peat containing a flora and a beetle fauna of tundra aspect was discovered; the layer had a C^{14} age of 30,500 BP. The organic layer both rested on and was buried by till, the overlying till being rich in limestone and moulded into drumlin form. The lower till was rich in sandstone and there was no indication that its surface had been weathered or affected by frost action before the organic material was deposited on it. Nonetheless the lower till was not considered to be of early Midlandian age; it was assigned to the Munsterian Cold Stage.

The second deposit was in a river section at Hollybrook not far away. Beneath the till of a drumlin there was a silt with washed-in vegetable debris derived from a tundra landscape, and this was given a C^{14} age of greater than 41,500 years. The silt passed downwards into varved clay, resting directly on calcareous till. Here it seems there cannot be any time interval between the retreat of the ice that deposited the till,

the formation of the varved clay, and the washing in of the silt and vegetable debris. It seems more likely that the deposition of the silt took place during a minor retreat of ice in the Midlandian Cold Stage, rather than during the preceding interglacial period. Both these sites appear to give strong indications that in Ireland ice did form during the early part of the Midlandian Cold Stage.

The table for the stratigraphy of the Irish Quaternary recommended by the Geological Society of London takes the opposite view – based largely on evidence from the English Midlands – and considers that the first formation of ice in this cold stage was after 26,000 BP. The table envisages an early Midlandian, before 50,000 BP, and a middle Midlandian, between 50,000 and 26,000 BP, during which the climate oscillated between boreal and arctic but ice was absent, with a late Midlandian from 26,000 to 10,000 BP, during which ice-sheets ebbed and flowed. Derryvree is placed in the middle Midlandian; work at Hollybrook is still incomplete, and its stratigraphical position cannot as yet be decided. The well-known mammalian fauna from Castlepook Cave, County Cork, which includes Woolly Mammoth (*E. primigenius*) and Spotted Hyaena (*Crocuta crocuta*), appears also to fall in the middle Midlandian. A mammoth femur has been dated by C^{14} at 33,500 BP. It is to be hoped that it will soon be possible to throw more light on the events of the early and middle Midlandian phases in Ireland.

Whenever Midlandian ice did first form in Ireland, there was first a major advance in the south-east. There was then a retreat and when it advanced again the centre of the ice-mass had migrated north-westwards. South-eastern Ireland was not again covered, the limit of advance running along a north-east to south-west line through Kells (Fig. 160). According to Synge the drumlins of Ireland (Fig. 161) are found only within this limit. At Derryvree the upper till of the drumlin must be younger than 30,000 BP. If there was no early Midlandian ice, then the till below the organic deposit must be of Munsterian age; but if there was early ice, then both the till below the organic deposit at Derryvree and the Midlandian till of south-eastern Ireland must be older than 30,000 but younger than 70,000 BP.

These uncertainties must be borne in mind when the apparent sequence of Midlandian events is being considered. The first formation of ice seems to have been an oval ice-cap, with its long axis running roughly from Belfast to Limerick. We can trace its southern and south-eastern limits, but the limits of its western extent lie concealed below the deposits of the later advance. On the south the ice was arrested against the northern slopes of the Galty Mountains south of Tipperary town. To the south-west the ice advanced across the low-lying ground of south Limerick until it was halted against the escarpment of higher ground that runs from Foynes to Drom-

colliher. Between Dromcolliher and the western end of the Ballyhoura Mountains it sent a lobe south towards Buttevant, from which melt-water carried

Fig. 160. Map to show location of warm stage sites, possibly of Ipswichian age: extent of ice-masses of Midlandian Cold Stage; distribution of drumlins; loation of Middle Midlandian interstadial sites; and some pingo localities.

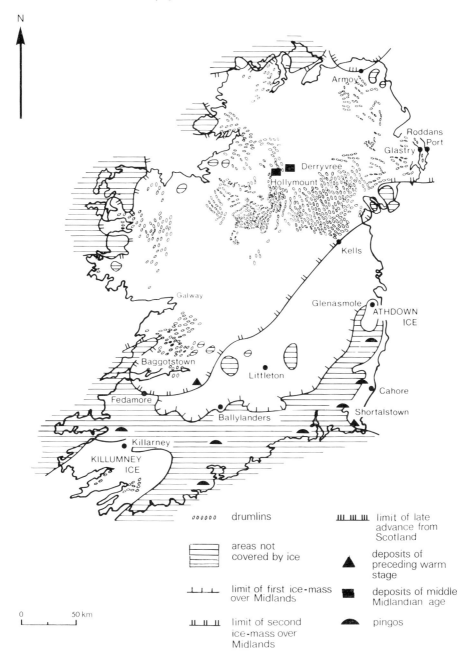

N

Armoy

Roddans Port
Glastry

Derryvree
Hollymount

Kells

Galway

Glenasmole
ATHDOWN ICE

Baggotstown

Littleton

Cahore

Fedamore

Shortalstown

Ballylanders

Killarney

KILLUMNEY ICE

oooooo   drumlins

⫽⫽⫽ ⫽⫽⫽ ⫽⫽⫽ limit of late advance from Scotland

▤ areas not covered by ice

▲ deposits of preceding warm stage

limit of first ice-mass over Midlands

■ deposits of middle Midlandian age

limit of second ice-mass over Midlands

◖ pingos

0   50 km

gravels down the valley of the Awbeg through Castle-
townroche to the valley of the Blackwater. The ice
front continued on along the north face of the Ballyhoura Mountains. Where these are separated from
the west end of the Slievenamuck ridge, around Ballylanders and Galbally, it again sent a lobe southwards
and spilled gravels down to the Blackwater valley.

Continuing south from the east end of the Slievenamuck ridge, the ice blocked the mouth of the Glen of
Aherlow and pushed south into the gap between
Cahir and Killenaule. It reached as far as Ardfinnan
where the moraine is perhaps in part responsible for
the great loop made by the Suir into the angle between
the Knockmealdown and Comeragh Mountains. To
the east the ice advanced down the valley of the
Suir as far as Carrick-on-Suir and sent tremendous

quantities of limestone gravels down the valley to
Waterford Harbour and beyond.

In its south-eastwards advance the ice failed to
over-ride the escarpment of Upper Carboniferous
rocks that runs from Killenaule to Timahoe. At
Durrow the escarpment is breached by the valley of
the Nore, which like several other rivers leaves the
low-lying Midlands, penetrates an escarpment, and
flows on in a south-easterly direction to reach Waterford Harbour. The ice also pushed through the escarpment and followed the valley of the Nore past Kilkenny as far as Thomastown. From the end-moraine
vast quantities of gravel went through the Inistioge
gorge to join the Barrow valley as it emerged from
a similar gorge above New Ross. East of Timahoe
the ice pushed down the Barrow Valley as far as

Fig. 161. Drumlins, Carrigullian Lough, 4 km north-north-west of Killyleagh, County Down.
Photograph J. K. St. Joseph, Cambridge University Collection: copyright reserved

Graiguenamanagh, and sent outwash gravels through the Barrow gorge towards New Ross and on into the head of Waterford Harbour. North of Mount Leinster it expanded south-eastwards and lay across the Slaney valley not far north of Bunclody. From here its margin ran north through Hacketstown to reach the Wicklow Mountains on the western slopes of Keadeen.

At its maximum advance the ice lay against the western flanks of the Wicklow Mountains, damming up a lake in the eastern part of the Glen of Imail and another much bigger lake, Glacial Lake Blessington, in the valleys of the Liffey and the King's River. South of Saggart where the ice reached its highest level, about 300 m, the margin turned east to run along the northern slopes of the Wicklow massif, damming up lakes in the northward draining valleys as it did so. Of these the lake in Glenasmole has the greatest stratigraphical significance.

When its passage was no longer opposed by the mountain slopes, the ice flowed strongly south-eastwards, passing over Killiney Hill and moulding it into roches moutonnées. The ice now met ice moving south down the basin of the Irish Sea, and turned in a southerly direction. At first it maintained its identity along the western margin of the ice-mass, pressing up against, but not surmounting the seaward edge of the Calary plateau. South of Wicklow town the margin was arrested by the transverse ridge of higher ground that reaches the sea in Wicklow Head. South of this point, till of Irish facies can no longer be recognised, being replaced by till largely composed of calcareous shelly mud dredged up by the ice from the floor of the Irish Sea. This till is very similar to the material that had also been dredged from the sea-floor by the earlier Munsterian ice, and indeed it may well in places incorporate large masses of the earlier till.

South of Wicklow Head the level of the ice seems not to have exceeded a height of 100 m. It flowed along with its flank pressed against the higher ground to the west, advancing still farther west wherever lower ground gave opportunity for such movement. Thus a lobe pushed south-west from Gorey at least as far as Camolin and sent a valley-train of gravel on to the Slaney. South of the Hill of Oulart the ice pushed west again, crossing the Slaney valley below Enniscorthy, and temporarily diverting the waters of the Slaney through the great overflow channel north of Taghmon and on to the sea in Bannow Bay. The ice flowed across the eastern end of the Forth Mountain ridge, and reached its limit at Kilmore Quay and the Saltee Islands.

Across St George's Channel the ice advance reached to the vicinity of St David's Head and to parts of the shores of Cardigan Bay. On the floor of the channel there are thick accumulations of drift, and these overlie shelly deposits thought to be Ipswichian in age.

In its retreat from the Carnsore Point/St David's Head line the ice deposited great quantities of almost impervious clayey till on which a soil of strongly impeded drainage, the Macamore Soil, has formed. If only very lightly grazed, or cultivated with a spade, this soil can be very fertile; but it will not carry heavy stocking or heavy agricultural machinery and presents great difficulties to modern agricultural methods.

Around Rosslare Harbour the sea has cut cliffs 20 m high in the till, which extends below sea-level to an unknown depth. North of Wexford the coast for many kilometres is formed of glacial deposits of this advance and in interglacial times the coast must have lain to the west of its present position. In places coastal erosion is endeavouring to restore the earlier coast-line. South of Wexford the interglacial marine clays at Shortalstown lie some distance from the modern coast. If — as seems likely — these are still approximately in their original position, they indicate that south Wexford also has been built up by glacial deposits. Borings made in the vicinity of Bridgetown in search of metalliferous deposits indicate that thick deposits of drift, in some cases extending below modern sea-level, exist in that area also.

From the maximum limits of advance there was, then, a substantial retreat. In its first falling-back the ice seems to have had a stillstand just north of Wexford town, because in the Curracloe area there is an enormous kettle-moraine of shelly sands and gravels, pitted by innumerable kettle-holes, both large and small.

When the ice re-expanded, it built up along an axis that had moved to the north-west, and lay roughly along a line from Galway Bay to Fair Head. It pushed farther south-westwards down the Shannon Estuary as far as Ballylongford, Scattery Island, and Kilrush; its eastern margin lay to the west of the Silvermine Mountains and then traversed the central lowlands in a north-easterly direction through Kells to reach the coast at Dundalk. Carlingford Mountain was not overridden, and a lobe of ice pushed down Carlingford Lough between Carlingford Mountain and the Mourne Mountains. The ice flowed round the Mourne Mountains and out into the basin of the Irish Sea.

North-eastern Ireland was covered by ice, but it is not clear how much of this ice was of Irish, and how much of Scottish, origin; complex movements took place in a give-and-take struggle. At Glastry in County Down shells in a lower till of Scottish origin gave a C^{14} date of 24,000 BP, and this till was buried by an upper till of Irish origin whose surface was moulded into drumlin form. The final retreat of Irish ice may have preceded that from Scotland, because a moraine that spans the Bann and Bush valleys may mark the limit of a late advance from Scotland.

On the north-west side the ice must have thinned abruptly, as it failed to override the Inishowen Peninsula and the points of high ground on the coast from Fanad Head to the Bloody Foreland. It reached the sea in Gweebarra Bay, but failed to override the Carrick Peninsula; it filled Donegal bay, and moulded its underlying till into some of the finest drumlins in Ireland. It did not surmount the higher ground of north-western Mayo or Connemara, but pushed in between out into Clew Bay, which it filled with splendid drumlins (Fig. 19). On the north shore of Galway Bay (and *cf.* Fig. 163), its action was erosional rather

Fig. 162. Esker, north-east of Dunmore, County Galway, looking south-south-westwards.
Photograph J. K. St. Joseph, Cambridge University Collection: copyright reserved

than depositional. Between Roundstone and Clifden there are vast areas of ice-scoured rock, now partly buried by blanket-bog. Still one cannot assume, just because the ground is generally free from drift, that the ice was free of debris, and isolated drumlins, typical in shape but widely scattered, occur occasionally on the scoured rock. Near Galway, drumlins become abundant and some of them have relict occurrences of *Dryas octopetala* and *Gentiana verna*.

Ice was present on the Wicklow Mountains, and was clearly subject to fluctuations in extent. Synge has recently described four major stages, of Middle and Late Midlandian age. The Midlandian ice-cap in south-western Ireland was much smaller than the Munsterian ice-cap in the same area. Again the ice advanced eastwards, but this time it stopped west of Cork at Killumney, whereas the earlier ice had passed over the site of the city and travelled east as far as Garryvoe. Unfortunately this ice-cap did not make contact with the ice of the Midlands at any point, and so it is not possible to determine their relative ages.

In the Munsterian Cold Stage there was substantial isostatic depression of the basin of the Irish Sea underneath accumulated weight of ice. Similar movement, but on a smaller scale, took place during the Midlandian Cold Stage, with the result that in north-eastern Ireland the sea, though still at a glacial level many metres below its present level, was able to flood in over the depressed land and form beaches at its margins (Fig. 168). Subsequent elastic recovery has raised these beaches to a height of 20 m above modern sea-level. There are younger glacial beaches at lower levels, and a start has been made on the work of relating beaches at different levels to stages of ice retreat.

Final Midlandian events

After 15,000 BP the world's ice-sheets could grow no more and great masses of ice became stagnant and then melted or evaporated away *in situ*, giving rise to what is known as 'dead-ice' topography, with kettle-holes, kames, and eskers (Fig. 162), as is well seen in the Irish Midlands and in south Tyrone. As areas of clay, sand, and gravel were exposed, they were invaded by the hardy plants of the pioneer vegetation and the plant cover started the slow process of re-establishing itself. This is not the place to enter the long-debated question of plant survival through glacial stages on nunataks or elsewhere, but it is noteworthy that Ben Bulbin in County Sligo (Fig. 105), which today carries a remarkable group of arctic-alpine plants, appears to have been a nunatak throughout the Midlandian Cold Stage.

If such plants did survive on Ben Bulbin, they would also have survived in the ice-free areas in the south of Ireland. But such vegetation, probably of northern grasses and arctic-alpine herbs, would have been very open, and as the plants re-expanded into areas formerly covered by ice the particular plants that grew in particular places would depend on soil and aspect more than on temperature. The very small output of pollen would have varied from place to place and local pollen records vary widely.

The Woodgrange Interstadial

About 14,000 years ago an amelioration of climate set in, enabling the plant cover to spread and develop a meadow-like aspect, with species of dock (*Rumex*) prominent in the meadows. This is the Gramineae–*Rumex* pollen-assemblage-zone. Here the interstadial opens, and as it was first documented at Woodgrange, County Down, by Gurdip Singh, it is called the Woodgrange Interstadial (Fig. 164). These first meadows lasted for perhaps 1,000 years, when they were invaded by juniper, which was enabled to spread widely and flower freely by the continuing rise in temperature during the period represented by the *Juniperus* pollen-assemblage-zone, which perhaps lasted from 13,000 to 12,000 years ago.

The vegetational developments of the interstadial were not only an expansion of plants that were already in Ireland; there was a massive immigration of new plants – and also of animals. Such movements into Ireland imply that land bridges from Britain must have existed. At this time sea-level, though rising, was probably still about 90 m below its present level, and there would have been one bridge to Scotland via Islay, a second to the Isle of Man and Anglesey and on east to the English mainland, and a third from Wicklow to the Lleyn peninsula. It is clear that movement into the Isle of Man presented no difficulty, because by 12,000 years ago at least eighty plant taxa had reached the island and many more were pushing in; a large number of beetles and the Giant Deer were also present. Ireland's richest Woodgrange flora comes from a site near the Leinster coast at Mapastown, County Louth, and the plants, the beetles, and the Giant Deer must have used bridges of glacial material with varied soil patterns as they pushed on westwards from the Isle of Man.

A beetle fauna of this Woodgrange phase at Shortalstown, County Wexford, closely resembles beetle assemblages from England and Wales that are approximately contemporaneous with it. These faunas suggest a climate at least as warm as, or at times even warmer than, that in the same areas at the present day. Finds of birch fruits show that tree-birches were in Ireland at this time, but, curiously enough, birch-woods appear to have been rare, though they did exist in the Killarney area. Instead of widespread birch-forests, the grasslands re-expanded and a Gramineae pollen-assemblage-zone developed, which lasted from about 12,000 to 10,500 years ago.

Some evidence from beetles suggests that temperature was now falling back and these conditions may have favoured the grasses. This is just the time that the Giant Deer (Fig. 165) became very common in Ireland, and so there is the dilemma – did the Giant

Fig. 163. Inishturk, off south Mayo, from the air. The ice-scoured surface displays tight, east-west trending first folds in greywackes and tuffs of the Sheefry Group (lower Ordovician: Chapter 3). There are conspicuous north-westerly trending minor shear planes.

Photograph reproduced by permission of The Controller, Stationery Office, Dublin.

Deer increase rapidly in numbers because there was ample food on the wide prairies, or did this animal graze on young birch shoots and thus keep growth of birch in check, enabling the grassland to expand at the expense of the trees? The Reindeer was also in Ireland at this time, though probably in smaller numbers.

The Nahanagan Stadial

Climate then deteriorated rapidly and ushered in the Nahanagan Stadial or Cold Phase. Periglacial conditions returned in strength on the lowlands; the continuous plant-cover broke up and *Artemisia* (Mugwort) became common, giving its name to the pollen-assemblage-zone. *Salix*, probably *herbacea*, *Rumex*, and arctic-alpine plants became more common. On the uplands ice re-occupied some corries. The stadial, though very cold, was also very short and may only have lasted 500 years, from 10,500 to 10,000 years ago.

The type-site, Lough Nahanagan, is a corrie lake at about 400 m in the Wicklow Mountains. It lies at the head of Glendasan, a valley that has been glaciated on more than one occasion. The corrie was probably occupied by a substantial ice-mass at some part of the Midlandian and a big moraine was thrown across its mouth. The modern lake behind the moraine was

harnessed in a pumped-storage generating-scheme (Fig. 59) and as part of the work the lake was drained. As water level fell, it exposed some very small moraines banked against the back-wall of the corrie. The moraines contained erratics of organic mud, which had a radiocarbon age of 11,500 years, a pollen picture that suggested the transition from the *Juniperus* to the Gramineae pollen-assemblage-zone (Fig. 164), and macroscopic remains of arctic-alpine plants. This mud had formed in an earlier lake behind the moraine in the Woodgrange Interstadial, and had then been ploughed up by the ice of a smaller later glacier. It is not yet known how widely ice formed elsewhere in Ireland at this time. In Scotland a small ice-cap formed on high ground, and its ice advanced as far south as Loch Lomond.

On the lowlands solifluction moved till downslope both at Howth in County Dublin and at Old Head, near Louisburgh in Mayo, where organic deposits of Woodgrange age were buried below till. Permafrost may have developed. Late Midlandian outwash gravels in County Tyrone are penetrated by ice-wedge-casts. These may have formed in the Nahanagan Stadial, and, if so, they indicate a mean annual temperature of less than −5° C. Pingos (Fig. 154) at Camaross in Wexford (indicating a similar temperature) have not produced any deposits older than the end of the Nahanagan Stadial and similar structures in Wales tell the same story.

Fig. 164. Pollen diagram to show development of vegetation in the Woodgrange Interstadial and in the Nahanagan Stadial at Woodgrange, County Down (after G. Singh).

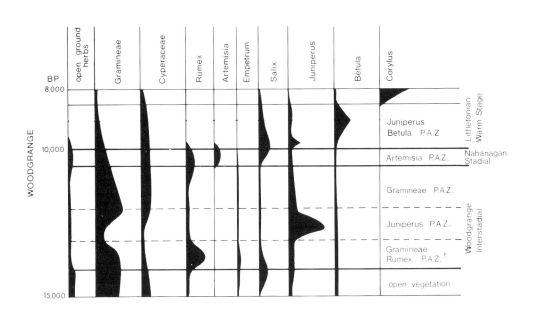

The fossil evidence also points to cold conditions. At Drumurcher, County Monaghan, a basin between late Midlandian drumlins contained a muddy silt, dated to 10,500 BP, which yielded remains of about 100 species of beetle. Many of these indicate an arctic or subarctic climate, such as is found today in the

Fig. 165. An artist's impression of the Giant Deer, *Megaloceros giganteus*. The frail but heavy antlers were used for display. Courtesy Field Museum of Natural History, Chicago. Artist Charles R. Knight.

mountains of Scandinavia or the northern tundras. The silt also produced a seed of the Arctic Poppy (*Papaver radicatum*), a plant that has today a strictly arctic-circumpolar distribution. The whole of Ireland must have been cold because arctic-alpine plants were growing at modern sea-level in west Kerry.

The opening of this cold phase brought about the disappearance of the Woodgrange grasslands and as they disappeared the Giant Deer went with them, unable to survive on the scanty vegetation that replaced them. The hardier Reindeer did survive the cold snap, but we have no knowledge of its presence in Ireland in the Nahangan Stadial.

About 10,000 years ago climate started to improve again, and *Juniperus* expanded and flowered freely once more. This time there was no reversal and continuing improvement allowed the birch to overshadow the juniper and to expand into true birch woods. A peak in birch pollen now replaced that in juniper and the grasses and herbs fell back as the woods became established in the period of the *Juniperus-Betula* assemblage-zone (Fig. 164). Finally, at about 8,500 years ago, the hazel arrived in Ireland. *Corylus* cannot grow in northern latitudes today and its arrival confirms that the improvement in climate 10,000 years ago did draw a final line across the Midlandian Cold Stage and ushered in the current warm stage.

BIBLIOGRAPHY

BOWEN, D. Q. — 1978 *Quaternary Geology. A Stratigraphic Framework for Multidisciplinary Work*. Pergamon, Oxford, pp. 221.

COLHOUN, E. A., DICKSON, J. H., McCABE, A. M., & SHOTTON, F. W. — 1972 A Middle Midlandian fresh-water series at Derryvree, Maguiresbridge, County Fermanagh, Northern Ireland. *Proc. R. Soc.*, **180B**, 273–292.

COLHOUN, E. A. & McCABE, A. M. — 1973 Pleistocene glacial, glaciomarine and associated deposits of Mell and Tullyallen townlands, near Drogheda, Eastern Ireland. *Proc. R. Ir. Acad.*, **73B**, 165–206.

COLHOUN, E. A. & MITCHELL, G. F. — 1971 Interglacial marine formation and lateglacial freshwater formation in Shortalstown townland, Co. Wexford. *Proc. R. Ir. Acad.*, **71B**, 211–245.

COOPE, G. R. *et al.* — 1979 The Lateglacial and Early Postglacial Deposit at Drumurcher, Co. Monaghan. *Proc. R. Ir. Acad.*, **79B**, 63–85.

JESSEN, K. — 1949 Studies in Late Quaternary deposits and Flora-History of Ireland. *Proc. R. Ir. Acad.*, **52B**, 85–290.

JESSEN, K., ANDERSEN, S. T., & FARRINGTON, A. — 1959 The Interglacial Deposit near Gort, Co. Galway, Ireland. *Proc. R. Ir. Acad.*, **60B**, 1–78.

KIDSON, C. & TOOLEY, M. J., (Eds). — 1977 *The Quaternary History of the Irish Sea*. Seel House Press, Liverpool, pp. 345.

McCABE, A. M. *et al.* — 1978 An Inter-till Fresh Water Deposit at Hollymount, Maguiresbridge, Co. Fermanagh. *Proc. R. Ir. Acad.*, **78B**, 77–89.

MITCHELL, G. F. — 1970 The Quaternary deposits between Fenit and Spa on the north shore of Tralee Bay, Co. Kerry. *Proc. R. Ir. Acad.*, **70B**, 141–162.

MITCHELL, G. F. — 1973 Fossil pingos in Camaross Townland, Co. Wexford. *Proc. R. Ir. Acad.*, **73B**, 269–282.

MITCHELL, G. F. — 1976 *The Irish Landscape*. Collins, London, pp. 240.

MITCHELL, G. F. — 1977 Periglacial Ireland. *Phil. Trans. R. Soc.*, **280**, 199–209.

MITCHELL, G. F.,   1973 A Correlation of Quaternary Deposits in the British Isles.
  PENNY, L. F.,   *Geol. Soc. Lond. Spec. Rep.*, **4**, pp. 99.
  SHOTTON, F. W., &
  WEST, R. G.

SYNGE, F. M.   1978 *In* Davies, G. L. H. and Stephens, N. *The Geomorphology
                                of the British Isles – Ireland. Methuen & Co. Ltd., London,
                                pp. 250.

SYNGE, F. M.   1979 Quaternary Glaciation in Ireland. *Quaternary Newsletter*,
                                No. **28**, 1–18.

WARREN, W. P.   1979 Stratigraphic position and age of the Gortian interglacial
                                deposits. *Geol. Surv. Ir. Bull.*, **2**, 315–322.

WATTS, W. A.   1967 Interglacial Deposits in Kildromin Townland, near Her-
                                bertstown, Co. Limerick. *Proc. R. Ir. Acad.*, **65B**, 339–348.

WATTS, W. A.   1977 The Late Devensian vegetation of Ireland. *Phil. Trans. R.
                                Soc.*, **280**, 273–293.

WRIGHT, W. B. &   1904 The Pre-glacial Raised Beach of the South Coast of Ire-
  MUFF, H. B.   land. *Scient. Proc. R. Dubl. Soc.*, **10**, 250–308.

17

THE LITTLETONIAN WARM STAGE – POST 10,000 BP

G. F. Mitchell

About 10,000 years ago an essentially uninterrupted amelioration of climate set in which enabled the forest trees to return to north-western Europe from the more southern areas where they had been forced to take refuge during the rigours of the last cold stage. This was the beginning of a warm stage which continues to the present day and is often called the 'post-glacial' or the Holocene. A type-site for the Irish deposits of this stage, where its base has been clearly defined, has been designated in a bog at Littleton, County Tipperary, and this gives its name to the stage in Ireland (see Table 15). In Britain the name Flandrian, used in mainland Europe for this warm stage, has been adopted; but there is a lack of precision about the definition of the base of the Flandrian on the continent, so this name has not been used in Ireland.

At a depth of 750 cm in a boring made in 1954 in the bog in Littleton Townland, County Tipperary (Fig. 166), pollen of *Juniperus* began to increase in relative abundance, and here the Littletonian Warm Stage opens at about 10,000 BP. At this time sea-level was perhaps still 35 m below its present level but was rising rapidly. Following on this first expansion of *Juniperus*, the woodlands of Ireland ought to have undergone the development typical of a Quaternary warm stage, and we can see them follow this course for some 5,000 years. But then farmers, who engaged in woodland clearance to create fields for themselves, arrived in Ireland, and from that point onwards the record is not one of natural woodland evolution, but rather one of man's progressive interference with the forests. As a woodland model was used as a background against which to follow the events of earlier warm stages, a similar scheme can show the phases of woodland development in Ireland during the Littletonian Warm Stage, with C[14] dates added to it (Fig. 167). Sketch-curves for temperature and for sea-level are shown.

The climatic rigours of the Midlandian Cold Stage had begun to collapse even before 10,000 BP, and the first re-expansion of plant cover (ILWA) had set in. The temperature curve shows the warm Woodgrange Interstadial and also the final Nahanagan Stadial. Then at about 10,000 BP *Juniperus* expands once more and begins (ILWB) the re-establishment of the Irish woodlands. *Betula, Corylus, Pinus, Ulmus,* and *Quercus,* all return, perhaps in that approximate order. By 7,700 BP, when sea-level was perhaps about 12 m below its present level, estuarine deposits were accumulating in the mouths of the Glens of Antrim, and before that date Ireland must have become an island separated from Britain by extensive tracts of water offering a substantial barrier to the further entry of plants and animals.

It seems almost certain that *Alnus* must have been present in Ireland before this time, but for some reason its pollen does not become abundant until later, at about 7,000 BP. The point at which *Alnus* begins to take its place in the woodlands can be taken as opening the climax phase of the Irish Littletonian woodlands, and here phase ILWB can be taken to end. This phase has previously been divided into a more elaborate series of Pollen-zones IV–VI, but these zones probably do no more than arbitrarily divide – on the basis of the dominant pollen of the moment – a period of tree migration into Ireland, and of the migration of other plants and animals also. This period of easy immigration was, of course, brought to an end by the separation of Ireland from Britain, which resulted in a flora and fauna in Ireland that are substantially more limited than those in Britain.

We can picture Ireland during this phase of immigration (Phase ILWB) as being densely wooded, though the composition of the woodlands was in a state of flux. Rivers threaded their way through the

forests, which were also punctuated by lakes and
ponds, perhaps at a rather lower level than they were
at a later period. Fen vegetation was invading the
margins of the lakes but as yet there was no development of bog. Towards the end of the stage, man
appeared for the first time in Ireland. A simple hunter
and fisher, without domestic animals and unaware
of the practices of tillage, and confined by the forests
to the margins of the sea, rivers, and lakes, he first
appears in the lower Bann valley and in the Shannon
basin about 8,500 BP, and rather later on the coast
of Antrim and on the shores of Lough Neagh. The
gravels of a raised beach spit in Larne Lough, County
Antrim, are especially rich in the flint debris he
created in forming implements. This major industry
is referred to as Larnian, an industry of a rather
impoverished Mesolithic type.

In the Midlandian Cold Stage there had been a
body of Scottish ice in the northern end of the Irish
Sea basin, bringing about an isostatic sinking of the
earth's crust below its weight. Substantial elastic
recovery had already taken place before the Midlandian ended, but uplift continued in north-eastern

Ireland into the Littletonian Warm Stage. At first,
eustatic rise in sea-level still exceeded the rate of
isostatic recovery. The sea flooded in on the coasts,
but, as the rate of eustatic rise fell away, elastic
recovery raised the earlier beaches above the reach
of the waves. In north-eastern Antrim the raised
beach at its highest level stands 8.5 m above modern
sea-level, but the actual area that was as severely
uplifted as this appears to have been relatively small
(Fig. 168).

About 7,000 BP the Irish woodlands entered on a
period of stability, and reached their climax phase
(ILWC). In these woods there would have been tall
well-grown forest trees with ivy on their stems, and
ferns and mosses on their branches, rising through a
dense undergrowth of bushes of considerable variety.
The trees would be of a size almost unknown in
Ireland today and the undergrowth would present a
degree of impenetrability equally unknown today.
Yet there would be no monotony because the variable
soil pattern would be reflected in the woodlands,
which are best pictured as a mosaic of differing tree-
stands, constantly and subtly changing.

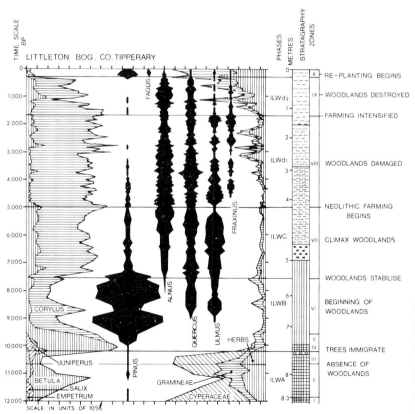

Fig. 166

Diagram for Littleton Bog,
County Tipperary, the type-site
for the Littletonian Warm Stage,
showing from left to right: time-
scale, pollen curves, phases of
woodland development, stratigraphy, zones, and explanation of
phases (after Mitchell, 1965).

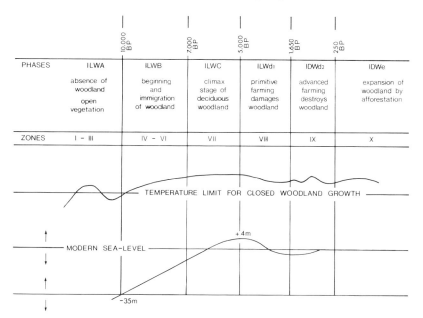

PHASES	ILWA	ILWB	ILWC	ILWd1	IDWd2	IDWe
	absence of woodland	beginning and immigration of woodland	climax stage of deciduous woodland	primitive farming damages woodland	advanced farming destroys woodland	expansion of woodland by afforestation
	open vegetation					
ZONES	I - III	IV - VI	VII	VIII	IX	X

TEMPERATURE LIMIT FOR CLOSED WOODLAND GROWTH

MODERN SEA-LEVEL

+4m

−35m

Fig. 167. Phases of woodland development in Ireland in the Littletonian Warm Stage, showing major features of phases, relationship of an older scheme of pollen-zones of phases, movement of temperature in relation to limiting temperatures for closed woodland growth, and movement of sea-level in relation to modern sea-level.

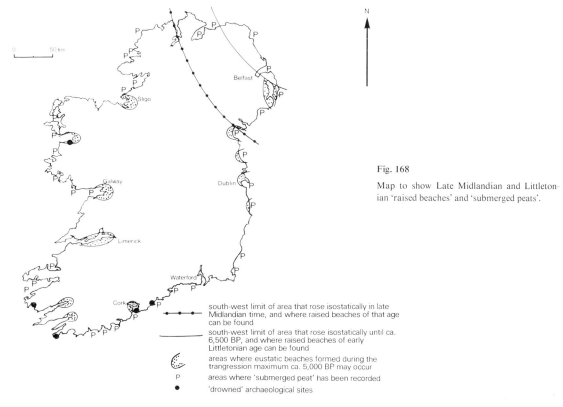

Fig. 168

Map to show Late Midlandian and Littletonian 'raised beaches' and 'submerged peats'.

south-west limit of area that rose isostatically in late Midlandian time, and where raised beaches of that age can be found

south-west limit of area that rose isostatically until ca. 6,500 BP, and where raised beaches of early Littletonian age can be found

areas where eustatic beaches formed during the trangression maximum ca. 5,000 BP may occur

P   areas where 'submerged peat' has been recorded

●   'drowned' archaeological sites

Red deer, wild boar, and probably bears would have lived on the woodland floors, with red squirrels and pine-martens in the branches. Wolves, foxes, and stoats on the ground, and eagles and other large birds of prey would have been the predators. The lakes and rivers would have teemed with fish and ducks all still unafraid of man, and if the simple equipment of the Larnian hunter-fishermen looks primitive, it must be remembered that both the numbers and the lack of fear of the creatures that they hunted made their task very much easier than that of the modern sportsman.

It seems very probable that at this time temperature was slightly higher than it is today and the climate generally may have been more genial. There is a general impression that Europe enjoyed a *Climatic Optimum* at this stage; but it is rather difficult to pinpoint this exactly, or to define it in terms of temperature. The molluscan fauna of the 'estuarine clay' of north-eastern Ireland indicates a water temperature rather warmer than that obtaining at present, and a figure of perhaps 2·5° C warmer than now has been suggested for air temperatures.

A considerable amount of evidence is now being assembled which suggests that at about 5,000 BP world sea-level was about 4 m higher than it is today. It is tempting to see this as a eustatic rise which reflected a world-wide melting of ice consequent on a rise in temperature. It seems very probable that in Ireland many of the post-glacial raised beaches that have hitherto been interpreted as evidence of isostatic uplift were in fact formed about 5,000 BP by this eustatic rise in sea-level (Fig. 169).

The Larnian folk were attracted to the sea-shores as an easy source of food, and particularly of molluscs, and their shell-middens have long attracted the attention of archaeologists. After they had come into contact with the invading Neolithic farmers, and had acquired new skills from them, they still frequented the shores, where their middens were washed away by the waves when the sea reached its high level about 5,000 BP. Both at Sutton in County Dublin and at Ringneill Quay in County Down middens which contained Neolithic artefacts and charcoal dated to about 5,300 BP were buried beneath beach deposits. The stages by which the sea fell back from this higher level to its modern position are not clearly understood. In the Bann valley Mesolithic and Neolithic artefacts became embedded in accumulating diatomite.

It is probable that the higher temperature was accompanied by higher humidity and higher rainfall, in fact by a more oceanic type of climate, and this has for long been the view of Scandinavian scientists who named these millenia *Atlantic*, implying a more oceanic climate than that of the opening phases of the warm stage, which were called *Boreal* to imply a more continental climate. At the opening of the Littletonian Warm Stage great areas of the more low-lying parts of the Midlands were covered by shallow lakes, in which muds rich in precipitated calcium carbonate were deposited. Sedges and reeds grew round the lake margins, and, as the lakes were shallowed by the deposition of mud, the surrounding reed-beds crept out towards the centres of the lakes, depositing a layer of vegetable debris or fen-peat as they did so. As the peat thickened its upper layers became poorer and poorer in variety of plant life, because the amount of inorganic nutrient available became progressively smaller and smaller.

When the climate became wetter two major developments took place. First the areas of impoverished fen-peat provided ideal growth conditions for *Sphagnum*, a moss whose leaves draw and store water directly from rain, and which can grow almost independently of soil nutrients. The environment was wet and slightly acid, decay of vegetable material was slow, and gradually the accumulating vegetable debris built itself up into a dome-like mass of *Sphagnum*-peat, forming the raised-bog which is such a feature of the Midlands and many other parts of Ireland today. Such bogs are rare or absent in the vicinity of the south and east coasts (Fig. 171). The formation of *Sphagnum*-peat and raised-bogs had started at least by 7,500 BP (Fig. 172).

Fig. 169. (above left)

Near Malin Head, County Donegal: Ballyhillin village lies along the curved crest of a Late Midlandian raised beach, now about 20 m above sea level. Strip fields follow the slope of the beach gravels seawards. Sea level rose eustatically about 4 m some 5000 years ago, cutting cliffs in the earlier beach gravels. More gravel was laid down as the sea retreated again.

Photograph J. K. St Joseph, Cambridge University Collection: copyright reserved.

Fig. 170

Pine stumps in blanket bog, near Slieve League, County Donegal, September 1965.

Photograph M. C. F. Proctor.

Secondly, increased humidity and rainfall caused water-tables to rise and ground that had hitherto been dry enough for trees to grow now became water-logged, with the result that the forest was replaced by fens and a layer of fen-peat buried the former forest floor. When this peat became thick enough to cut off soil nutrients it was invaded by the *Sphagnum*-association and further raised-bog started to form. The masses of peat created in the raised-bogs formed new obstacles to natural drainage-channels, and in this way the water-logging of the soil became further aggravated, enabling bog to expand still farther (Fig. 172). Major growth of the raised-bogs appears to have been interrupted rather irregularly by forces which again are not clearly understood; but had it not been for human interference bringing artificial drainage to many raised-bogs, their growth would probably have continued to the present day.

About 5,000 BP, or more probably some centuries earlier, the Neolithic farmers who had been pushing across Europe from their original homeland in the Middle East reached their western limit when they

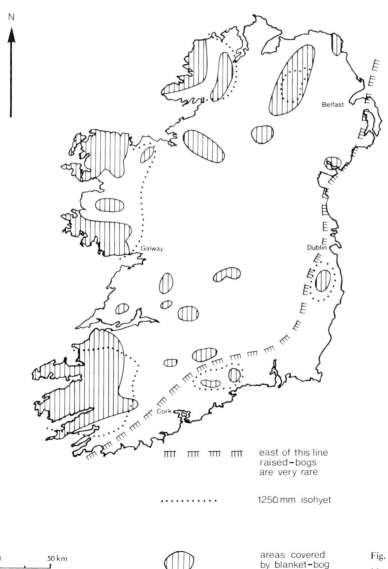

N

Belfast

Galway

Dublin

Cork

ꟘꟘꟘ   ꟘꟘꟘ   ꟘꟘꟘ   ꟘꟘꟘ   east of this line
raised—bogs
are very rare

············   1250 mm isohyet

0   50 km

areas covered
by blanket—bog

Fig. 171

Map to show distribution of bog in Ireland.

crossed the Irish Sea into Ireland. If they were enjoy-
ing a climatic optimum, then living conditions would
have been favourable and population pressures high.
Thus the dangerous and difficult sea-crossing may
have been worth while. To have transported a foun-
dation-stock of domestic animals across the Irish Sea
was no mean feat.

In Ireland as everywhere else the farmers took up
their polished stone axes to clear the woodlands and
their hoes to till the soil. Through trial and error they
had come to recognise that certain types of woodland
implied fertile soils, and that certain types of stone
were superior to others as raw material for polished
stone tools. The qualities of flint and chert for imple-
ment-making had long been known, and it was now
learned that fine-grained tough igneous rocks such as
dolerite and metamorphic rocks such as hornfels
could be shaped and polished into durable implements. The first geological survey revealed the bluish
Tertiary porcellanites of Tievebulliagh and Rathlin in
Antrim, and the first factories to mass-produce such
implements quickly sprang up and were soon export-
ing their wares as far as the south of England (Fig.
173).

Ireland has a rock foundation of many different
geological formations, varied relief, a complex history
of glaciation, and a climate dominated by low evapor-
ation-rates and these variables gave rise to a pattern
of poorly drained soils of considerable complexity,
which were certainly reflected in the early woodland
communities. *Ulmus* would have been particularly
abundant where the soil was well drained and had a
high base status, while *Quercus* and *Alnus* would have
dominated the more poorly-drained and less fertile
areas. About 5,000 BP the relative amount of *Ulmus*

pollen being trapped in lakes and bogs fell dramatically, while pollen of herbs and spores of *Pteridium*
(bracken) increased, and pollen of *Plantago lanceolata* (plantain), a common weed of agriculture today,
first appears. Though argument remains as to how
what must initially have been a small Neolithic population could have brought about such a drastic reduction in the amount of *Ulmus* pollen produced, it is
now generally agreed that this change marks the first
major interference by man with the virgin woodlands.

And so the climax phase of the Littletonian woodlands – ILWC – came to what certainly was a premature end at about 5,000 BP and a phase of woodland
damage – ILWd₁ – set in. After this, human influences
were the dominant factor in the Irish environment
and changes in the fossil content of bogs and lakes
do not reflect the natural changes that would have
taken place in the woodlands and elsewhere had the
Littletonian Warm Stage proceeded along its path
solely in response to developments of climate and soil.

In the raised-bogs, layers of highly humified or
decomposed peat, thought to have formed slowly with
opportunity for contemporary decay, alternate with
layers of fresher peat thought to have formed more
rapidly, possibly under cooler and wetter conditions,
less conducive to contemporary decay. On the whole
the upper layers of the bogs are composed of such
fresh peat (Fig. 172), and for long the initiation of the
formation of this upper slightly humified peat was
thought to have been contemporaneous throughout
much of north-western Europe, developing in response
to a climatic deterioration that set in about 2,350
years ago. This was reflected in the terminology which
pictured a drier Sub-Boreal phase giving way to a
cooler wetter Sub-Atlantic phase about 400 B.C. But

Fig. 172. Sketch-section of typical midland raised-bog: 1, wood-peat; 2, glacial deposits; 3,
open-water mud; 4, fen-peat; 5, wood-fen-peat; 6, *Sphagnum*-peat (highly humified); 7, *Sphagnum*-peat (slightly humified). Numbers within the diagram refer to C¹⁴ dates in years BP. (The
section is based upon work by R. Hammond).

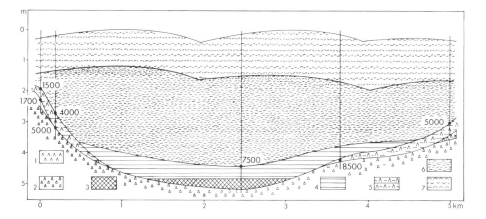

more detailed pollen-studies and close series of C[14] dates have shown that the alternation from humified to fresh peat is not synchronous from bog to bog. It can in some cases be shown that even within a single bog fresh peat had started to form at some places while humified peat was continuing to form at others. Nonetheless it is impossible to overlook the fact that, generally speaking, the upper layers are less humified than the lower, and this may indeed reflect a significant deterioration in climate.

What did the Neolithic farmers do to reduce so drastically the quantity of *Ulmus* pollen produced? As we have seen, *Ulmus* was probably growing in concentrated stands on well-drained soils with a high base status – soils particularly suitable to simple agriculture. All the farmers had to do was to clear and burn the undergrowth, and then ring-bark the trees and so kill them. The skeletal branches of a dead tree cut off almost no light and it would not have been necessary to fell and remove the dead trees. They may well have cut green branches of *Ulmus* to feed to their cattle and the lopped trees may not have produced pollen in quantity; but such practices are unlikely to have cut off the supply of *Ulmus* pollen in the almost total way that did take place.

When the soil in the clearance patch was superficially exhausted, the farmers moved on and the abandoned field was slowly invaded, first by shrubs

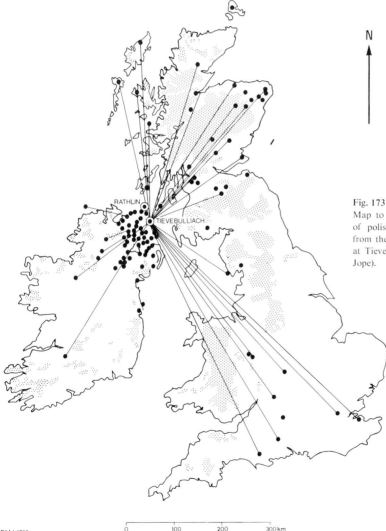

Fig. 173

Map to show distribution in the British Isles of polished axes of porcellanite originating from the 'axe factories' on Rathlin Island and at Tievebulliagh. County Antrim (after E. M. Jope).

EMJ·1952

0   100   200   300 km

among which *Corylus* was prominent, and then by secondary woodland. In Ireland *Ulmus* sometimes returned in the secondary woodland and this confirms that its reduction was due to man and not a climatic deterioration, as has been suggested. In their wanderings the farmers might return to the now re-habilitated woodlands, and a further clearance of similar intensity would take place.

Knowledge of metals was now spreading through Europe and may first have reached Ireland about 4,000 BP. Just as the Neolithic folk had an eye for the type of natural vegetation that would indicate fertile soil, so those of the Bronze Age had an eye for the type of landscape and type of rock that might yield metallic ores. Before long copper was being won in Waterford and in Kerry and gold was being extracted in Wicklow. The outcrops when first examined would have been very much more deeply concealed by dense vegetation than they were in historic times, and very detailed prospecting must have been carried out by a population that can never have been very large.

Agriculture probably continued on a nomadic basis, woodland clearance was an ever-present chore, and wood must have been the prime construction material, just as today the log cabin is still the mark of the frontiersman everywhere in northern latitudes. When the group moved on, the wooden buildings would be swallowed up in the regenerating woodland, and, when the woodland was cleared again, all coherent trace of the former settlement would disappear. This may be the reason that so little is known of the dwelling-sites of these early peoples. We know their tombs and their implements, but of where and how they lived we really have very little knowledge.

The clearance of woodland with relatively primitive implements which lacked the cutting-edge of iron and steel must have been a back-breaking process and the uplands, where woodlands were perhaps thinner, and sloping ground favoured soil drainage, must have offered attractions. Climate may have been more genial than it is today and it is coming to be realised that many Irish uplands, now buried by blanket-bog, were under cultivation at this time. How and when did this turnover from fertile farmland to barren blanket-bog take place?

Here two points must be kept separate. *First* not all blanket-bog is situated on former farmland, yet *secondly* on many upland areas blanket-bog did bury former fields. Where did blanket-bog form? In Ireland today the amount of rainfall is not high, ranging from a minimum of 750 mm to more than 1,500 mm p.a., but the number of rain-days is high and the evapo-transpiration-rate is low. This amount of moisture, combined with poor soil drainage, is quite sufficient to maintain waterlogged ground surfaces over much of the country. The occurrence of blanket-bog can be roughly related to the 1,250 mm isohyet (Fig. 171). Where the rainfall exceeds 1,250 mm p.a., the ground is covered by a continuous sheet of peat interrupted only where slopes are steep. Thus in much of the west of Ireland the blanket-bog continues down to, and below, sea-level, giving great stretches of country buried by peat. Below much of the peat there is a layer of tree-stumps, chiefly of *Pinus* (Fig. 170) and *Betula*. Away from the west coast, rainfall exceeds 1,250 mm only on higher ground and the blanket-bog is confined to hill-tops.

During the climax phase of the woodlands – ILWC – it is probable that the uplands were covered by woodland, even though the forest may not have been as dense as on the lowlands. Even where the trees have all disappeared, the forest soils which developed below them can be traced in some places. The early farmers cleared and cultivated some upland areas and the associated pollens, principally that of *Plantago lanceolata*, can be found in the upper layers of the soil. Podzolisation then appears to have set in and it is not easy to say whether this was produced by the constant turning of the soil, allowing a downwards movement of iron and other constituents, or by a deterioration of climate causing increased leaching after the farmers had occupied the area. At any rate impeded drainage resulted in the formation of blanket-bog and at Goodland, County Antrim, where the peat overlies former fields, the peat had started to form before 4,500 BP.

If there was a deterioration in climate about this time, with increased wetness and increased windiness, conditions may have become impossible for tree-growth on the uplands and in the west of the country. As the trees faded out they too were replaced by blanket-bog, which thus obliterated both the primeval woodlands and the upland fields that had been created after their clearance. In the Glenamoy district in Mayo depressions can be found below the blanket-peat, and in some of these that had been lakes, sediment started to accumulate at the beginning of the warm stage. Pollen in these early deposits suggests that in early Littletonian time woodland development in the area was similar to that in the rest of the country, and that the area was covered with typical forest. The lake deposits are then succeeded by blanket-peat and the tree-pollens fall away in number and variety, suggesting that the landscape that we see today was being established. Neolithic farmers were early into the area, and they enclosed large areas with stone walls, built houses, and erected megalithic tombs. Peat continued to form, but nonetheless in Bronze Age times man continued to farm the areas that were still free of peat. The land was cultivated in ridges thrown up by spades, and on the western slopes of the Ox Mountains such ridges have been traced over several hectares, where the peat which subsequently smothered the fields has been removed either by cutting for fuel or by archaeological excavation.

Today at many points on the uplands of eastern and of south-western Ireland the blanket-bog is being vigorously eroded away. The vegetation surface has broken, deep erosion channels are active, and on some tops over areas of several hectares the peat has been entirely stripped away and the mineral soil exposed once more. It is not known whether this process is climatic or anthropogenic in origin. It does not seem to be a process of very long duration or more peat would have been removed. It has been said that the failure of the surface vegetation, which probably initiated the process, was brought about by overgrazing by sheep, or by burning the older elements of the surface vegetation in order to promote young growth and improve the grazing.

The pollen-diagram (Fig. 166) for this first phase of damage of the Irish woodlands – ILWd$_1$ – shows how agriculture fluctuated in intensity in the vicinity of Littleton Bog. Peaks in the amount of herb and weed pollen reaching the bog alternate with increases in the pollen output of *Ulmus* and *Fraxinus*. The herb peaks rise still higher as the phase progresses, and here perhaps we can also see a general increase in human population. There appears to have been an increase in wealth because, as the Bronze Age progressed, more and more people were able to assemble hoards of bronze; in other words the metal had become more abundant, and it was possible to maintain a stock-pile, rather than have all metal in usable form as servicable implements. But the pattern of migration seems to have continued; as the farmers moved on, *Ulmus* and *Fraxinus* established themselves in the abandoned fields and over the abandoned log stockade. After an interval the farmers returned, cleared the trees, and established their farms once more. Two such major cycles are clearly seen in the diagram.

Then something different happened. About 1,650 BP (300 A.D.) a prolonged period of recovery by *Ulmus* and *Fraxinus* was abruptly ended, and the pollens of these trees fall back to low values, from which they never again recover. There may well have been agricultural revolution followed by population explosion at this time, brought about by the acquirement of new skills from the continent and from Roman Britain. By 300 A.D. Roman methods of agriculture had been established in Britain for 250 years. With the opening of the fourth century, Roman power in Britain was weakening, and Irish raiding was intensifying. Not only was the manpower of the slaves carried back into Ireland utilised, but advantage may have been taken of their familiarity with more advanced techniques of agriculture. The early Irish sagas certainly contain material going back to

this period, and there are numerous references to plough teams and to ploughshares. The early Iron Age in Ireland remains obscure but by this time iron must have been becoming abundant, and more efficient axes and saws were available.

So at about 1,650 BP, a phase of woodland destruction opens – ILWd$_2$ – which continued with gathering momentum until some 250 years ago, when the planting of exotic trees on country estates initiated the reversal of the process. The rapid reduction in the amount of timber available had two effects: first the woodlands could no longer re-expand to engulf an abandoned farm, and secondly there was no longer an inexhaustible supply of wood available for the construction of farm buildings; earth and stone had to be used instead. As a result the abandoned farmsteads of the period, the earth-built rath and the stone-built cashel – the most common-field monuments in Ireland today – are known in numbers that run into tens of thousands.

With their new iron saws and axes the farmers could now clear the woodlands more closely; with their iron ploughs they could disturb the soil more deeply; so it is very probable that significant movement of earth or soil erosion took place at this time. This is an aspect of Irish geomorphology that has been almost completely neglected – when did slopes in Ireland acquire the degree of stability that they have today, so that soil erosion is practically unknown even on relatively steep slopes? It seems that *two* factors are probably important here. First, in the ebbing of the Midlandian Cold Stage there was certainly some solifluction on slopes and some cutting of periglacial valleys, from which material was removed not by water flow but by sludging in a semi-liquid state. This has left the valley with a flat and not an incised floor. As has been recently pointed out for Britain it can be 'argued that solifluxion can take place on slopes very much gentler than those required to promote present-day creep. The result could be that the very gentle slopes of Britain are still in equilibrium with Ice Age periglacial processes and are not capable of being affected by present processes. This general possibility should be carefully considered in the explanation of practically any landforms in Britain'.

Secondly, the consequences of deforestation are also coming to be realised more and more clearly. Evaporation and transpiration are reduced, and there is more run-off water available to transport soil particles. In many of the drumlin areas of Ireland, Monaghan for example, flood plains through which misfit streams thread their way separate many of the drumlins. Drainage trenches in such flood plains reveal layers of peat and prostrate trunks of *Quercus*, many of large size overlain by silts and clay. Such investigations as have been done suggest that these trees are late, and the flood plain and its embedded vegetable material may well date from this phase of woodland clearance. On a Wexford slope charcoal and organic debris (probably from a hearth) with a C^{14} date of 500 A.D. was buried by 1 m of hillwash. Such a phenomenon is well known in the United States where archaeological material of Indian origin and only some hundreds of years old may be buried to a depth of more than a metre in a young flood-plain terrace.

In the phase of woodland destruction – ILWd₂ – the course of the curve for grasses and herbs (including weeds) is of more interest than the curves for the disappearing trees. The curve climbs to a peak at about 1050 BP (900 A.D.) and then falls away sharply; it is tempting to view the rise as indicating the spread of early monastic farming, and the fall as due to the disruption of that agriculture by the Viking raids.

A little later the curve for grasses and herbs surges up again and the detailed counts show that cereal pollen was relatively abundant at this time. Here we are at about 750 BP (1200 A.D.), and must be seeing the record of Anglo-Norman farming following the invasion in 1169 A.D. The Anglo-Normans certainly chose the right moment to enter Ireland, for they did so at a time of very favourable climate (Fig. 174), which was to last for about one hundred years. During this time the invaders were able to carry on corn-farming on the manorial system with considerable success. The curve for herbs and grasses then falls away, while that for *Corylus* rises, and this may indicate a disruption and contraction of farming consequent on climatic deterioration. The 'Black Death' of the fourteenth century may have been due as much to malnutrition as to infection.

The final *coup-de-grâce* was given to the Irish woodlands after the Elizabethan re-conquest had been completed about 350 BP (1600 A.D.). A new type of invader, the Tudor businessman, appeared. To him the woods were not only a source of danger, for they gave shelter to Irish rebels and to wolves, but also a source of quick profit as raw materials for iron-smelting, shipbuilding, barrel-stave making, and the tanning of leather. Just how rapidly the woodlands

melted away is seen in the diagram (Fig. 166).

Until about 250 BP (1700 A.D.), large landholders in Ireland thought it prudent to live in castles or tower-houses, with only narrow slits for windows. About 1700 A.D. political conditions became more stable and wealthy people began to build houses with large rooms and large windows. Through their windows they wanted to see a pleasant wooded prospect, and not the typical 'naked, bleak, dreary view for want of wood' made famous by Arthur Young. On their estates they commonly planted beech (not previously known in Ireland), pine, and elm, and pollen of these planted trees is present in the uppermost layers of Littleton Bog (and of other bogs where these upper layers have survived).

Thus about 250 BP (1700 A.D.) the current phase – ILWe – opened, when afforestation began a re-expansion of the woodlands. One hundred years ago some three per cent of the country had been reclothed with trees, but in the following fifty years political uncertainties led to the extensive felling of demesne timber and by the 1920s the wooded area had fallen to one per cent. Since then vigorous state afforestation programmes have raised the area to about four per cent, by world standards still a very low level.

Without human activities, perhaps 80 per cent of Ireland would be covered by woodlands, 10 per cent by bogs, and 10 per cent by lakes, rivers, and by ground too steep or otherwise unsuitable for the development of forest or bog. However, having been reduced by man to covering less than one per cent of the country, woodland is now slowly re-expanding.

Peat (page 290) cut by hand has been used since time immemorial as a domestic fuel, and in the nineteenth century desultory attempts were made to find economical ways of winning this material on a large scale. The fuel shortages of two world wars, first in 1914–18 and later in 1939–45, gave renewed impetus to these searches, and in 1946 the mechanised production of peat fuel for use in electric power stations and for general industrial and domestic consumption was firmly established. In 1970 10 per cent of the bogland area (one per cent of the area of the country) was under active exploitation. This perhaps represents

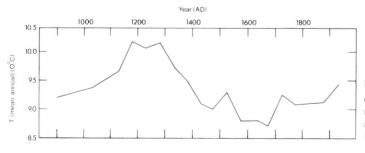

Fig. 174

Graph to illustrate changes in mean annual temperature in England by 50 year averages over the last 1000 years (after H. H. Lamb).

a peak level of activity, for only relatively small areas of the total peatlands lend themselves to mechanical exploitation and from this level there must inevitably be decline.

From all this activity there will be certain geological consequences. Large areas of mineral soil have been re-exposed, run-off has been increased, artificial drainage-channels have been created, and care will have to be taken to ensure that long-term problems are not created.

Blanket-bog started to form about 4,500 BP, a time when sea-level was probably some height above its present level, and might, had human interference not intervened, still be forming at the present day. At many localities on the west coast of Ireland blanket-bog is today being eroded by the sea and 'submerged forests' of Littletonian age are known from many places in the south and east (see Fig. 168). At the time the blanket-peat was forming it was free from marine influence. Therefore, after its high level at about 5,000 BP, sea-level fell to below its present level and blanket-bog then invaded the ground that emerged from below the sea. At a later time – 'after the end of the Late Bronze Age in Ireland' according to Knud Jessen, say around the beginning of the Christian Era – a late rise in sea-level enabled the waves to attack the margins of the blanket-bogs. In many places the peat of the blanket-bog proper has been removed and a layer of wood-peat rich in *Pinus*-stumps exposed. At Roundstone, County Galway, the wood-peat is 2·5 m below modern high-tide level; C^{14} dates for such 'submerged forests' in the south

and west of Ireland centre on 4,000 BP. Some coastal archaeological sites were also 'drowned' by this late rise in sea-level (see Fig. 168).

The question of sea-level changes in the Littletonian Warm Stage is one of world-wide importance. Thus it would be of great value if these late movements in Ireland could be dated. But the problem is a rather intractable one. Pollen analysis is of little help, because by the time that the blanket-peat started to form the local forests had disappeared, due either to climatic change or to human interference. When the sea cut a cliff in the blanket-bog, the natural development of the bog ceased, but plants still continued to grow on its surface and to send roots deep into the underlying peat. Modern carbon has thus been introduced, and it is not possible to apply C^{14} dating even to determine the point in time at which the cliff was cut. But the investigation of the problem has barely started, and when more data have been accumulated some answer may appear.

Lyell showed that it was imperative to study current earth processes in order to be better able to understand the events of the past. The record of the immediate past must now be put under much more detailed scrutiny to see if rhythms and patterns can be deciphered in it. If patterns can be recognised, then it may be possible to project these patterns forwards, and so forecast geological events rather than record them subsequently. Well-founded forecasting is one of the most urgent needs of a world that must endeavour to supply the needs of an ever-increasing population from resources that are ever-diminishing.

BIBLIOGRAPHY

CASE, H. G., DIMBLEBY, G. W., MITCHELL, G. F., MORRISON, M. E. S., & PROUDFOOT, V. B.   1969   Land Use in Goodland Townland, Co. Antrim, from Neolithic Times until today. *J. R. Soc. Ant. Ir.*, **99**, 39–53.

CULLETON, E. B. & MITCHELL, G. F.   1976   Soil Erosion following Deforestation in the Early Christian Period in South Wexford. *J. R. Soc. Antiq. Ir.*, **106**, 120–123.

DAVIES, G. L. H. & STEPHENS, N.   1978   *The Geomorphology of the British Isles – Ireland*. Methuen & Co. Ltd., London, pp. 250.

HERITY, M. & EOGAN, G.   1977   *Ireland in Prehistory*. Routledge & Keegan Paul, London, pp. 302.

JEFFREY, D. W., GOODWILLIE, R. N., HEALY, B., HOLLAND, C. H., JACKSON, J. S., & MOORE, J. J. (Eds.).   1977   *North Bull Island Dublin Bay – a modern coastal natural history*. The Royal Dublin Society, pp. 158.

JESSEN, K.   1949 Studies in Late Quaternary Deposits and Flora-history of
                                    Ireland. *Proc. R. Ir. Acad.*, **52B**, 85–290.

MCCRACKEN, E.   1971 *The Irish Woods since Tudor Times: Their distribution
                                    and exploitation.* David & Charles, Newton Abbot, pp.
                                    184.

MITCHELL, G. F.   1965 Littleton Bog, Tipperary: an Irish Vegetational Record.
                                    Spec. Pap. geol. Soc. Am., **84**, 1–16.

MITCHELL, G. F.   1965 Littleton Bog, Tipperary: an Irish agricultural record. *J. R.
                                    Soc. Antiq. Ir.*, **95**, 121–132.

MITCHELL, G. F.   1972 Soil Deterioration associated with Prehistoric Agriculture
                                    in Ireland. *Proc. 24th. Int. geol. Congr. Montreal, Symp.*
                                    1, 59–68.

MITCHELL, G. F.   1976 *The Irish Landscape.* Collins, London, pp. 240.

MITCHELL, G. F. &   1974 Is there evidence for a Holocene sea-level higher than that
   STEPHENS, N.   of to-day on the coasts of Ireland? *Colloques int. Cent.
                                    natn. Res. scient.*, **219**, 115–125.

WOODMAN, P. C.   1978 The chronology and economy of the Irish Mesolithic:
                                    some working hypotheses. *In* Mellars, P. (Ed.). *The Early
                                    Postglacial Settlement of Northern Europe.* Duckworth,
                                    London, pp. 411.

18

ECONOMIC GEOLOGY

G. D. Sevastopulo

The kinds of geological activities which may be grouped under the broad title of economic geology fall into two fairly distinct categories. The first concerns the application of geology in such fields as civil engineering and agriculture; and the second, the exploration for, and exploitation of earth resources. The first category should be of major importance in Ireland, but is outshone in the public eye by the more dazzling aspects of the second.

Much of the geological contribution to civil engineering is concerned with the site investigation of foundation conditions and other aspects of the construction of buildings, bridges, dams, and so on. Geological information is also important in the siting, design, and construction of tunnels, buried pipelines, roads, cuttings, and embankments. To cater for the increased demand by engineers for geological information, the Geological Survey of Northern Ireland has compiled a 1:21,200 scale special engineering geology map of the Belfast area.

Pedology, geochemistry, and Quaternary geology, are applied in agricultural research; personnel of the Soil Survey division of An Foras Taluntais (The Agricultural Institute) have been systematically mapping during the last 20 years, and have completed a soil map of the whole country on a 1:750,000 scale, as well as more detailed maps of some counties. Geochemistry has important applications in the area of animal (and also human) health, as may be seen from studies correlating the distribution of selenium in soils in County Clare and the incidence of selenosis in sheep. Although these applied aspects of geology are not dealt with at length here, it must be stressed that they have an important contribution to make, and a potential not yet fully realised.

Ireland's earth resources may be conveniently discussed under the following headings: Metals; Industrial Minerals and Rocks; Water; and Fossil Fuels.

Metals

There is a long tradition of metal mining in Ireland, and prehistoric mines are known at a number of sites, particularly in Munster where many of them were preserved (and some probably still remain) under blanket bog. Small mines on Mount Gabriel, near Schull (Fig. 175) in west County Cork, were driven to exploit the copper minerals present in the Old Red Sandstone. The ore was mined by fire-setting: the rock face was heated, and then rapidly cooled by dousing with water, and the shattered rock was ripped away from the face with stone mining mauls. The tip-heaps contained charcoal fragments which have yielded radio carbon dates of approximately 1500 B.C. (Bronze Age). Mining mauls similar to the Mount Gabriel examples and other artefacts have been discovered at several sites, including Derrycarhoon, County Cork, which contained a wooden shovel and a crude wooden ladder, and Ross Island, Killarney, County Kerry.

No direct evidence of prehistoric gold mining has been found, but it seems very likely that the gold of the ornaments now on display in the National Museum of Ireland is of Irish origin, despite the claim by some authorities that its trace element composition is incompatible with indigenous gold.

There is little documentary evidence of the mining of non-ferrous metals in historical times until the end of the seventeenth century. Nevertheless, it is clear that there was some exploitation of lead and silver ores, and Gerrard Boate, in his 'Ireland's Natural History', recorded that mines were operating at Silvermines and elsewhere before the rising of 1641. Iron mining was at its peak in the seventeenth and eighteenth centuries, mainly because wood, which was burned to make the charcoal used in smelting, was much cheaper in Ireland than in Britain.

273

Fig. 175. Locality map of economic deposits mentioned in the text.

From the beginning of the eighteenth until the latter part of the nineteenth century, the Irish mining industry prospered. The production of copper, lead, and pyrites, was at its peak around the middle of the nineteenth century; at that time there were copper mines at Allihies, County Cork; Bunmahon, County Waterford; and Avoca, County Wicklow; and a number of lead mines, including those around Glendalough, County Wicklow (Fig. 175).

The production of metals, particularly copper, had dropped drastically by 1880, and remained at a low level until the beginning of the 1939–45 war. The beginning of the present phase of enhanced exploration and mining activity in the Republic of Ireland can be traced to the Minerals Development Act (1940), which provided the legislative framework for prospecting and mining, and brought into being a state company, Comhlucht Lortha agus Forbartha Mianrai, Teo. (Minerals Exploration and Development Co. Ltd.), which in 1945 became Mianrai Teoranta. During the war years, the company investigated strategic resources, including the East and West Avoca mining areas, from which pyrite for the manufacture of sulphuric acid was produced. Further investigations of the Avoca deposits by Mianrai Teoranta led to underground mining by the St. Patrick's Copper Mines Ltd. Mianrai Teoranta also carried out investigations of the Abbeytown, County Sligo lead-zinc deposit in 1958. The current level of intense prospecting activity in Ireland followed the discovery in 1961 of the Tynagh, County Galway lead-zinc-silver-copper deposit. During the last seventeen years, ore bodies have been discovered at Gortdrum, Avoca, Silvermines and Navan (Fig. 175). In Northern Ireland, there has been considerable exploration activity following the introduction, in 1969, of the Minerals Development Act (N.I.), under which mineral rights were vested in the Ministry of Commerce.

The pattern of changing activity in the Irish metal mining industry over the years must be examined against a background of metal demand and prices; innovations in mining techniques, mineral processing, and prospecting; and in the context of the general industrial development of the country. It is no accident that the phase of increased activity since 1945 followed the development of new prospecting techniques.

Most companies prospecting in Ireland select, and try to obtain prospecting licences for, those areas which are available and judged to be most likely to contain mineralisation. If a licence is granted, the prospector may use a range of techniques to try to define smaller target areas, which after detailed investigation may be further reduced in size, and eventually tested by drilling. It is worth pointing out that a typical prospecting licence covers an area of 25 square kilometres, whereas the projection to the surface of an orebody may cover less than 50,000 square metres, a ratio of 500 to 1.

Geochemistry has been the most widely applied and most successful prospecting tool. Anomalies identified in stream sediment and reconnaissance soil geochemical surveys are usually investigated by more detailed soil surveys. Each of the mines and major prospects found to date has had a geochemical anomaly associated with it; the lead and zinc anomalies which led to the discovery of the important deposit at Navan are shown in Figure 176. Despite its successes, geochemical prospecting is subject to severe limitations: there is little doubt that overburden of more than 10 m (and in some cases considerably less) effectively masks surface anomalies; there is also little understanding of the dispersion of metals through a cover of peat bog. Relatively recent departures from the standard techniques of soil and stream sediment sampling include sampling by power auger from the base of the overburden, the use of mercury gas detectors to pinpoint mercury anomalies which may be related to base metal sulphide occurrences, and the use of geochemistry of bedrock as a guide to mineral

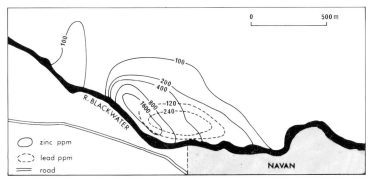

Fig. 176

Lead and zinc soil anomalies associated with the Navan deposit (redrawn from Morrissey and Romer 1975, Figure 3).

haloes around ore bodies. These more sophisticated (and more costly) techniques now play an essential part in exploration in Ireland, particularly since over the last few years many of the more obvious geochemical anomalies have been tested, and there now remain to be assessed the much more numerous subtle anomalies (those with less contrast between anomalous and background values).

Various geophysical techniques have been applied in Irish exploration. Probably the most successful has been induced polarization (IP), which has generally been used after the definition of a target by soil geochemistry. An example of the IP response at Gortdrum, and its relationship to mineralisation is shown in Figure 177. Both airborne and ground-based electromagnetics (EM) surveying, using a variety of methods, including very low frequency (VLF) and INPUT have been applied with limited success. Gravity and magnetic surveys in general have not been used as specific exploration tools, but both contribute in important ways to the understanding of regional geology and structures which may be related to base metal mineralisation. For this reason, the lack of an aeromagnetic map of the Republic of Ireland is a considerable hindrance. Prospecting for uranium, which started in Ireland recently, has mainly involved radiometric surveys carried out using gamma ray

scintillometers, either mounted in vehicles or aircraft, or hand held.

In the last few years, there has been a growing interest in the application of techniques other than geochemistry and geophysics in exploration. As prospecting companies have evolved more sophisticated and specific models for the genesis and localisation of Irish mineral deposits, so the appreciation of detailed geological mapping and stratigraphical and structural synthesis has increased. A recent development in this field has been the drilling of short boreholes to improve geological maps in areas of widespread overburden. Detailed mapping of float boulders, including those cleared from fields and incorporated into walls, has led to an improved knowledge of bedrock geology, and has also shown up areas of mineralisation; almost all the mines and major prospects discovered so far are now known to have had mineralised float close to them.

An increasing use is being made of photogeological interpretation, and the recent completion of aerial photographic coverage of the Republic of Ireland, complementing the coverage of Northern Ireland, is particularly welcome. The interpretation of photographs and other data provided by remote sensing from orbiting satellites seems likely to be a powerful new method for identifying structures which may be linked with mineralisation.

In the following account* the Irish metalliferous occurrences are grouped according to their mineralogy and the stratigraphical age of the host rocks.

Few significant mineral deposits have been discovered in the Pre-Cambrian and early Palaeozoic metamorphic rocks of the north and west of Ireland. Lower Palaeozoic rocks form the hosts to a number of deposits in eastern Ireland, of which the Avoca ore

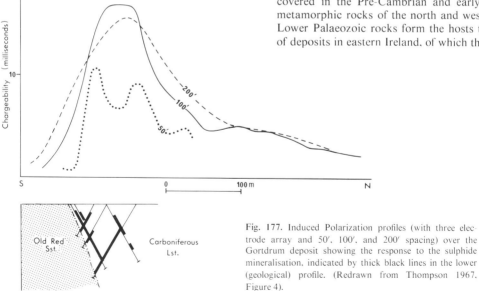

Fig. 177. Induced Polarization profiles (with three electrode array and 50′, 100′, and 200′ spacing) over the Gortdrum deposit showing the response to the sulphide mineralisation, indicated by thick black lines in the lower (geological) profile. (Redrawn from Thompson 1967, Figure 4).

* Only slight modifications have been possible to the statistical material in this chapter since 1978.

bodies are the best known and only currently commercially exploited examples.

The Avoca District (Fig. 178a), situated in a northeast to south-west belt of folded Ordovician volcanic and sedimentary rocks, is an historic mining area, from which copper, iron, sulphur, lead, silver, and zinc, have been produced intermittently since prehistoric times. Current mining activity is centred west

of the Avoca river (West Avoca) but earlier mining, particularly in the nineteenth century, also developed underground workings in East Avoca at Tigroney, Cronebane, Connary, and Kilmacoo. J. W. Platt, who has substantially revised the interpretation of the geology of the Avoca mining district, has described two different ore types in West Avoca: a stratigraphically lower 'stringer' ore, which consists of

Fig. 178. (a) Sketch map of East and West Avoca
(b) Cross-section of the West Avoca Orebodies (looking south-west)
(c) Cross-section of the Cronebane open pit (looking south-west) (Based on Platt 1977, Figures 6, 7, 8).

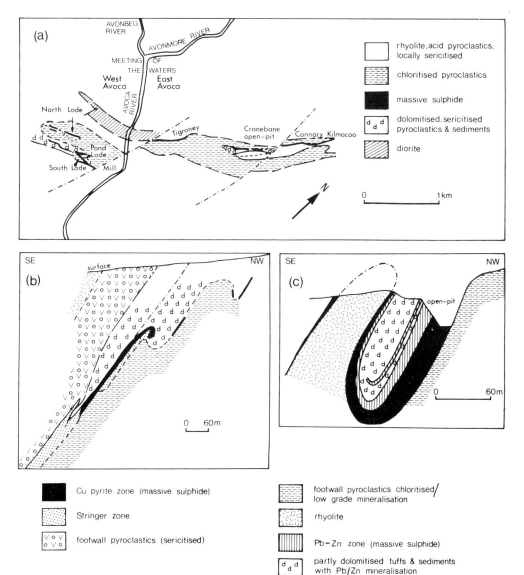

ramifying and cross-cutting quartz-veinlets (stock-work), carrying chalcopyrite and pyrite, within a strongly chloritised acid tuff; and an overlying strati-form massive or banded cupriferous pyrite ore. The ore bodies are developed on the north-west limb and in the core of an isoclinal syncline (Fig. 178b) with its axial plane inclined to the south-east at 55°, and with a 35° south-westerly plunge. The banded sulphide ore of the north-west limb forms the Pond Lode, which has a strike extension of some 350 m and a variable width, averaging 10 m where mined, with an overall grade of about 1·15% copper. The South Lode con-sists mainly of 'stringer' ore; it has a width of approxi-mately 20 m and an average grade of about 0·85% copper. The South Lode grades stratigraphically downwards into sericitised and silicified tuffs, which overlie rhyolites. In the core of the isocline is a sequence of strongly sericitised and dolomitised schistose ashes and agglomerates. The North Lode, a banded pyrite deposit with insignificant copper values, was exploited in the nineteenth century; it may be the Pond Lode horizon, repeated by folding.

The Cronebane orebody, East Avoca (Fig. 178c) has recently been worked by opencast methods. As in West Avoca, a stratiform cupriferous pyrite body overlies 'stringer' ore in chloritised pyroclastics. At Cronebane, however, the cupriferous pyrite is over-lain by a dense fine-grained pyritic lead-zinc-copper ore, a type which is poorly developed in West Avoca. The mineralised horizons are folded into an isoclinal syncline, whose core is occupied by dolomitised tuffs.

The other East Avoca deposits are poorly known. The Tigroney deposit (Fig. 178a) consisted of both massive and 'stringer' ores, which were last mined by the St. Patrick's Copper Mines Ltd. in the 1950s. Between Tigroney and Cronebane, in the so-called 'Dead Ground', massive sulphides were unknown, but recent exploration has shown the presence of 'stringer' mineralisation. It is likely that the Connary and Kil-macoo mines exploited a continuation of the Crone-bane ore body. At all three localities significant values of lead and zinc were encountered; there is a sugges-tion that the ratio of these metals compared to copper increased from the south-west to the north-east. The Kilmacoo mine gave its name to Kilmacooite, a com-plex copper, lead, zinc, iron sulphantimonide, also called 'blue-stone' ore.

It has been estimated that up to the 1939–45 war, about 4 million tonnes* of ore were produced from East and West Avoca. Between 1958 and 1962, a further 2·6 million tonnes, grading 0·7–0·8 per cent copper were extracted. The present mining operation started in 1970, and by the end of 1975, about 4·2

million tonnes of ore had been milled, providing 153,000 tonnes of copper concentrates and 2·8 million tonnes of pyrite. Estimates of future reserves in West Avoca have varied from 3·6 million tonnes, grading 0·8 per cent copper (calculated at the begin-ning of 1976), to higher figures. In East Avoca, recent exploration has indicated approximately 41 million tonnes of low grade (less than 0·5 per cent) copper.

The genesis of the Avoca deposits has been dis-cussed since the time of Thomas Weaver, who had studied under Werner and was manager of the mines in the first decade of the nineteenth century. Weaver recognised the stratiform nature of some of the sul-phides, but most later observers concluded that the mineralisation was discordant with the host rocks, a view which is reflected in the use of the term 'Lode' in the names of the ore bodies. The mineralisation was generally thought to be related to the Leinster Granite intrusion. More recently, the stratiform nature of the banded sulphides and their intimate relationship with Ordovician volcanic rocks have been clearly demon-strated. On the basis of their stratigraphy, mineralogy, associated volcanic rocks, and geological setting, the Avoca ore bodies have been classed in a group of volcanic exhalative deposits, usually associated with island arc volcanism, which includes other examples in the Caledonian/Appalachian belt, such as Parys Mountain, Anglesey and Buchans, Newfoundland. The models of the genesis of such deposits, developed chiefly by study of the Miocene Kuroko ores of Japan, involve metal-rich brines (possibly derived from the interaction of heated water and volcanic rocks, or possibly partly of magmatic origin) rising through the volcanic pile, depositing the stockwork 'stringer' ore, and issuing onto the sea floor, precipi-tating the massive sulphides.

No other metalliferous deposit in Lower Palaeozoic host rocks is now being worked. In the past, there was production from several mines in both Leinster and Ulster. The most important was at Bunmahon on the coast of County Waterford (Fig. 175), where mining started in prehistoric times. The ores con-sisted of chalcopyrite in large steep-dipping quartz-veins, which trended south-east to north-west, normal to the strike of the folded Ordovician (Caradoc) volcanic and shale country rocks. The wall rocks are strongly silicified. Old Red Sandstone basal con-glomerates may be seen to unconformably overlie mineralised veins, indicating a pre-Upper Devonian age of emplacement of the ore. It has been estimated that during the most active phase of mining (1824–76) over 22,000 tonnes of copper metal were shipped as ores and concentrates. Small lead and zinc vein

---

* Throughout this chapter all measures of reserves and production are written in metric units. The tonne (metric ton) is equivalent to 1,000 kg.

deposits in Lower Palaeozoic slates were worked at Caime and Barrystown, County Wexford, and also occur widely in the Longford–Down Lower Palaeozoic inlier, where they were formerly worked around Castleblayney.

Most of the gold which has been discovered in Ireland has been from Lower Palaeozoic terrain. Very small amounts have been recorded in quartz veins in Wicklow, in a stibnite-arsenopyrite vein at Clontibret, County Monaghan (Fig. 175), and in gossans at Avoca. Commercial production in the past has been from the neighbourhood of Woodenbridge, County Wicklow. It is possible that some of the prehistoric gold was from this area (although the Avoca gossans are more likely to have been the source), but the main enterprise in historic times began in 1795, when local people learned that alluvial gold was to be found in the Goldmines River and a large number of them dug the sands and gravels. It has been estimated that between that time and the present, between 230 and 280 kg of gold were produced, most of it before 1850. There has been much speculation as to the location of the mother lode of the alluvial deposit; extensive trenching of the northern slopes of Croghan Kinshela to the south of the river was undertaken in 1801 and 1802 but no trace of gold was found in bedrock.

Mineralisation directly associated with Caledonian granites is known from a number of places, but none is being exploited at present. Molybdenite occurs along the margins of the Murvey granite, County Galway, where 255,000 tonnes of 1·3 per cent MoS_2 have been reported, and also in the Mace–Carna area. A number of lead-zinc vein deposits along the margins of the Leinster Granite were formerly worked, the best known being around Glendalough, Glendasan, and Glenmalure, County Wicklow, and at Ballycorus, County Dublin (Fig. 175). The veins, carrying galena, (some of it argentiferous), sphalerite, subsidiary chalcopyrite, and barytes and carbonate gangue, were steep and trended north and north-east, cutting the granite/schist contact; metal values were highest within the granite. Some of the veins were of considerable extent; the Luganure vein at Glendalough was stoped to a depth of some 200 m, and along its length for 1,260 m. The Glendalough mines are reported to have yielded approximately 51,000 tonnes of lead metal in concentrates. On the eastern margin of the granite near Myshall, County Carlow, pegmatites containing the lithium-bearing mineral spodumene have been discovered. The Caledonian granites are also targets for uranium exploration.

Mineralisation within the Old Red Sandstone occurs mainly in Munster. The most important deposits were in the neighbourhood of Allihies, County Cork (Fig. 175), and were exploited from 1811 until the 1880s, and for a short period in the 1930s. Steeply dipping quartz-veins with both east-west and approximately north-south trends cut the folded Old Red Sandstone and contained chalcopyrite, with minor tetrahedrite-tennantite. The most important deposit was the Mountain Lode, which trended easterly, turned north for some 90 m, and then easterly again; the middle element carried the payable ore and was mined to a depth of approximately 550 m, the deepest mine in Ireland. It has been estimated that ores totalling 27,500 tonnes of copper metal were shipped from the Allihies area, and exploration in the 1950s indicated reserves of at least 1·5 million tonnes of ore grading 1·68 per cent copper. Vein deposits similar to those at Allihies occur elsewhere in West Cork and some of them in the Glandore area contain manganese minerals and barytes.

Strata-bound copper mineralisation (chalcocite, bornite, and chalcopyrite) also is widespread in Counties Cork and Kerry. The sulphides generally occur within grey and green sandstone beds within the varied red and paler strata of the fluviatile Old Red Sandstone. The mineralisation is clearly earlier than the Hercynian folding as the sulphides are commonly deformed.

Almost all the significant metalliferous deposits discovered during the last seventeen years have been within Carboniferous rocks. They may be most conveniently grouped into copper deposits (Gortdrum, Aherlow, Mallow, and Ballyvergin) and those which are predominantly of lead and zinc (Tynagh, Silvermines, Navan, and others) (Fig. 175).

The Gortdrum deposit (Fig. 179) was discovered in 1963 through the use of stream sediment geochemistry, followed by soil geochemistry and an induced potential (IP) geophysical survey (Fig. 177). The open pit mine went into production in 1967 and closed in 1975. The mineralisation was localised in Courceyan aged calcareous shales and bioclastic limestones in two areas (east zone and west zone) on the north side of the east-north-easterly trending and generally northerly dipping Gortdrum Fault, which has an Old Red Sandstone foot-wall. The hanging-wall shales and limestones are intruded by east-west trending basic dykes (altered to soft pale green or buff material, consisting of carbonate, chlorite, and clay minerals) and two plug-like basic bodies. The ore minerals were bornite, chalcocite, chalcopyrite, tennantite, and tetrahedrite, which occurred disseminated and also in thin veinlets and as discrete blebs, with calcite, dolomite, and rare barytes gangue. The Gortdrum ores carried notable amounts of mercury (mainly in the tennantite, but also as cinnabar), antimony, arsenic, and silver. The sulphides were zoned, with tennantite and chalcopyrite dominant near to the surface, and bornite and chalcocite at depth. Pre-production estimates of reserves were 3·8 million tonnes, grading 1·19 per cent copper. During the life of the mine, approximately 3·4 million tonnes of ore are reported to have been milled, producing some 45,000 tonnes of copper, 2·7 tonnes of mercury, and 9·12 tonnes of silver. Very little information has been published on which to base hypotheses concerning the age or genesis of the Gortdrum deposit. The mineralisation is almost certainly post-Courceyan in age, because many of the altered basic dykes (probably related to the Chadian or Asbian volcanics of the region) are themselves mineralised. The close spatial relationship of the orebodies and the Gortdrum Fault is surely significant; the fault is likely to be Hercynian in age, but may have had a protracted history of movement from Dinantian times onward. J. A. Greig and his co-workers have analysed the isotopic composition of lead in a galena from Gortdrum and have calculated a model age of 130 or 75 m.y. (depending on the constant used). The significance of this date may be questioned, firstly because galena forms such a small

proportion of the sulphides that its formation may be unrelated to the emplacement of the copper ore, and secondly because the assumption of a single stage evolution of the lead may not be correct. The temperature of the fluids from which the ore was precipitated is thought to have been less than 200° C, because of the stability range of some of the silver and mercury minerals present.

Copper deposits at the Glen of Aherlow and near Mallow (Fig. 175) are both similar in many respects to the Gortdrum deposit. The Aherlow deposit (Fig. 180), reported to contain 5·5 million tonnes grading 0·89 per cent copper and 44·9 gm/tonne silver, was discovered by soil geochemistry. The mineralisation, disseminated and coarser chalcopyrite, chalcocite, and bornite, with calcite, dolomite, and barytes gangue, occurs in a steeply dipping zone of fractured and sheared Courceyan sub-Waulsortian shales and limestones, which is up to 30 m wide and has an east-west strike length of approximately 600 m. There is some zoning of sulphides across the ore zone, with low

Fig. 179. a and b. Sections across the west and east zones, Gortdrum, looking west. (Carboniferous Limestone on location map left blank). (Redrawn from Steed 1974, Figure 2).

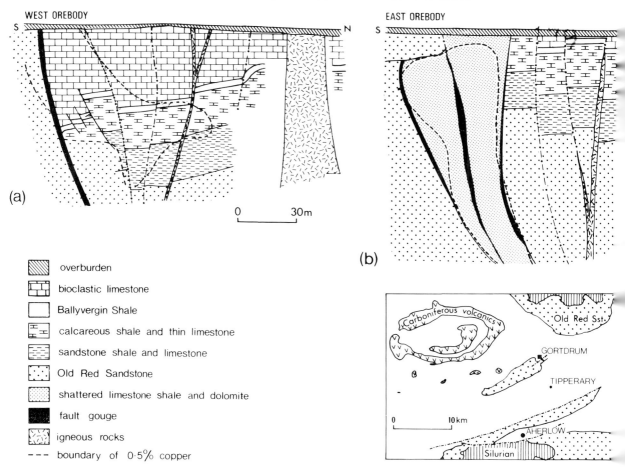

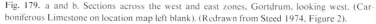

grade disseminated chalcopyrite (and locally galena and sphalerite) around the margin of the zone, and chalcopyrite, chalcocite, and bornite in the higher grade interior. Silver occurs as the native element, and also in stromeyerite. In contrast to the Gortdrum mineralisation, tennantite and tetrahedrite are uncommon and mercury has not been detected. As at Gortdrum, the localisation of the mineralisation is structurally controlled; it seems likely that the structures are Hercynian in age.

The discovery, in 1973, of the Mallow deposit through geochemical and geophysical surveys prompted by finds of weakly mineralised limestone outcrops, has been described by D. G. Wilbur and J. J. Royall. The deposit is reported to contain 3·6 million tonnes, grading 0·7 per cent copper and 27·4 gm/tonne silver. The mineralisation consists of disseminations and veinlets of chalcopyrite, bornite, chalcocite, and tennantite, with subordinate native silver, galena, and sphalerite, and calcite, dolomite, and quartz gangue. It occurs within limestones and shales up to 120 m above the Old Red Sandstone at the crest and on the northern flank of an anticlinal flexure, on the north-west margin of the Old Red Sandstone inlier some 6·5 km north of Mallow. The Ballyvergin deposit, approximately 136,000 tonnes grading 1 per cent copper and 17·1 gm/tonne silver, also occurs in shales and limestones close above the Old Red Sandstone. The mineralisation consists mainly of disseminated chalcopyrite, localised in a small elongated dome.

The common factors linking the four copper deposits are, firstly, their location in the south of the country (however, small copper deposits have been worked in historical times farther north – for example, at Beauparc, County Meath, a short distance east of Navan); secondly, their stratigraphical position – all fairly close to the Old Red Sandstone; and thirdly, the localisation of the ore by structures (of various types) which are probably Hercynian in age.

The majority of deposits found in Carboniferous rocks have been of lead and zinc. The first of these to be mined in recent times was at Tynagh, County Galway (Fig. 175). It was discovered in 1961 through the use of soil geochemistry, an EM survey, and subsequent drilling, in an area in which the Geological Survey of Ireland had previously mapped a train of sandstone boulders with copper mineralisation. Opencast production started in 1965 and underground production in 1972.

The deposit lies on the northern side of the Tynagh Fault, an east-west trending normal fault with a displacement probably in excess of 600 m, which brings Old Red Sandstone and Courceyan and Chadian limestones into contact in the mine area (Fig. 181). The lower limestones and shales in the hanging wall are similar to those encountered elsewhere in the south (see p. 152), but the Waulsortian Limestone Complex is atypical and shows considerable lateral variation. Normal *in situ* mudbank limestones are confined to areas close to the fault, and the bulk of the Complex consists of limestones including coarse

Fig. 180. North-south cross-section of the Aherlow copper deposit (redrawn from Cameron and Romer 1970, Figure 2).

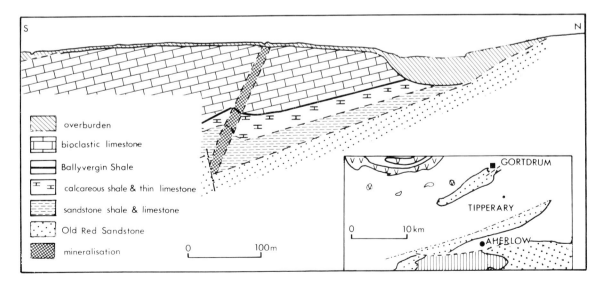

conglomerates and breccias, which were derived (in part, probably by slumping) from mudbank limestones; the conglomeratic limestones become thinner, finer-grained, and better bedded northwards. The lower part of the Complex interfingers with the Tynagh Iron Formation, alternations of graded limestones and cherty ironstones, which extends for at least 1,800 m along strike and 600 m north-south. The ironstone beds, which in some sections make up between quarter and half the formation, consist of hematite and chert with subordinate iron carbonates and silicates, and very little alumina. Individual beds range in thickness up to a metre or more, and some contain structures interpreted by R. W. Schultz as being of algal origin. Overlying the Waulsortian Limestone Complex, are dark argillaceous and locally pyritous limestones, informally termed 'Calp'.

The deposit contained both primary ore (sulphides in a limestone host) and a secondary residual ore, composed of metal-rich rubble and mud, formed by the weathering of primary ore. The primary mineralisation, sphalerite (low iron variety), argentiferous galena, chalcopyrite, tennantite, and a number of rarer sulphosalts, associated with pyrite, marcasite,

barytes, calcite, and dolomite, occurs as replacements, cavity lining and fillings, and veinlets; micritic limestones of the Waulsortian Limestone Complex were the favoured host lithology, but close to the fault, other limestones are also mineralised.

The secondary residual ore (Fig. 181b), which was exploited by open cast methods and is now exhausted, has been described by C. J. Morrissey and D. Whitehead. It consisted of a complex body of mineralised rubble and mud, nearly 700 m long, up to 165 m wide, and up to 75 m deep, overlying, and in some places grading into, the western part of the primary mineralisation. The residuum included fragments of primary ore up to 2 m or more across, decalcified 'Calp' Limestone, clay, and brown, yellow, orange, and multi-coloured rubble and mud, formed by oxidation of primary ore and limestone. As well as varied primary sulphides, sulphosalts, and gangue minerals, thirty-eight supergene minerals were identified; these included carbonates (cerussite, smithsonite, malachite, azurite, and others), arsenates, sulphates, silicates, oxides, and metals (native copper and silver). C. J. Morrissey and his co-workers in 1971 estimated that the primary deposit contained 8·5 million tonnes,

Fig. 181. (a) Sketch map of the Tynagh area.
          (b) Cross-section of the Tynagh deposit looking west.
               (Figure 181a redrawn from Moore 1975, Figure 1, and Figure 181b from Derry, Clark, and Gillat 1965, Figure 2).

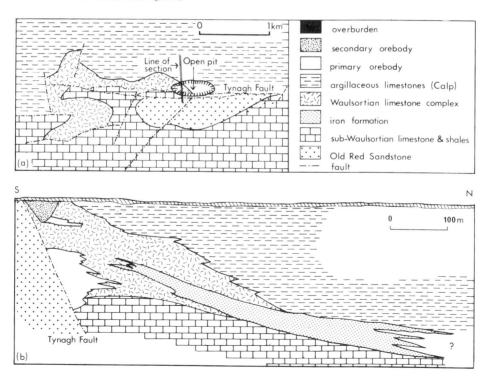

grading 3 per cent lead, 3·2 per cent zinc, 0·3 per cent copper, and 34·3 gm/tonne silver; and the secondary residual deposit 3·8 million tonnes, grading 9·1 per cent lead, 7·4 per cent zinc, 0·6 per cent copper, and 109·7 gm/tonne silver. Up to the beginning of 1978, approximately 7·5 million tonnes of ore had been mined, and it is unlikely that more than 2 million tonnes remain.

The genesis of the primary ores is controversial; some authorities have favoured a late (post-Dinantian) age for the mineralisation, but others believed that the sulphides were deposited whilst at least part of the host limestones were forming. It is generally agreed that the Tynagh Fault was in some way linked to the localisation of the deposit, and most of the arguments have been about the age of the faulting, the interpretation of textural relationships of sulphides and host limestones, and the association of the sulphide mineralisation and the Tynagh Iron Formation (Fig. 181b).

The views of R. W. Schultz, who made a detailed study of the deposit, may be summarised as follows. The iron and silica of the Iron Formation were derived by intense chemical weathering of Dinantian sediments, uplifted during mid-Dinantian movements, and were transported into a sheltered basin where they were precipitated with limited dilution by other sediments. The lead-zinc-copper mineralisation occurred later (an opinion in accordance with model lead ages of 230 (or 175) m.y. obtained by J. A. Greig and his co-workers from two samples of galena); the ores formed replacements and filled solution cavities, which cross-cut the primary calcite-filled cavities of the Waulsortian mudbanks. Mineralisation was intimately associated with the Tynagh Fault, for which there was no evidence of Dinantian movements.

D. R. Derry and his co-workers suggested that submarine springs, related to local volcanic activity, occurred along the line of the Tynagh Fault, which was thought to have been active and discharged solutions rich in barium, lead, zinc, iron, silica, copper, and silver. The iron and silica were precipitated in a protected basin off the margins of the mudbanks (forming the Iron Formation), whilst the other elements moved less far, and formed sulphides both at the sediment surface and in cavities within the carbonates of the Waulsortian Complex.

Recent work has supported some features of Derry's model. J. McM. Moore has shown that the Tynagh Fault has a complex history of movement with initial normal faulting, followed by reverse-oblique slip movements (?Hercynian) which postdated the sulphide mineralisation. There is no evidence in the stratigraphy that the fault was active during the deposition of the sub-Waulsortian succession, but thickness variations, and the prevalence of

conglomeratic and graded limestones, north of the fault, point to movement during the deposition of the Waulsortian limestones. M. J. Russell has compared the Tynagh Iron Formation to the recent iron-rich sediments being formed within the hot brine pools of the Red Sea. He attributed anomalous concentrations of manganese and zinc within limestones of the Waulsortian Complex, found up to 7 km away from the mine, to dispersion from submarine springs near the Tynagh Fault. The springs produced the exhalative Iron Formation and were fed from a hydrothermal system which gave rise to the apparently epigenetic sulphide mineralisation. It is unlikely that the hydrothermal activity was related to local volcanicity.

The secondary residual deposit is thought to have begun to form in the late Tertiary (page 233) when mineralised Waulsortian limestones, probably rich in pyrite and marcasite, were exposed on a land surface some 6–15 m higher than the present surface. Oxidation of the sulphides at the surface caused very acid groundwater, which progressively etched out an elongate, steep-sided cavern; this was gradually filled by the settling and collapse of disaggregated primary ore, and by dark mud, formed from the decalcification of 'Calp' limestone and transported into the depression from the north. The continuing dissolution of limestone at depth and the differential compaction of the residuum resulted in local depressions which became filled with newly-formed and reworked residuum, producing an extremely complex stratigraphy. During much of its existence the bulk of the residuum was probably water-logged, which may explain its surprisingly high sulphide content. Ground water movement was, in general, downwards and to the north, and there was extensive movement of metals towards the periphery of the deposit; some were precipitated as supergene sulphides (logs of the fossil wood *Sequoia* associated with the 'Calp', were replaced by sphalerite and cadmium sulphides); and large quantities formed carbonates at the margin of the deposit by reactions between metal-bearing solutions and the limestone wall rock. Gossans formed where the deposit was above the local water table and in areas of high ground-water flow. The gossan developed about primary ore rich in galena and tennantite in the central part of the deposit was enriched in silver.

The second significant lead-zinc deposit found in the last seventeen years was in the Silvermines district, County Tipperary (Fig. 175), where mining has been carried on sporadically since at least the seventeenth century. The mineralisation was discovered by drilling, mainly in 1963–64, following a soil geochemical survey, and IP and EM geophysical surveys; it occurs in Old Red Sandstone and Carboniferous Limestone mostly on the north side of the east-north-east trending Silvermines Fault, part of a major fault complex which may be traced westwards for some 25 km to the Cratloe hills, County Clare.

The exploration outlined a number of mineralised zones, along some 3500 m parallel to the fault. The present underground mine came into production in 1968 and exploits the 'G' and 'B' zone orebodies, which lie approximately 2000 m and 1400 m west of Silvermines village and just north of the Ballynoe barytes deposit. A cross section through the more important 'G' zone is shown in Figure 182. In the mine area the fault has an Old Red Sandstone footwall. Few details of the stratigraphy of the hanging wall limestones have been published, but it appears that the Courceyan section is similar to, but substantially thinner than, equivalent successions in the vicinity, and that much of the bedded limestones, and also the Waulsortian mudbank limestones, have been strongly dolomitised. In the 'G' zone, two developments of ore have been recognised. The lower orebody parallels the Silvermines Fault and the mineralisation, generally coarse-grained sphalerite and galena, with less abundant pyrite, chalcopyrite, and tetrahedrite, occurs as fracture fillings, replacements, and disseminations, and is clearly discordant. The upper orebody lies at the base of the Waulsortian mudbank limestones and is a stratiform body of dominantly fine-grained massive sulphides, which exhibit banded and colloform textures; pyrite forms some 75 per cent of the sulphides, sphalerite 20 per cent, and galena 5 per cent.

The 'B' zone deposit is similar to, and at the same stratigraphical level as, the upper 'G' zone orebody. The other orebodies known are all discordant and closer to the fault: the Shallee mine, approximately 3700 m west of Silvermines, exploited low grade lead mineralisation in fractured Old Red Sandstone in the footwall of the fault; the 'K' zone orebody, approximately 600 m south-south-west of Silvermines, consists of zinc and lead mineralisation in fractured Old Red Sandstone and sub-Waulsortian dolomites in both the footwall and the hanging wall; and the 'C' zone, 600 m south-south-east of Silvermines, contains mainly secondarily oxidised ores in fractures in the Old Red Sandstone in the footwall.

The upper 'G' zone and 'B' zone orebodies are estimated to have totalled 12·7 million tonnes, grading 2·4 per cent lead, 8·31 per cent zinc, and 28·4 gm/tonne silver. The lower 'G' zone orebody contained an estimated 1·9 million tonnes, grading 4·5 per cent lead, 3·4 per cent zinc, and 38·7 gm/tonne silver. The 'K' zone orebody may contain approximately 2 million tonnes, grading better than 5 per cent lead and zinc combined.

The Silvermines orebodies have been studied more

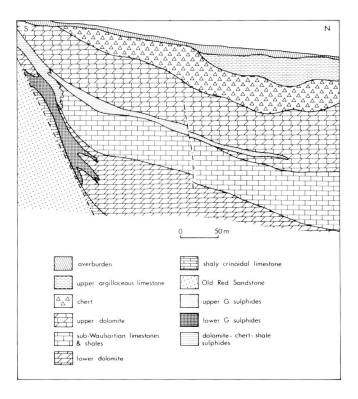

Fig. 182

Cross-section of the Silvermines deposit looking west (based on Greig et al. 1970, Figure 2).

intensively than any other lead-zinc deposits in Ireland. There is no doubt that in the lower 'G' zone and similar orebodies close to the fault, the sulphides were emplaced after the lithification and tectonic fracturing of the host rocks; but the stratiform nature and colloform, banded texture of the upper 'G' zone and 'B' zone orebodies and the presence of features interpreted as slumps, strongly suggest that the sulphides there accumulated on the sea floor.

One model of the mineralisation is as follows: during the late Courceyan, metal-bearing hydrothermal brines were channelled up the then active Silvermines Fault complex; as they ascended, they reacted with the sub-Waulsortian limestones to form the Lower Dolomite shown in Figure 182, and deposited sulphides in fractures in the Old Red Sandstone and the overlying carbonates and shales. The brines flowed out onto the sea bed through submarine springs and precipitated the stratiform sulphides and the barytes of the Ballynoe deposit. The hydrothermal system continued after the deposition of the sulphides, and the brines caused the alteration of Waulsortian mudbank limestones to the Upper Dolomites and Breccias.

Several separate analytical studies have thrown more light on the formation of the deposits, but many of the data are difficult to interpret. Greig and his co-workers suggested that the temperatures of deposition of the Lower 'G' zone orebody ranged from about 150° C to 257° C with most values around 225° C; their estimates were based on the homogenisation temperatures of a few fluid inclusions, and on the partitioning of sulphur isotopes between pairs of sulphur-bearing minerals assumed to have been deposited in isotopic equilibrium. P. G. Coomer and B. W. Robinson determined a greater range of temperatures, using similar isotopic techniques. The sulphur isotopes of the lower orebody fall in a narrow range (δ^{34}S of 8 per mil to 4 per mil) and show a distinct distributional trend, becoming relatively depleted in δ^{34}S upwards along the fault. This has been interpreted as resulting from the reaction of hydrothermal fluids with the carbonate host rocks and the attendant rise in pH and oxygen fugacity of the fluids. According to this model the mainly negative δS^{34} values would be derived from a fluid with an initial δS^{34} of zero, the value of sulphur of juvenile origin. However, the sulphides of the 'B' and upper 'G' zones have a wide range of isotopic values (δ^{34}S of 12 per mil to 35·8 per mil), which, according to Coomer and Robinson, suggest that they were biogenically precipitated. Furthermore, the isotopic composition of the barytes in the Ballynoe deposit, and in veins in the sulphide bodies, is not very variable (δ^{34}S of 17·0 per mil to 20·8 per mil) and is similar to that of Lower Carboniferous seawater sulphate. Coomer and Robin-

son have suggested that while the sulphur of the lower 'G' zone was of magmatic origin, that of the barytes and stratiform sulphides was derived from seawater sulphate. Greig and his co-workers obtained a model age of 115 m.y. (or 60 m.y., depending on the constants used) from the isotopic composition of lead in galenas; this date conflicts with the geological evidence for a Carboniferous age for the upper 'G' zone sulphides.

The third major lead-zinc deposit was discovered in 1970 approximately 1·5 km west of Navan, County Meath (Fig. 175). A geochemical survey (Fig. 176) revealed an extensive area of anomalously high lead and zinc values in the soil. Following encouraging results from an IP survey, a systematic diamond drilling programme was undertaken, which outlined a large orebody with reserves probably in excess of 80 million tonnes of ore with a grade better than 11 per cent lead and zinc combined. An underground mine on the south side of the river Blackwater came into production in 1977. The near-surface portion of the orebody on the north side of the river is to be mined by open-cast methods.

Few details of this fascinating and extremely important deposit have yet been published. The mineralisation occurs in Courceyan limestones, not far south of the Lower Palaeozoic/Carboniferous contact. The stratigraphical succession in the mine area is shown in Figure 183. Red sandstones and conglomerates, probably generally less than 30 m thick, rest unconformably on the Lower Palaeozoic and pass upwards into laminated, burrowed sandstones and siltstones, overlain by argillaceous bioclastic limestones ('Muddy Limestones'). The 'Pale Beds' which form the host to the sulphides consist of variably sandy bioclastic limestones and oolites, with a well-marked unit of micrites near their base. The 'Upper Dark Limestones' are dark basinal limestones which overlie limestone boulder conglomerates resting on an eroded surface of 'Pale Beds'.

The mineralisation is concentrated between two converging faults, the 'A Fault', a north-easterly trending high angle reverse fault, and the 'B Fault' (Fig. 183), which has a normal displacement and trends east-west. The 'Pale Beds' and the orebody both dip south-westwards at 20°. A massive development of ore in the north-east splits down dip into separate tongues which parallel the stratification within the 'Pale Beds'. The ore is mineralogically simple, consisting of sphalerite and galena, with a zinc/lead ratio of 5/1, subsidiary pyrite, barytes, and rare fluorite. The 'Pale Beds' are extensively dolomitised in the mineralised zones. The sulphides are generally fine-grained with textures varying from massive to fine fracture fills and disseminations; the massive sulphides show banding of light and dark sphalerite and galena, well-developed colloform textures, and spectacular brecciated sulphides in which several episodes of brecciation of pre-existing sulphides and recementation with banded sulphide can be made out.

One of the most intriguing questions regarding the Navan deposit is whether the mineralisation is in some way related to the unconformity below the 'Upper Dark Limestones'. The erosion surface has a channel-like cross-section and rises rapidly to the west of the deposit, where there are substantial thicknesses of Waulsortian mudbank limestones and underlying bedded limestones and shales, which are cut out in the area shown in Figure 183. The base of the 'Upper Dark Limestones', a few kilometres east of the deposit, is Arundian in age and so Chadian strata, if ever deposited, have also been eroded. It seems likely that the unconformity resulted from local uplift and erosion and it is therefore extremely interesting that the erosion surface truncates the 'B Fault'. It also appears to truncate the ore horizons, which themselves are shifted by the 'B Fault'; this indicates that the emplacement of the sulphides occurred between late Courceyan and early Arundian times. It is tempting to postulate that Chadian faulting and uplift, resulting in tectonic fracturing and limestone solution, opened up the 'Pale Beds' to become a conduit; other

features of a genetic model for the deposit, such as the source of the metals, of the sulphides, and the nature of the transporting fluids, will only emerge from detailed research.

A number of other significant discoveries made since 1961 (Fig. 175) either have not been of sufficient size to warrant development, or are still being assessed. The deposit at Keel, County Longford, was discovered in 1962 by detailed geochemical soil and IP surveys and by diamond drilling, following encouraging results from an initial stream sediment geochemical survey. Further underground exploration and assessment was carried out through the sinking of a 180 m deep shaft. The deposit is reported to contain 1·8 million tonnes grading 7 per cent zinc and lead combined. The mineralisation occurs on the down-faulted southern flank of the Lower Palaeozoic inlier some 10 km south-south-east of Longford town, in conglomerates and sandstones, and overlying mudstones, sandstones, and carbonates ('Mixed Beds'), which form the lower part of the local Carboniferous (Courceyan) succession. Sphalerite is the dominant sulphide and contains high concentration of cadmium and inclusions of silver-bearing tetrahedrite; galena is subsidiary. The mineralisation occurs as breccia and fracture fillings and replacements related to a series of

Fig. 183.   Cross-section of the Navan deposit looking south-east (redrawn from Mining Magazine, July 1975, Figure 1).

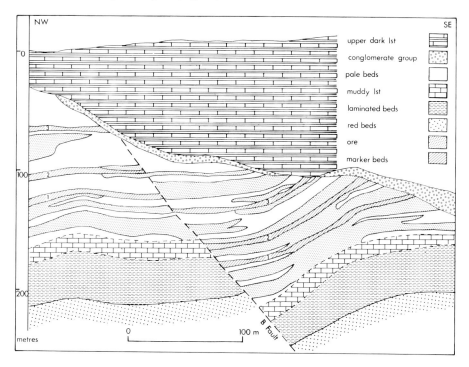

north-east south-west trending faults. A later north-south trending set of faults shifts both the early faults and the mineralisation. A model lead age of 270 m.y. (or 215 m.y. depending on the constant used) was obtained from galenas from Keel. Limited homogenisation temperatures of fluid inclusions in sphalerite suggest that the mineralising fluids were at least as hot as 175° C.

The deposit at Ballinalack, County Westmeath, was discovered through a reconnaissance geochemical survey, followed by detailed soil geochemical and IP surveys and by diamond drilling during 1969–1970. It is reported to contain over 3 million tonnes with a grade of 8·5 per cent lead and zinc combined. The mineralisation of sphalerite, pyrite, and subordinate galena, with calcite, dolomite, and barytes, occurs as fracture fillings and replacements in Waulsortian mudbank limestones; some of the sulphides appear to be an early component of the fill of cavities in the bank limestones. Although faulting occurs, it is not known whether it controls the localisation of the ore.

Significant but non-economic deposits have been discovered near Moate, County Westmeath (sphalerite, pyrite, and subordinate galena occurring as fillings in steeply-dipping fractures in sandy and oolitic limestones close to the local base of the Carboniferous succession); near Ferbane, County Offaly; and Carickittle, County Limerick. In all of these, the host rocks are Courceyan in age; the only deposit worked recently for which the host rocks are known to be younger is at Abbeytown, near Ballisadare, County Sligo. Mining has continued there sporadically since the seventeenth century and about 1 million tonnes of low grade lead and zinc ore (probably less than 5 per cent lead and zinc combined) are estimated to have been extracted up to 1961 when operations ceased. The mineralisation consisted of sphalerite, galena, and pyrite which occurred as high grade replacement bands, disseminations, and in breccias within a block of shallow-dipping Chadian and Arundian limestones and dolomites (close to the local base of the Carboniferous succession), bounded by two east-west trending faults.

There has been considerable speculative discussion regarding the genesis and localisation of the many Carboniferous base metal deposits, which have earned Ireland the tag of a 'metallogenetic province'. In the search for a unifying factor or factors there has been a tendency to regard all the deposits as having been formed at the same time and by the same processes. However, while there are many similarities between individual deposits there are equally many differences. One fundamental aspect on which it is hoped that there will be further research is the age of the mineralisation. The balance of the evidence available suggests that the Navan, Silvermines, Tynagh, and Ballina-lack deposits were formed in mid-Dinantian times (although this runs counter to the lead isotope dating), and the Gortdrum, Aherlow, and Abbeytown deposits later. Further lead isotope dating together with potassium/argon dating of clays, altered and formed during the mineralisation, is required.

Almost certainly, components of the deposits were transported by heated chloride-rich brines, but what proportion of the latter originated as connate water, deeply circulating meteoric waters, or juvenile waters is not known, although the association of pyrobitumens with a number of deposits suggest that connate waters played at least some part. The few rather uncertain estimates of the temperatures of deposition of the ores (almost all in excess of 100° C and some close to and above 200° C) are rather higher than those found in the deposits of the Mississippi Valley mineral district of North America with which Ireland has often been compared. Such temperatures have a particular significance in the cases of Silvermines and Tynagh (if, as suggested above, the ores formed in mid-Dinantian times) since they could not have been generated within the local Courceyan and Upper Devonian sedimentary pile unless the geothermal gradient was substantially higher than the present usual 30° C/km. Morrissey and his co-workers have suggested that higher geothermal gradients may have existed; certainly magma chambers at shallow depth in the Limerick region during Chadian times must have produced high gradients locally.

A number of theoretically possible sources existed for both the sulphide and the metals. The sulphide could have been derived from Carboniferous sea-water sulphate, from Carboniferous evaporites, from the bacterial or thermal degradation of long-chain organic molecules within Carboniferous sediments, or from magmatic sources. The metals may have been scavenged from Upper Devonian, Carboniferous, or Lower Palaeozoic sedimentary rocks and volcanics, or from Caledonian Granites, or may have been derived from mantle sources. Greig has argued that the isotopic composition of lead from various deposits suggests a deep regional, rather than local, source.

In addition to our ignorance about the origin of the components and their transport, we know very little about the reasons for the localisation of the Irish metal deposits. The association of easterly to north-easterly trending faults with many of the deposits is impressive, but as Morrissey has pointed out, mineralisation is restricted to a very small proportion of the strike length of each fault. Clearly the fracturing associated with the faulting may have provided favoured conduits, and seismic pumping associated with the repeated movements of a fault may have allowed the rapid passage of the large quantities of hydrothermal fluids required to form deposits such as that at Navan. Although there has been very little research on the topic, it seems likely that the permeability of the Courceyan shale and carbonate sequences (including the Waulsortian mudbank limestones) was already very much reduced when the sulphides of deposits such as Tynagh and Silvermines were precipitated. It may be that faulting was also important in providing an upwards passage for formation waters from the underlying sandstones, whose permeability may have been greater. Several commentators have suggested other specific controls of the localisation of mineralisation. M. J. Russell has postulated that the metal deposits occurred at the intersection of deep-seated north-south fractures (related to incipient opening of the North Atlantic) with the easterly to north-easterly trending faults mentioned above. According to R. R. Horne, the deposits in Carboniferous and older rocks lie along regularly spaced north-west trending fracture zones which were derived from transform faults in a Lower Palaeozoic Proto–Atlantic Ocean. These fundamental fractures acted as channel ways, through which hydrothermal fluids carrying metals derived from Caledonian oceanic crust moved upwards into the high-level east to north-easterly trending faults in Carboniferous rocks. Ingenious though both hypotheses are, there does not appear to be very much independent evidence for either fundamental north-south geofractures or regularly spaced north-west trending structures. Other authors have pointed out the coincidence of base metal deposits in Ireland (and Britain) and Caledonian granites, either at surface or inferred from gravity data, and have suggested that the granites may have acted as channel ways for solutions of deep-seated origin because of their clean vertical tension fractures. Caledonian granites may also have affected the localisation of any metal deposits formed by hydrothermal solutions originating as formation water in Carboniferous basins; the granites are likely to have been overlain by thin accumulations up-dip of the thicker 'basinal' sequences from which brines may have been expelled by compaction. The Silvermines area presents an interesting association of a metal deposit, gravity low, and thin Upper Palaeozoic succession; there and elsewhere a great deal more research is required before the genesis and localisation of Irish lead, zinc, copper, and silver deposits is even partially understood.

Iron ores (of very low grade, judged by the standards of today) were extensively worked in Ireland from the sixteenth to the early part of this century, and the remains of old ironworks may be seen in many places. In most cases the furnaces were put out when the supply of local timber dwindled. The most important ores were hematite-bearing veins and hematitic cherts in the Lower Palaeozoics and Old Red Sandstone; Upper Carboniferous clay ironstone concretions and bands, particularly in the Leinster and Connacht Coalfields, and around the Shannon estuary; laterites from the Tertiary Interbasaltic Formation of County Antrim (which were last exploited during the 1939–45 war); and bog iron. The Interbasaltic Formation of County Antrim was also worked for bauxite in this century.

Industrial minerals and rocks

Within this category are included the varied non-metallic minerals and rocks which, in their natural state or after processing, are the raw materials of industry. Although they lack the glamour of the base metal sulphides, they are important natural resources and their exploitation results in a significant contribution to Ireland's economy, not least by providing widespread employment. In what follows, those minerals and rocks used in agriculture, and in the manufacture of chemicals and other products, are discussed before those used without elaborate processing in the construction and allied industries. This division, it should be recognised, is arbitrary and results in certain materials, for instance limestones, falling in both categories.

Most industrial minerals and rocks are used locally, but one exception is barytes, of which Ireland is a major producer and exporter, almost entirely from the deposit at Ballynoe, County Tipperary (Fig. 175). There barytes, accompanied by hematite and pyrite, occurs at the base of the Waulsortian mudbank limestones, in the same position as the sulphide mineralisation of the nearby Silvermines deposit to which it is clearly genetically related. The deposit has been worked by opencast methods since 1963 and the barytes is exported for use mainly in drilling mud. As with many of Ireland's industrial minerals, there is a lack of published firm estimates of reserves. However, production is now in excess of 250,000 tonnes a year, and it is likely that future reserves and past production together total more than 5 million tonnes. Barytes also occurs as a gangue mineral in the Tynagh sulphide deposit and is now being won from the tailings. The Benbulben Barytes Mine, a relatively small deposit with reserves likely to be less than 400,000 tonnes, has been exploited intermittently since the last century and is at present in production. The barytes occurs within a vein, a metre or so wide, cutting the Carboniferous Dartry Limestone on top of Kings Mountain, County Sligo. In the past, barytes-filled fractures in Old Red Sandstone were worked at a number of mines in west Cork, one of which, the

Ladys Well mine at Duneen, near Clonakilty, is now being reassessed.

In contrast to barytes, which is a relatively rare mineral, calcite, as the main constituent of limestone, is readily available over most of Ireland, although deposits of very high purity are not so common. Most of the limestone quarried (apart from that produced for aggregate and roadstone) is used in the manufacture of cement and agricultural ground limestone; almost all the quarries are in Carboniferous Limestone, but the Chalk, also, is exploited in Ulster. Smaller amounts of limestone are used in an enormous range of industries, including the production of glass, chemicals, and foodstuffs. Considerable quantities of burned lime are used in the clarification of sugar and for agricultural purposes and hydrated lime is supplied to the building industry. Small deposits of high grade calcite, occurring as veins within the Carboniferous Limestone, have been worked near Ennis and in north County Clare.

Clays and shale are exploited for use in the production of cement and for the manufacture of land-drainage tiles, pipes, and bricks. The use of concrete in buildings and the trend towards more centralised production of natural materials has resulted in a drastic reduction in the number of operating quarries and pits. G. H. Kinahan, writing in 1888, recorded clay deposits used for brickmaking in almost every county. Many of the bricks used in Belfast and Dublin during the last and early part of this century were produced locally; from glacial clays, boulder clay and Keuper Marl in Belfast; and from boulder-clay, picked clean of stones by hand, in Dublin. Now probably less than twenty deposits are worked, most of them in Ulster. They include Ordovician mudstones at Slane, County Meath; Upper Carboniferous shales and fireclays from the Leinster Coalfield, and from around Coalisland and Dungannon, County Tyrone; Permo-Triassic mudstones at Kingscourt, County Cavan; Tertiary clays from around Lough Neagh (page 231); and glacial and alluvial clays from a number of localities.

Dolomite occurs commonly within the Carboniferous Limestone, but large deposits of high purity are largely restricted to the east and south-east part of the country. One such deposit is quarried at Bennettsbridge, County Kilkenny, with production reported to be in excess of 200,000 tonnes a year. The dolomite is crushed and transported to Dungarvan, County Waterford, where it is burned and reacted with sea water to form magnesite (magnesium carbonate) which is mainly exported.

Gypsum and halite (rock salt), both evaporite minerals, occur in commercial quantities in the Permo-Triassic rocks of Ulster. Gypsum has been mined for over forty years from Kingscourt, County Cavan, where it occurs at two horizons, 20–35 m and 6–10 m thick, within the lower part of the Permian sequence (page 202). Current production is reported to exceed 350,000 tonnes a year, and reserves are believed to be considerable. Most of the gypsum is used in the manufacture of plaster and plaster board. Gypsum and anhydrite have also been recorded from the Carboniferous of Ulster, particularly in the basal sandstones, shales, and limestones; whether commercial deposits occur is not known. Large amounts of halite occur in Triassic Keuper Marls between Carrickfergus and Larne, County Antrim. At Carrickfergus, where extraction by mining or brining has been carried out for over a century, the salt occurs in three beds totalling 40 m in thickness. The succession is known to thicken northwards and a borehole put down at Larne by the Geological Survey of Northern Ireland encountered 488 m of salt. At present, rock salt is mined at Kilroot and mostly exported; its main use is in melting ice and snow on roads.

Phosphate in the lower part of the Namurian in north County Clare was first discovered in 1924. It occurs as nodules in shales and as more continuous thin beds and lenses at the base of the Clare Shale Formation (see page 177) and was mined and quarried at Doolin and Noughaval from 1940 to 1947, during which time approximately 105,000 tonnes are reported to have been extracted. With the increasing price of phosphate on world markets and the intensive use of fertiliser there is renewed interest in the north County Clare deposits and they are currently under study by the Geological Survey of Ireland.

Silica is used in several industries but part of Ireland's requirements are met by imports and local production (for purposes other than use in the building industry) is small. Silica sands of high purity suitable for glass making are reported to occur in Carboniferous rocks at Kildress, County Tyrone; Ballycastle, County Antrim; and in County Fermanagh. A deposit on Muckish Mountain, County Donegal, has been exploited for some years and the Namurian Carrickleck Sandstone near Kingscourt, County Cavan, has been worked recently. Moulding sand for use in foundries has been obtained mainly from dune, beach, and fluvioglacial deposits. Diatomite, a fine-grained siliceous sediment formed from the frustules of diatoms, has long been exploited in the Bann Valley, County Antrim, and is used in the manufacture of insulating refractory bricks. Very finely divided silica, probably derived from the solution of siliceous limestones, occurs in a number of the many solution pipes and cavities known in the Carboniferous limestone. One such deposit near Cloyne, County Cork, has been exploited in the past for use as an abrasive and also as a raw material for the manufacture of pottery.

Of the rocks quarried in Ireland, the greater amount by far is used as aggregate in the preparation of concrete and in the construction of roads. Fluvio-glacial sands and gravels, suitable as aggregate for concrete, are widespread and enormous amounts (probably in excess of 10 million tonnes) are removed every year. Nevertheless, in some areas, for instance Dublin, local deposits are scarcely adequate to satisfy demand. Crushed rock has now to an important extent replaced gravel for concrete and aggregates. Crushed rock aggregates are also used in large quantities in the construction of roads. In general, the rock-types used are those locally available; they include Lower Palaeozoic greywackes and igneous rocks, Devonian sandstones, Carboniferous Lime-stone, Tertiary basalt, and granites. Major trunk roads and motorways carrying a high density of traffic require a wearing-course surfaced with an aggregate giving high polished stone values. Lower Palaeozoic greywackes from Counties Armagh and Down are reported to have such characteristics. Perlite obsidian from the Tertiary rhyolite lavas near Tardree, County Antrim, has been exploited as a source of lightweight aggregate.

The use of local materials in buildings in the past has contributed to the variety of the Irish urban and rural landscape. Contrast Cork, with its mixture of red Devonian sandstones and white limestones; Dublin with its granite and dark calp; Belfast with its brown Triassic sandstones and red brick; and south County Galway with its grey limestone walls. All reflect their local geology. Stone as a structural material has been superseded by concrete, but it is still used, both indoors and outdoors for a number of purposes. Sadly, the use of Irish stone has declined dramatically and, although a good range of different types are available locally, much of what is needed is imported. Probably the most characteristic of Irish building stones are the ornamental marbles. Of these the green and fawn Dalradian Connemara marble is still exploited but many of the well-known Carbon-iferous 'marbles', the Cork Red and other reds, and the Merlin Park Black (County Galway) are no longer quarried. Granite from Counties Wicklow and Down is still wrought for building and monumental pur-poses. The Namurian Liscannor Flags from north-west County Clare, with their bedding plane surfaces covered with elaborate trails or burrows, are popular for paving and facing, as are some Old Red Sand-stones from west County Cork.

Water

Water, unlike metals and fossil fuels, is a renewable resource. Because rain is such a familiar aspect of the Irish climate, it might appear at first sight that there is little need for the careful management and development of our water resources; this is not the case. A large proportion of the water used is obtained from surface sources such as rivers and lakes; for instance, the Dublin area is served by reservoirs in the Wicklow Mountains and Belfast by reservoirs in the Mournes, in the Carrickfergus area, and by water raised from Lough Neagh. Ground water has con-tributed only some 15 per cent of the water used, but is in increasing demand. Unconsolidated aquifers, mainly sands and gravels of fluvioglacial origin, are widely distributed and are probably underdeveloped. Extensive deposits are reported to occur at the Cur-ragh, County Kildare, in eastern County Wexford, and elsewhere. Porous consolidated aquifers are found only in the Triassic Bunter Sandstone, which is the main source of ground water in the Belfast area. The other rock units provide reasonable aquifers where they are fissured. In general, the Pre-Cambrian, Lower Palaeozoic slates and greywackes, granites, Old Red Sandstone, much of the Carboniferous Lime-stone and Upper Carboniferous, and Tertiary basalts form poor aquifers. Fractured Lower Palaeozoic vol-canics in County Waterford are reported to have yielded reasonable flows. The Carboniferous Lime-stone, where it is strongly fractured in the south, provides high permeability, and good yields have also been obtained from the north side of the Longford–Down inlier. The Upper Carboniferous Clay-Gall Sandstone of the Castlecomer coalfield, although it is not very permeable, provides good artesian flows.

Fossil fuels

The fossil fuels which have been, or will be, exploited in Ireland are peat, coal, and natural gas. No assur-edly commercial discoveries of oil have yet been made.

Peat has accumulated in bogs during the last 10,000 years and over the centuries has provided a significant proportion of the fuel requried for domestic use. It has been estimated that roughly half of the approximately 600,000 hectares of land originally covered by deep peat had been cut away before the large-scale mechanised exploitation of the bogs from 1939 onwards. Bord na Mona (the state sponsored body entrusted with the development of the country's peat resources) has established 22 production centres covering 52,000 hectares of bog, mainly in the mid-lands, and production from an additional 18,800 hectares is anticipated in the next few years. Since 1939, some 77 million tonnes of peat have been pro-duced and the annual output over the last five years has averaged 4·35 million tonnes. Production in 1976 was 4·9 million tonnes, of which over 60 per cent was used to generate electricity. Reserves of peat are reported to be sufficient to sustain production, at levels slightly higher than at present, for a further 30 to 40 years.

Coal

Coal-bearing strata have a limited distribution in Ireland and because mining has been carried on since the seventeenth century, many of the seams have been worked out. Richard Griffith (see Chapter 19) wrote the first comprehensive accounts of the coalfields in a series of reports on the Leinster Coal District (1814), the Connaught Coal District (1818), and the Coal Districts of Counties Tyrone and Antrim (1829), all commissioned by the Royal Dublin Society. There have been several additional investigations of the coalfields, apart from the original mapping of the Geological Survey which led to the production of 1″ maps and explanatory memoirs published between 1858 and 1888. The geology of the Leinster and Slieve Ardagh Coalfields was revised by E. T. Hardman in the 'Explanatory Memoir on the Geology of the Leinster Coalfields' (1881). The Geological Survey of Northern Ireland has remapped the Tyrone Coalfield (described in the memoir on the Dungannon area, published in 1961), and the Ballycastle Coalfield (described in the memoir on the Ballycastle area, published in 1966, which had previously been revised in 1924). In 1921, the Commission of Inquiry into the Resources and Industries of Ireland published a 'Memoir on the Coalfields of Ireland', in which the total reserves were reported to be 2077 million tonnes, a figure which must have been an overestimate by a factor of at least 20. Mianrai Teoranta and the Geological Survey of Ireland have carried out drilling programmes to establish more realistic estimates of reserves in the Slieve Ardagh, Leinster, and Connaught Coalfields in the last 30 years and the results are available in unpublished reports. Native coal will never satisfy more than a small percentage of our energy needs. Nonetheless, coal mining makes a contribution to the economy. It seems that there may be potential for development of the industry, but, without further exploration to establish firm estimates of reserves, this will remain no more than a possibility.

Namurian and late Dinantian coals were once to be seen in the cliffs around Ballycastle, County Antrim, and were probably worked from an early date. The heyday of the coalfield was in the mid-eighteenth century when the annual production exceeded 10,000 tonnes. There has been little mining during this century and operations ceased in 1967. The most important seam was the Main Coal (Fig. 121) which was up to 1·4 m thick and had low chlorine, sulphur, and ash contents and a moderate calorific value; it is unlikely that much workable coal remains. Other late Dinantian and Namurian coals were also worked, but they were thinner and generally of poor quality. Substantial reserves of low-quality Dinantian coals are believed to occur under Fair Head, some 5 km east-north-east of Ballycastle.

Coal was mined in east County Tyrone from the seventeenth to the middle of the present century. Workable coals occurred in a small down-faulted block of Namurian and Westphalian strata between Dungannon and Coalisland, and in the small fault-bounded Westphalian Annaghone Coalfield, 6·4 km north of Coalisland. Four Namurian coals were wrought to the north of Dungannon: the Main Coal (Fig. 121) was the most important of them and it was worked out by 1907. It varied in quality, and in thickness from 1·5 to 3·4 m, of which between 0·9 m and 1·5 m were coal and the remainder partings of shale and fireclay. The younger Namurian coals formerly worked were, in ascending order, the Sixteen-inch, Lower Two-foot and the Yard; the latter is reported to have been a bituminous coal of excellent quality and about 0·9 m thick. In the Coalisland area, about 2·5 sq. km are underlain by Westphalian rocks approximately 275 m thick and containing at least thirteen coal seams, of which eight have been worked in the past (Fig. 122). The most important were the Derry Coal (up to 1·5 m thick), the Brackaville Coal (up to 1·8 m thick) and the most valuable seam of the coalfield, the Annagher Coal (usually about 2·7 m thick). Only the highest seams of Coalisland have been recognised in the diminutive Annaghone Coalfield, where the most important coal, the Main Coal, is correlated with the Annagher Coal.

The Connaught or Arigna Coalfield lies in Counties Sligo, Leitrim, and Roscommon. The coals, which have been exploited for nearly two centuries, are of early Namurian (E_2) age and occur as gently-dipping beds in the high land surrounding Lough Allen. Most of the mining, both opencast and underground, has been to the west of Arigna, on Kilronan and Altagowlan Mountains. The stratigraphy of the coal-bearing strata in the coalfield is poorly known; the best information is to be found in the unpublished report of the Geological Survey of Ireland recording the results of a programme of diamond drilling undertaken between 1960 and 1962. The drilling proved five coals within some 50 m of sandstones and shales to the west of Lough Allen; in ascending order, these were the Lower Crow, Middle Crow, Upper Crow, Main and Top Coals. The Main Coal has been the principal seam mined; production has been approximately 50,000 tonnes a year in recent years, with most of the coal being supplied to a local power station, but reserves are now almost exhausted. The seam averages approximately 0·46 m thick and the coal is bituminous with an ash content less than 10 per cent. The Top and Upper Crow Coals are too impersistent and thin to be economic and only in a relatively small area is the Lower Crow Coal thick enough to work. The best prospect for future mining is the Middle Crow Coal with probable reserves of approximately 6 million tonnes. The seam is rather variable in thickness, reaching 0·91 m in places and the coal has an ash content almost everywhere in excess of 25 per cent, and in some places as high as 50 per cent. It has been reported that such coal could be burned in a power station using fluidised beds. To the east of Lough Allen, there are three seams, the Top, Middle, and Bottom Coals (Fig. 121), but how they equate with the coals to the west is unknown. Of the three, only the Bottom Coal is economically significant. The seam varies in thickness, generally between 0·46 m and 0·76 m, and the coal has an ash content around 40 per cent. Reserves of some 9 million tonnes have been indicated. Small reserves are also believed to exist north of Lough Allen.

The Leinster or Castlecomer Coalfield situated in parts of Counties Carlow, Kilkenny, and Laois, has been mined since the beginning of the eighteenth century. The coal, generally good quality high rank anthracite, was in great demand and production is estimated to have reached 153,000 tonnes a year at the beginning of the nineteenth century. As the easily exploited thicker coals were exhausted production dropped and now only a single mine is still working, producing some 15,000 tonnes a year. The Namurian and Westphalian strata form an upland area, called the Castlecomer plateau, with steep scarp slopes falling to the limestone plain below. The coalfield is structurally and topographically a shallow basin except along its western boundary where there are a number of north-south trending folds. The earliest (Namurian) workable coal, the No. 1, Rockafoil, or Kingscoot Coal (Fig. 120), extends throughout the coalfield but is everywhere thin. It was worked by bell-pitting in the north-east of the region, where it reached a thickness of 0·25 m; it is unlikely to be economic now or in the future. The second workable (No. II) coal consists of two leaves, the Skehana Coal below and the Marine Band Coal above (Fig. 122). The Skehana Coal is restricted in distribution; in the drilling programme undertaken by the Geological Survey of Ireland between 1959 and 1963 it was found to be up to 0·33 m thick in the west-central part of the coalfield, but thinned and disappeared northwards and eastwards. Where it was formerly mined in Firoda and Skehana collieries, 4 km north-west and 3 km north of Castlecomer, respectively, the seam was up to 0·75 m thick. The Marine Band Coal is thin in the west of the coalfield but has been worked in the north

and east, where it is usually between 0·3 and 0·5 m thick, exceptionally reaching 0·7 m. To the south of an east-west line through Castlecomer, the Skehana and Marine Band Coals have been cut out by the unconformity at the base of the Clay-Gall Sandstone. The Geological Survey investigation suggested that reserves of 2·1 million tonnes of workable Skehana Coal and 6·7 million tonnes of Marine Band coal remain. The third coal, Ward's Seam, was worked in a few pits but was thin, pyritous and of poor quality. The fourth coal, the Jarrow Coal, a fair quality anthracite, generally 0·23 to 0·30 m thick, was worked until recently in the central part of the coalfield. It was cut by the Jarrow Channel, an oxbow-shaped channel approximately 11 km long and 250 m wide, which contained a 1·22 m thick, poor quality, coal, now mined out. About 7 million tonnes of remaining Jarrow Coal might possibly be workable although the seam is rather thin. The highest coals were limited to the central part of the coalfield and have long been exhausted.

The small Slieve Ardagh Coalfield consists of a number of north-east trending basins with a succession similar to that of the Leinster Coalfield, to which it obviously once was connected. Mining started there in 1825 and the last working pit closed a few years ago, but has been reported possibly to be reopening. The higher coals (Fig. 122) are very limited in distribution and have long been worked out. Of the lower coals, the most important seam is the Upper Glengoole Coal, a good quality anthracite usually about 0·8 m thick. The Lower Glengoole Coal (at the level of the Marine Band Coal of the Leinster Coalfield) is very pyritous and usually less than 0·37 m thick.

The Kanturk Coalfield in north County Cork was mined in the eighteenth and nineteenth centuries. Its geology is poorly known because of the lack of records, poor outcrop, and structural complexity. It appears that four coals were worked (Fig. 122). The Fourpenny Vein (Namurian) is recorded as usually ranging from 0·30 to 0·51 m in thickness; the Sweet Vein (Namurian) from 0·38 to 0·46 m; and the Rock Vein from 0·46 to 0·76 m. The Bulk Vein exhibits extreme variation from less than 0·3 to over 2 m. The coals are anthracites but are crushed and pulverised, and this, allied with the steep dips and numerous faults, make the estimation of reserves of mineable coal difficult.

Small amounts of coal have been worked in the past from the Cratloe coalfield, County Limerick, and from the Namurian south of the Shannon.

Oil and natural gas

The most recently discovered fossil fuel in Ireland is natural gas. Exploration for oil and gas began in

1960, when, following the enactment of the Petroleum and Other Minerals Development Bill 1960, Ambassador Irish Oil was granted an exploration licence giving it sole rights to exploration over the entire Republic of Ireland, including the sea bed beneath the territorial waters, and beneath the high seas over which Ireland exercised jurisdiction. Ambassador was joined in this venture by the Continental Oil Company and Marathon Oil Company, and following geological and seismic appraisal, the first well was drilled in 1962 at Rathmolyon, near Trim, County Meath (Fig. 175). By the end of 1963, a further five wells had been drilled, near Doonbeg, County Clare; Dowra, County Cavan; Ballyragget, County Kilkenny; Meelin, County Kerry; and Macnean, County Leitrim. Of these, the Dowra well encountered a small non-commercial flow of gas which, nevertheless, was the first discovery in Ireland, and the remainder were dry. Ambassador, operating through a subsidiary company, then obtained an exploration licence from the government of Northern Ireland, and drilled three further wells at Big Dog, Owengar, and Glenoo, County Fermanagh, all of which were unsuccessful. The onshore exploration was aimed at testing the Carboniferous and all of the wells drilled were spudded into late Dinantian or Namurian strata. The results of this phase of exploration were very disappointing. The reservoir characteristics of most Irish Carboniferous rocks are now known to be very poor and it seems likely that the thermal history of the Carboniferous basins, particularly in the south, has been such that much of any original hydrocarbons has been destroyed.

In 1966 Ambassador (by then merged into the Anadarko Production Company) and Continental Oil withdrew from the venture and Marathon were assigned Ambassador's rights. Under the terms of the original agreement the concession holders were to cede one quarter of their original acreage every five years. However, after negotiations with the Irish government, Marathon agreed to relinquish their claim to substantial portions of the continental shelf, so that following the enactment of the Continental Shelf Act 1968, and the designation order of that year, they were awarded exclusive licences to explore in three areas: a large tract in the Celtic Sea and smaller areas off Galway and Sligo Bays.

It seems appropriate at this point to turn from the history of exploration for oil and gas to a consideration of the geology of the offshore areas where exploration has been focussed since 1968. Although interest in the geology of the seabed around Ireland dates back to as early as 1823 when the engineer Alexander Nimmo published a map showing the distribution of sediment in the Celtic Sea, the Western Approaches, and the English Channel, little factual information was available before 1968. However, exploration in other areas of the north-west European continental shelf, notably the North Sea, had established the presence of large prospective sedimentary basins with thick sequences of post-Carboniferous rocks, whose presence, in many cases, was scarcely hinted at in the onshore geology. That some of these basins contained commercial accumulations of hydrocarbons had been confirmed by the discovery of several gas fields in the Southern North Sea, the first of which, the West Sole Field, was found in 1965.

Since 1968 there has been a spectacular increase in the information relating to the geology of the areas offshore of Ireland. The bulk of the new data has been acquired from seismic and gravity surveys and drilling carried out by commercial concerns in the search for hydrocarbons; very little of it has yet been released. Nevertheless, enough work undertaken by government and academic institutions in Britain, Ireland, and elsewhere, and enough information from industry has been published to allow an outline picture to be drawn.

The results of this decade of exploration have revealed that the geology of the offshore areas is very different from that on land. As is clear from the earlier chapters of this book, the geology of the land area is concerned mainly with Carboniferous and older rocks and their Quaternary cover; Permian, Mesozoic, and Tertiary sedimentary rocks are, with few exceptions, confined to the north-east of the country. The offshore areas, in contrast, contain a number of sedimentary basins filled with post-Carboniferous rocks (Fig. 184), whose total surface area certainly exceeds the land area of Ireland.

The Celtic Sea, that is the region stretching south-westwards from a line drawn between Carnsore Point, County Wexford, and St David's Head, Dyfyd (Pembrokeshire), is a convenient starting point in a brief description of the offshore geology. G. H. Kinahan, in 1879, had speculated that Mesozoic rocks might occur off the south-east coast of Ireland and might have been the source of the abundant flints found in the Quaternary deposits of Wexford and elsewhere. Information from bottom sampling and seismic surveying has confirmed this hypothesis: except for a narrow north-western shelf, floored by the continuation of the Palaeozoic rocks of Counties Wexford, Waterford, and Cork, and a similar extension in the south of the Upper Palaeozoic geology of south-west England, the sub-Quaternary floor of the Celtic Sea is formed almost entirely of Mesozoic and Tertiary rocks.

Seismic profiles, such as those published by D. Naylor and S. N. Mounteney in their account of the geology of the offshore areas west of Britain, have revealed that the Celtic Sea covers a pair of fault-bounded east-north-easterly trending grabens, the North and South Celtic Sea Basins, separated by a narrow basement high which has been called the Pembroke Ridge (Fig. 184). The North Celtic Sea Basin at its north-eastern end is linked to the basins of the Irish Sea, described below; its western extension has been called the Fastnet Basin. The South Celtic Sea Basin extends eastwards into the Bristol Channel Basin. Little direct information regarding the stratigraphy of the Celtic Sea has been released, but limited published seismic information (Fig. 185), together with data from surrounding areas, allows the con-

struction of speculative and diagrammatic cross sections such as that shown in Figure 186.

The interpretation of the history of the Celtic Sea reveals many parallels with other sedimentary basins of the north-west European continental shelf. The North and South Basins were probably initiated in the Permian as grabens cutting obliquely across the east-west Hercynian structural trend. Above the folded Palaeozoic 'basement' within these grabens is a relatively thick unit, thought to be of Permo-Triassic age, which by analogy with outcrops in south-west England, south Wales, and farther north in the Irish Sea, is likely to be formed of non-marine mudstones

Fig. 184. Sedimentary basins around Ireland. CISB-Central Irish Sea Basin; CISH – Central Irish Sea High; BIT – Bardsey Island Trough; CBB – Cardigan Bay Basin. (Based on various sources including Reeves, Robinson, and Naylor 1978, Fig. 1).

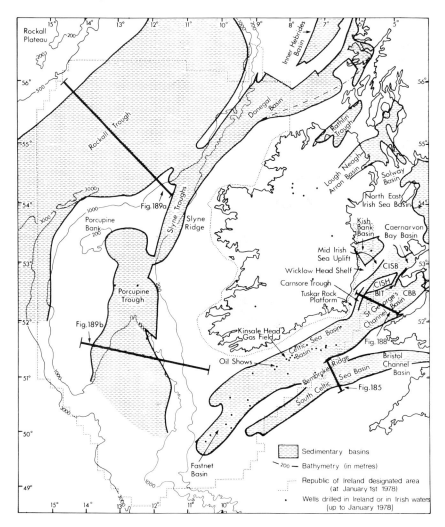

and sandstones. There is evidence in the seismic profiles of thick salt, generally assumed to be Triassic in age.

The Liassic marine transgression, which inundated much of north-west Europe, heralded a period of mainly marine conditions within the Celtic Sea Basins, which lasted through much of the Jurassic. Both seismic information and comparison with adjacent areas suggest that the Jurassic section in the Basins is thick and generally dominated by mudstones: over 1,300 m of Liassic clays were proved in the Mochras borehole in the north-east of the Cardigan Bay Basin (Fig. 184), and approximately 1,500 m of clays with some sands and rare limestones in the Bristol Channel Basin are believed to thicken to perhaps 3 km in the eastern part of the South Celtic Sea Basin. It has been reported that thick Upper Jurassic with undisclosed thicknesses of Middle and Lower Jurassic have been encountered in wells in the North Celtic Sea Basin.

Throughout north-west Europe, there was a reduction in the area of marine deposition during latest Jurassic and early Cretaceous times. Thick sequences of non-marine and deltaic shales and sands (typified by the Wealden deposits of south-east England) accumulated in structural depressions, probably in response to epeirogenic movements. Most commentators have suggested that Wealden-type shales and sands are present within the Celtic Sea Basins and it is widely believed that some of the sands form the reservoir rocks of the Kinsale Head gasfield. Following the deposition of the Lower Cretaceous sands and shales, there was an important episode of folding, uplift, and erosion, which has been widely recognised in north-west Europe. Seismic profiles in the Celtic Sea (for instance, Figure 185) show Upper Cretaceous chalk resting discordantly on folded Jurassic, Lower Cretaceous, and older rocks. The chalk crops out extensively on the sea-floor south of Ireland, where it is gently folded along east-west axes. Probably as much as 600 m is present in places within the Basins, and thick deposits also occur over the Pembroke Ridge. To what extent Mesozoic rocks covered the platform areas north of the Celtic Sea Basins has been debated for a long time. The discovery of chalk at Ballydeanlea, County Kerry (page 211), provides evidence that the widespread Upper Cretaceous transgression did flood the south of Ireland (although the

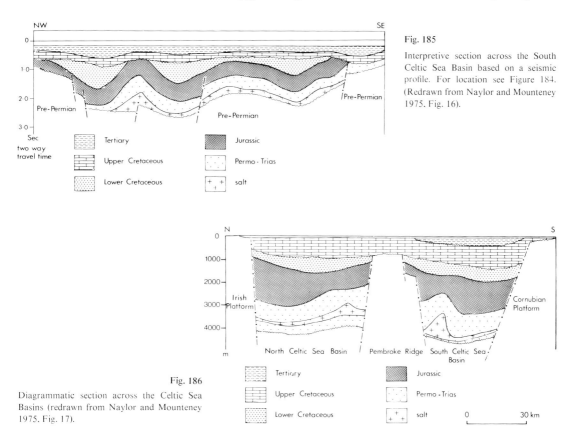

Fig. 185

Interpretive section across the South Celtic Sea Basin based on a seismic profile. For location see Figure 184. (Redrawn from Naylor and Mounteney 1975, Fig. 16).

Fig. 186

Diagrammatic section across the Celtic Sea Basins (redrawn from Naylor and Mounteney 1975, Fig. 17).

thickness of chalk deposited there is likely to have been much less than in the Basins), but evidence for the extent of earlier Mesozoic deposits probably has been removed by late Jurassic–Cretaceous uplift.

Tertiary rocks extend eastwards from the edge of the continental shelf (where relatively thick sections are developed) into the South Celtic Sea Basin and thence northwards into the St George's Channel Basin. In the North Celtic Sea Basin, much of the Tertiary has been stripped; isolated outliers have been reported to the west of Cork but the main occurrence is a narrow outlier, fault-bounded on its northern

margin, between Cork and Carnsore Point, which connects to the narrow fault-bounded Carnsore Trough farther east. Seismic profiles in the Celtic Sea show two units above the chalk. The lower is thought to be Palaeogene in age, probably consisting of Palaeocene chalk unconformably overlain by Eocene carbonates and calcareous muds; the upper has generally been regarded as Neogene, but recently has been suggested to be largely pre-Devensian Pleistocene. The Oligocene was a time of regression, and is represented by an unconformity near the edge of the continental shelf, and by non-marine clays and lignites in a

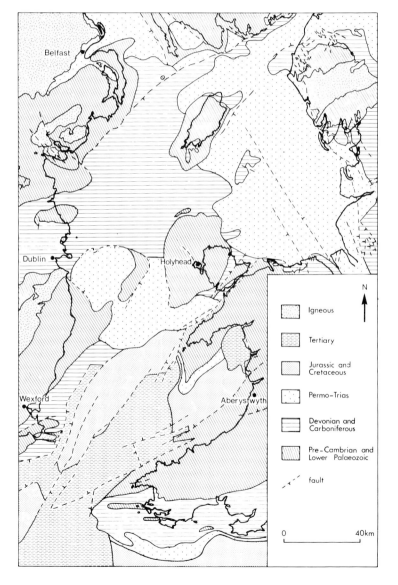

Igneous

Tertiary

Jurassic and Cretaceous

Permo-Trias

Devonian and Carboniferous

Pre-Cambrian and Lower Palaeozoic

fault

0   40km

Fig. 187

Geology of the Irish Sea (redrawn from Dobson 1977, Fig. 1).

number of isolated basins. Thick Miocene–Pliocene sections are thought to occur to the south-west of Ireland.

Mesozoic and Tertiary deposits extend northwards from the Celtic Sea into the Irish Sea (Fig. 187), an area whose geology has recently been reviewed by M. R. Dobson and by J. E. Wright. Dobson and his colleagues have given an account of the extensive work undertaken by the University College of Wales, Aberystwyth, and others, in the South Irish Sea (that is south of Dublin and Anglesey). Gravity surveys have shown that, just as in the case of the Celtic Sea, the South Irish Sea is not a single sedimentary basin but contains a number of basins and highs, most of them with a conspicuous north-easterly trend (Fig. 184). Between Dublin and Anglesey, is a narrow north-east trending gravity high, which is caused by a ridge, termed the Mid-Irish Sea Uplift. It extends south-westwards into a broader region of high gravity values called the Wicklow Head Shelf. In both areas, the bedrock is masked by Quaternary cover, but behaves seismically as acoustic basement and has been interpreted as the offshore continuation of the Lower Palaeozoics of Counties Wicklow and Wexford. North-west of the Mid-Irish Sea Uplift is a large gravity low. It marks the position of the Kish Bank Basin, which is thought to contain between 2·5 and 4 km of strata, probably thick Permo–Trias and Tertiary and thin Jurassic. The basin margins of the south-western and northern sides appear to be fault-controlled.

To the south-east of the Wicklow Head Shelf and Mid-Irish Sea Uplift lies a north-east trending gravity low, flanked on its south-east side by a gravity high. These have been interpreted as arising from a basin, the Central Irish Sea Basin, and an associated high, originally rather unfortunately named the Irish Sea Geanticline, but called here the Central Irish Sea

High. The Central Basin at its north-eastern end is joined to the Caernarvon Bay Basin whose sedimentary fill appears on seismic profiles to consist of a lower unit with persistent strong reflecting horizons, and an upper unit with weaker reflectors. Comparisons with the onshore geology of Anglesey suggest that the two units represent Dinantian and younger Carboniferous rocks; it is probable that the upper unit also includes Permo–Trias farther to the south-west. The sedimentary fill of the Central Basin includes two units with seismic characteristics similar to those of Caernarvon Bay, and the interpretation that the main fill of the basin (probably in excess of 2,000 m) is of Carboniferous and possible Permo–Trias age is supported by comparison of the structures revealed in seismic sections offshore of south-east County Wexford, with those in the Dinantian rocks of the Wexford syncline. The Central Irish Sea High is separated from the offshore continuation of the Lower Palaeozoics of the Lleyn Peninsula by the narrow, but deep, Bardsey Island Trough. Seismic profiles across the high reveal an acoustic basement with uneven relief overlain by a variable thickness of bedded strata. The basement, which gives rise to a magnetic high, is thought to be formed of Lower Palaeozoic and Pre-Cambrian rocks similar to those of north-east Wales and south-east County Wexford. The overlying bedded strata which may total 1,000 m in thickness, are folded and faulted, and can be traced into the St George's Channel Basin to the east, where they have been interpreted as being of early Mesozoic age.

Between the Central High and the Welsh Coast is a large gravity low which delineates the St George's Channel Basin and its north-east extension, the Cardigan Bay Basin. A section across St George's Channel at the south end of this basin is shown in Figure 188. In the west, bounded by the Lower Palaeozoic rocks

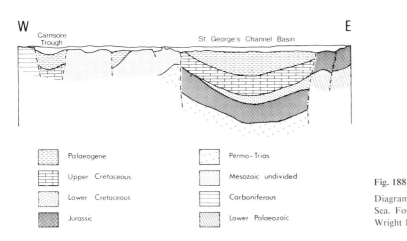

W   E

Carnsore
Trough   St. George's Channel Basin

Palaeogene

Upper Cretaceous

Lower Cretaceous

Jurassic

Permo-Trias

Mesozoic undivided

Carboniferous

Lower Palaeozoic

Fig. 188

Diagrammatic section across the south Irish Sea. For location see Figure 184. (Based on Wright 1975, Fig. 12).

of the Tuskar Rock Platform, is a narrow graben, the Carnsore Trough, which connects southwards with the Tertiary Basins of the North Celtic Sea and north-wards cuts across the Central High into the Central Basin. Interpretations of gravity and seismic data suggest that it contains a thick Tertiary and Mesozoic sequence. To the east is a horst of probable Mesozoic rocks, which dip southwards off the Central High; it flanks the main development of the St George's Channel Basin (which lies almost entirely within the British sector). The nature of the sedimentary fill of the St George's Channel Basin has been inferred from seismic and gravity information and from compari-son with borehole sections in the adjacent Cardigan Bay Basin. Probably as much as 5–7 km of Permian to Tertiary sediments are represented. Thick, prob-ably Palaeogene, sands and shales are inferred above the prominent reflector marking the top of the chalk. The Upper Cretaceous may be in excess of 875 m thick in parts of the basin and probably rests discord-antly on Lower Cretaceous and Jurassic. Probably Upper and Middle Jurassic, as well as Lias, are pre-sent above a Permo–Trias sequence which may include salt, since there is geophysical evidence in the south of the basin of a strongly diapiric structure.

The western portion of the north Irish Sea is devoid of post-Carboniferous basins, but on the eastern side are the large Permo–Trias North-east Irish Sea Basin and the neighbouring Solway Firth Basin. Both are entirely within British waters but are of interest be-cause the North-east Basin is known to contain gas.

Farther north, the Mesozoic deposits of Ulster, described in Chapter 12, are known to extend off-shore (Fig. 184). The Permo–Trias and younger rocks of the Lough Neagh to Belfast region continue east-wards; a southerly graben-like extension may exist in the North Channel. North of the Highland Border Ridge thick Mesozoic deposits fill the Rathlin Trough, which is bounded by the Lough Foyle and Tow Valley Faults and extends from the south of Islay to the Ulster coast between Lough Foyle and Ballycastle. Farther north and west are a number of poorly-known Mesozoic and Tertiary basins associated with major north-east trending fractures; the largest of them is probably the westward extension of the Inner Hebrides Basin. As may be judged from the account above, the interpretation of the geology of the Celtic and Irish Seas and the region to the north is to a large extent speculative and relies heavily on comparisons with areas, both onshore and offshore, where the Mesozoic and Tertiary stratigraphy is well known from outcrop or boreholes. Interpretation of the geology of the continental shelf west of Ireland in-volves more extreme speculation, because the only direct control comes from a few boreholes drilled as part of the Deep Sea Drilling Project, and some dredged rock samples. Few deep seismic profiles have been published and the results of commercial drilling are likely to remain confidential for a number of years. Nevertheless, a number of comprehensive re-views, particularly by D. G. Roberts and R. J. Baily, indicate how much has been achieved in understand-ing this most interesting area.

The bathymetry of the continental margin west of Ireland reflects the positions of a number of large Mesozoic and Tertiary basins discovered by geo-physical surveying. The main features are a deep embayment, the Porcupine Sea Bight (Fig. 184), which extends from Ireland westward to the Porcu-pine Bank (where it joins the Porcupine Ridge, bounding the west of the Sea Bight); and the Rockall Trough, a large sedimentary basin, separating the shelf immediately west of Ireland from the Rockall Plateau.

Both the Rockall and Porcupine Troughs are clearly implicated in the early evolution of the North Atlantic, since there is geophysical evidence that both are underlain partly by either oceanic or thinned continental crust. The Rockall Plateau, on the other hand, is clearly underlain by normal continental crust. It consists of the relatively shallow areas, the Rockall Bank on the east side and the Hatton Bank on the west, separated by an approximately north-easterly trending sedimentary and bathymetric trough, the Hatton–Rockall Basin. Both the Hatton Bank and the Hatton–Rockall Basin lie to the west of the limit of the map in Fig. 184, but are important because of the light they throw on the evolution of the Rockall and Porcupine Troughs. The Banks are thought to be formed mainly of high-grade metamorphic rocks; samples from the Rockall Bank include a Laxfordian granulite and another granulite which yielded a Gren-ville age. In addition, probable late Cretaceous to Tertiary igneous rocks are widespread, and Rockall Isle, itself, is made up of an aegerine granite, which has yielded an early Tertiary (52 ± 9 m.y.) age. The Hatton–Rockall Basin appears to be fault-bounded and contains 1,500 m or more of sediments. The upper part of this section was penetrated in two bore-holes (drilled as part of the Deep Sea Drilling Pro-gramme), sited within the basin (Site 116) and on its eastern margin (site 117). At Site 116, a thin (approxi-mately 60 m) unit of Pleistocene pelagic ooze overlies 640 m of Miocene and Pliocene oozes and 40 m of more cherty Upper Oligocene oozes. 110 m of Lower Oligocene and Upper Eocene consolidated chalks complete the section. The Lower/Upper Oligocene contact apparently represents a break in sedimen-tation, which can be recognised throughout the basin because of its proximity to a very prominent seismic reflector. At Site 117, the reflector occurs close to an unconformity between Lower Miocene to Oligocene cherty limestones and Lower Eocene clays. The latter overlies Upper Palaeocene shallow water mudstones, silty clays, and conglomerates, resting on weathered basalt. On the seismic profiles, the strata above the unconformity are nearly horizontal; they thin towards the trough margins and eventually overstep the sub-Oligocene sequence to rest directly on the Pre-Cambrian of the Banks. The nature and age of the fill below the unconformity is conjectural as the rocks are acoustically transparent. It is probable that the Palaeocene and Cretaceous are represented.

The Rockall Trough (Fig. 189a) separates the Rockall Bank from the Porcupine Ridge and the shelf off north-west Ireland. Seismic profiles show that it is fault-bounded and contains more than 2,000 m of nearly horizontal strata. A number of reflectors can be followed. One is correlated with the Oligocene unconformity met with in the Hatton–Rockall Basin. Independent evidence of the unconformity has been obtained in samples dredged from the margins of the trough, which include Oligocene limestones containing reworked Eocene foraminifera. On the west side of the Trough the succession above the unconformity is like that in the Hatton–Rockall Basin, with perhaps 1,000 m of pelagic ooze above Oligocene cherts and limestones; but in the east, north of the Porcupine Ridge, there appear to be fans of easterly derived terrigenous sediments. Below the unconformity several reflectors can be traced which have been tentatively assigned Cenomanian, Upper Cretaceous, and Palaeocene ages. The central portion of the trough is probably underlain by oceanic crust, which is difficult to date but most probably is of Lower Cretaceous age.

The Porcupine Sea Bight Trough (Fig. 189b)

appears to be underlain by a median zone of oceanic or thinned continental crust at its southern end. It, too, is fault-bounded and contains from 2 km to more than 5 km of nearly horizontal strata with a number of widespread reflectors, which are difficult to date. One prominent reflector has been correlated by D. G. Roberts with the basal Oligocene unconformity of the Hatton–Rockall Basin. Above this horizon, the section thins towards and oversteps onto the Trough margins; in the east, as in the Rockall Trough, terrigenous sediments predominate, but they are replaced by pelagic oozes to the west over the Porcupine Bank. The sub-Oligocene section is confined to the Trough and extends down probably at least as far as the Lower Cretaceous. In the northern part of the Trough possible diapiric structures have been recognised.

The Slyne Ridge, north of the Porcupine Sea Bight, is the westerly continuation of the Pre-Cambrian and Lower Palaeozoic basement of Connaught; crossing it are north-easterly trending complexly fault-bounded troughs, originally mapped as a single structure, the Slyne Trough. They contain a thick sequence of gently folded rocks below rather thin horizontal strata. The age of the sedimentary fill is not known, but R. J. Bailey has suggested that the formation of the troughs may date back to the early Mesozoic. Whether the basins to the west of Ireland are as old as their counterparts in the Celtic Sea, with the implication that the Rockall and Porcupine Troughs underwent a period of graben formation and filling, prior to the Lower Cretaceous introduction of oceanic crust, is a question which will only be answered by deep drilling. Information about the shelf west of Ireland, north of the Slyne Troughs, is limited but

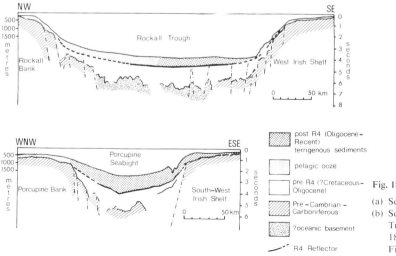

post R4 (Oligocene–Recent) terrigenous sediments

pelagic ooze

pre R4 (?Cretaceous–Oligocene)

Pre-Cambrian – Carboniferous

?oceanic basement

R4 Reflector

Fig. 189

(a) Section across the Rockall Trough.
(b) Section across the Porcupine Trough. For location see Figure 184. (Redrawn from Roberts 1975. Fig. 7).

relatively thick sedimentary sequences are known to occur in several areas, one of which has been termed the Donegal Basin.

Returning now to the history of exploration, it is worth emphasising that much of the geological information outlined above was not available when Marathon was granted off-shore licences. The exploration of the Celtic Sea began with seismic surveying in 1969 and the first well was spudded in 1970 and provided indications of hydrocarbons. Marathon's third well, spudded in 1971 some 50 km south-east of the Old Head of Kinsale, was the discovery well for the now operational Kinsale Head Gas Field. Two further wells delimited the field which is estimated to contain reserves of approximately 28,300 million cubic metres of high quality gas. The pay zones are at relatively shallow depths (between 823 and 1,067 m in the discovery well) and are believed to be within Lower Cretaceous Wealden sands. Production is from two platforms, the gas being piped ashore east of Cork City and, according to present plans, used to generate electricity and in the manufacture of fertiliser.

Up to the end of 1977, 27 wells had been drilled in the original Marathon acreage, part of which had been farmed out to ESSO in 1972. Of these, a number contained shows of hydrocarbons and two resulted in flows of oil which remain to be assessed (Fig. 184). Non-exclusive exploration licences were issued in 1971, and, following a period of intensive geophysical surveying, exclusive licences were awarded to a number of companies in 1975, covering blocks within the Fastnet Basin to the west of the Marathon acreage. So far, five wells have been drilled in the Fastnet Basin, without success.

Exclusive licences covering blocks off the west coast and over the Kish Bank Basin were awarded, also in 1975. In 1977, two wells were completed in the northern part of the Porcupine Trough and a single well in the Kish Bank Basin. The number has increased and the search has been extended to the Donegal Basin. In the late summer of 1979 BP reported oil flows from a well in the Porcupine Trough situated in water some 370 m deep about 190 km from the Aran Islands and directly west of Galway Bay.

BIBLIOGRAPHY

BAILEY, R. J., JACKSON, P. D., & BENNELL, J. D. 1977 Marine geology of Slyne Ridge. *Jl. geol. Soc. Lond.*, 133, 165–172.

CAMERON, D. E. & ROMER, D. M. 1970 Denison copper-silver deposit at Aherlow, County Limerick, Ireland. *Trans. Inst. Ming. Metall.*, 79B, B171–173.

COOMER, P. G. & ROBINSON, B. W. 1976 Sulphur and sulphate-oxygen isotopes and the origin of the Silvermines deposits, Ireland. *Mineralium Deposita*, 11, 155–169.

DERRY, D. R., CLARK, G. R., & GILLATT, N. 1965 The Northgate base-metal deposit at Tynagh, County Galway, Ireland: a preliminary geological study. *Econ. Geol.*, 60, 1218–1237.

DOBSON, M. R. 1977 The geological structure of the Irish Sea. *In* Kidson, C. and Tooley, M. J. (Eds.). *The Quaternary history of the Irish Sea*. Seel House Press, Liverpool, 13–26.

GREIG, J. A. *et al.* 1971 Lead and sulphur isotopes of the Irish base-metal mines in Carboniferous carbonate host rocks. *Soc. Mining Geol. Japan*, Spec. Issue 2, 84–92.

HORNE, R. R. 1975 Possible transverse fault control of base-metal mineralisation in Ireland and Britain. *Ir. Nat. J.*, 18, 140–144.

MOORE, J. McM. 1975 Fault tectonics at Tynagh mine, Ireland. *Trans. Inst. Ming. Metall.*, 84B, B141–145.

MORRISSEY, C. J., DAVIS, G. R., & STEAD, G. M. 1971 Mineralisation in the Lower Carboniferous of central Ireland. *Trans. Inst. Ming. Metall.*, 81B, B174–185.

MORRISSEY, C. J. &   1973   Mineral exploration in glaciated regions of Ireland. *In*
  ROMER, D. M.   Jones, M. J. (Ed.). *Prospecting in Areas of Glacial Terrain*,
                                   Institute of Mining and Metallurgy, London, 25–29.

MORRISSEY, C. J. &   1970   Origin of the Tynagh residual orebody, Ireland. *In Mining*
  WHITEHEAD, D.   *and Petroleum Geology*, Publ. Proc. 9th Commonwealth
                                   Mining Met. Congr., **2**, 131–145.

NAYLOR, D. &   1975   *Geology of the north-west European continental shelf.*
  MOUNTENEY, S. N.   *Volume 1*. Graham Trotman Dudley, London, pp. 162.

PLATT, J. W.   1977   Volcanogenic mineralisation of Avoca, County Wicklow,
                                   Ireland and its regional implications. *In Volcanic Pro-*
                                   cesses in Ore Genesis, Institute of Mining and Metallurgy,
                                   London, 163–170.

REEVES, T. J.,   1978   Ireland's Offshore geology. *Irish Offshore Review*, **1**,
  ROBINSON, K. W., &   25–28.
  NAYLOR, D.

ROBERTS, D. G.   1975   Tectonic and stratigraphic evolution of the Rockall Plateau
                                   and Trough. *In* Woodland, A. W. (Ed.). *Petroleum and the*
                                   continental shelf of north-west Europe, Vol. 1. Inst. Petrol.,
                                   London, 77–92.

RUSSELL, M. J.   1968   Structural controls of base-metal mineralisation in relation
                                   to continental drift. *Trans. Inst. Ming. Metall.*, **77B**,
                                   B117–128.

RUSSELL, M. J.   1975   Lithogeochemical environment of the Tynagh base-metal
                                   deposit, Ireland and its bearing on ore deposition. *Trans.*
                                   Inst. Ming. Metall., **84B**, B128–133.

SCHULTZ, R. W.   1966   Lower Carboniferous cherty ironstones at Tynagh, Ireland.
                                   Econ. Geol., **61**, 311–342.

SCHULTZ, R. W.   1971   Mineral exploration practice in Ireland. *Trans. Inst. Ming.*
                                   Metall., **80B**, B238–B258.

STEED, G. M.   1974   The geological setting of the Gortdrum deposit, Ireland. *In*
                                   Mineral Exploitation and Economic Geology. University
                                   of Wales Inter-collegiate Colloquium 1974. Mineral Ex-
                                   ploitation Department, University College, Cardiff, (this
                                   paper pp. 16).

THOMPSON, I. S.   1967   The discovery of the Gortdrum deposit, County Tipper-
                                   ary Ireland. *Trans. Can Inst. Ming. Metall.*, **70**, 85–92.

WILBUR, D. G. &   1975   Discovery of the Mallow copper-silver deposit, County
  ROYALL, J. J.   Cork, Ireland. In Jones, M. J. (Ed.). *Prospecting in Areas*
                                   of Glacial Terrain, Institute of Mining and Metallurgy,
                                   London, 16–31.

WRIGHT, J. E.   1975   The geology of the Irish Sea. *In* Yorath, C. J., Parker,
                                   E. R., and Glass, D. J. (Eds.). Canada's continental
                                   margins and offshore petroleum exploration. *Can. Soc.*
                                   Petrol. Geol. Memoir, **4**, 295–312.

19

THE HISTORY OF IRISH GEOLOGY

Gordon L. Herries Davies

The pioneers 1770–1820

Modern geology was born in late eighteenth-century Europe, and among the many perplexing problems that awaited the votaries of the infant science there was one which loomed particularly large: what was the origin of basalt? Was it a chemical precipitate as the influential Werner and his Neptunian followers claimed, or were Desmarest and the Vulcanists correct in regarding it as an igneous melt? Ireland was well endowed to shed light upon this important issue and it was therefore the basaltic plateau of Ulster that first attracted the attention of the pioneers of Irish geology. Irish opinion in the controversy was divided. The Neptunian interpretation was adopted by the renowned chemist Richard Kirwan (1733–1812) and by the Rev. William Richardson (1740–1820), a sometime Fellow of Trinity College, Dublin, who earned international prominence through his claim to have discovered ammonites amidst the olivine-dolerite of the Portrush sill in County Antrim (Fig. 190). He had, of course, mistaken the fossils within the baked Liassic shales adjacent to the sill for fossils enclosed within the sill itself, but his 'discovery' seemed a confirmation of the Neptunian theory, and in consequence Portrush became for a while one of Europe's most famed geological localities.

The earliest Irish member of the opposing Vulcanist school was Frederick Augustus Hervey (1730–1803), the Bishop of Derry and the fourth Earl of Bristol. By about 1770 he had recognised the volcanic origin of the Giant's Causeway, and for some time he employed an Italian artist to make sketches both there and at other Irish sites of geological interest. A better known Irish Vulcanist was the Rev. William Hamilton (1755–97), who in 1786 published both an excellent vulcanistic interpretation of north-eastern Ireland and a rudimentary geological map of the Antrim coast between Fair Head and Portrush. This is one of the earliest cartographic representations of Irish geology, and in a 1790 edition of the book Hamilton widened his purview by including a map of the whole of north-eastern Ireland illustrating the limits of the basaltic plateau. This was certainly the first attempt to represent the extent of one of Ireland's geological formations, and it is sad that Hamilton's murder in County Donegal in 1797 should have cut short so promising a geological career. By that date, however, Hamilton and his contemporaries had made the geology of Antrim so familiar throughout the scientific world (Fig. 191) that the expression 'a Giant's Causeway' was universally accepted as a technical term applicable to any outcrop of columnar basalt wheresoever it might occur.

In Ireland the debate between the Neptunists and the Vulcanists chiefly involved academics centred upon the University of Dublin (Trinity College) and the Royal Irish Academy, but by the 1780s there existed within the country another group of men possessed of a more practical interest in geology – the members of the Dublin Society. The Society (it became the Royal Dublin Society in 1820) had been founded in 1731 for the encouragement of Irish agriculture and industry, and by the closing decades of the eighteenth century its members were increasingly aware that the study of geology might yield rich rewards. England's mineral wealth was beginning to bring her unparalleled prosperity; why should the same not happen in Ireland if only there could be discovered the mineral basis for an Irish Industrial Revolution? Thus in 1786 the Society commissioned Donald Stewart, a Scotsman, as its 'Itinerant Mineralogist' and his first assignments were to survey County Wicklow and to examine the exposures along the line of the Grand Canal then under construction from Dublin to the Shannon. The Dublin Society continued to employ him for a quarter of a century, but he was a mineralogist rather than a stratigrapher and his investigations provided no clear picture of Ireland's geological structure. Such a picture would have emerged had it proved possible to give effect to a scheme that Richard Kirwan placed before the Society in 1802. He recommended the establishment of an Irish Mining Board consisting of twelve expert members, the Board to be responsible both for all Ireland's mines and for the production of a series of county geological maps. Sadly, the scheme was still-born, but had it been acted upon Ireland would have been the first nation in the world to receive the benefit of a detailed official geological survey.

Kirwan's scheme may have been premature, but the Dublin Society can certainly take credit for the publication of four early geological maps. Although little known, these four maps, contained in the

Fig. 190. Portrush Foreshore, County Antrim, east side of promontory. Ammonites (*Palt echioceras*) in indurated Liassic shales ('Portrush Rock') adjacent to the Portrush Sill. This olivine-dolerite intrusion was discovered about 1798 by William Richardson, who failed to distinguish between the sill and the adjacent baked shales. Noting the presence of fossils in what he termed 'a silicious basalt', he offered the site as conclusive proof of the Neptunian belief in the sedimentary origin of basalt. His claim to have disproved the Vulcanist interpretation of basalt attracted much attention and he circulated samples of his 'fossiliferous basalt' to many geologists. In Edinburgh Sir James Hall, John Playfair, and Lord Webb Seymour examined specimens and recognised Richardson's mistake. Playfair visited the sill soon after 1802 and in 1816 Berger and Conybeare pronounced a final verdict when they observed that the fossiliferous stratum 'was no other than the slate-clay of the lias formation in an indurated state.' *Photograph* Geological Survey of Northern Ireland.

Society's series of county statistical surveys, are deserving of honourable mention in any history of geological cartography. In the order of their appearance the maps are County Wicklow, by Robert Fraser (c. 1760–1831), published in 1801; County Kilkenny, by William Tighe (1766–1816), and County Londonderry, by the Rev. George Vaughan Sampson (1762–1827), both published in 1802; and County Cork, by the Rev. Horatio Townsend (1750–1837), published in 1810 with a second but by no means improved edition published in 1815. On the maps by Fraser and Sampson geological symbols or colour-washes have been added only to those localities where rock-outcrops had received positive identification, and large areas of their sheets are therefore left as geological blanks. Such maps are commonly termed 'geo-

gnostical' rather than 'geological', but the caution of the two authors is understandable because theirs was an age when the lack of any secure theoretical basis seemed to render dangerous the extrapolation of geological lines from one outcrop to another. Tighe and Townsend, however, threw such caution to the winds. Their maps are coloured throughout, and the two sheets thus stand as the earliest modern geological maps of any part of Ireland. Tighe's map of Kilkenny, at a scale of one inch to 2·5 miles (1:158,400) is for its day a particularly fine production. Perhaps such rock-categories as 'secondary siliceous schistus and ferruginous argillite' (the Namurian shales) and 'siliceous breccia and red argillite' (the Old Red Sandstone) ring strangely in the ear of the modern geologist, but Tighe's mapping of the various formations

Fig. 191. As early as the seventeenth century the Giant's Causeway, County Antrim, was one of the most famed geological localities in Europe. This engraving was published 1 February 1743/4 and is based upon one of a series of paintings of the Causeway by Susanna Drury for which she was in 1740 awarded a premium by the Dublin Society. By the 1780s the members of the Vulcanist school had recognised that the Causeway was a product of former Irish igneous activity.

was surprisingly good and in 1802 his sheet was by far the most sophisticated geological map available for any part of either Ireland or Great Britain.

Save for Donald Stewart and Robert Fraser, all the geologists mentioned thus far were Irish-born, but it was during the years around 1800 that Ireland began to receive her first geological visitors from across the water. Arthur Young toured the country collecting specimens in 1776; John Whitehurst, a member of Birmingham's famed Lunar Society, visited County Antrim in 1783; and in 1797 that ardent Wernerian, Robert Jameson, travelled from Edinburgh to Dublin expressly to inspect the geological treasures housed in the museums of the Irish capital. Humphry Davy made geological excursions through Ireland in 1805 and 1806, accompanied on the latter occasion by George Bellas Greenough who was later to become the first President of the Geological Society of London. That Society, founded in 1807, was soon displaying its own interest in Irish geology because in 1812 the members despatched the Genevan geologist Jean François Berger to northern Ireland to conduct a survey on their behalf, and in the following year Greenough himself returned to Ireland where he spent most of his time geologising in western Connaught. Two other visitors from among the ranks of the Geological Society were the Rev. William Buckland (1784–1856) and the Rev. William Daniel Conybeare (1787–1857) who together re-examined Berger's ground in northern Ireland. The result of their labours was a major memoir published by the Geological Society in 1816 and accompanied by a geological map depicting the whole of Ireland to the north-east of a line drawn from Dundalk to Derry. This memoir was perhaps the inspiration for a paper on the geology of south-eastern Ireland read to the same Society in 1818 by Thomas Weaver (1773–1855), the English-born and Freiberg-trained manager of the metalliferous mines at Cronbane and Tigroney, County Wicklow. When it was published in 1819 his study, too, was illustrated by an excellent geological map, in this case a sheet showing the whole of south-eastern Ireland as far westwards as the borders of County Limerick.

Thus as a result of the debate between the Neptunists and the Vulcanists, as a result of the concern of the Dublin Society for economic geology, and as a result of the activities of her geological visitors, there had emerged by 1820 an outline picture of the geology of at least the eastern half of Ireland. But when in 1802 the Society of Arts in London offered an award for the completion of a mineralogical map of Ireland at a scale of at least one inch to ten miles there was no claimant; nor was there any more enthusiastic a response when in 1808 the Dublin Society offered a prize of £200 for a mineralogical map of County

Dublin. By 1808, however, there was already present in the country the man who was destined to complete the first geological map of Ireland – Richard Griffith, the widely acclaimed 'father of Irish geology'.

Richard Griffith and his map
1809–1839

Richard John Griffith (1784–1878) was the son of a landowner in County Kildare, and after a brief dalliance with the profession of arms, he resolved to apply himself to the study of mining geology. To this end he in 1802 repaired to London there to learn the general principles of science, and in 1804 he visited Cornwall in order to familiarise himself at first-hand with rocks, minerals, and the latest mining practice. A tour of the other British mineraliferous districts followed, and he concluded his apprenticeship by spending two years in Edinburgh. There he attended the classes of Robert Jameson and assisted Sir James Hall in some of his experimental work on the origin of igneous rocks. In 1808 Griffith returned to reside in Ireland and during the following year the Dublin Society commissioned him to make a detailed survey of the Leinster coalfield, the Society requiring of him a large-scale geological map, horizontal sections of the strata, and an explanatory memoir. While this survey was still in progress, Griffith was in 1812 appointed to the newly-created post of Mining Engineer to the Dublin Society, and this office, together with his considerable private practice as a mining consultant, allowed him to travel the length and breadth of the country laying the foundations of a knowledge of Irish field-geology so extensive as perhaps never to have been surpassed.

Griffith's memoir on the Leinster coalfield was published in 1814 together with sections and a geological map at a scale of one inch to 1·32 miles (1:83,600). No previous Irish geological map had sought to depict a region's structure in such detail, but sadly the map was only a qualified success because Griffith had found difficulty in coping with the multitude of small faults that traverse the area. Failing to appreciate the tectonic complexity, he joined up coal-seams in neighbouring fault-blocks and treated them as continuous, when in reality they are fault-dislocated strata lying at a variety of different stratigraphical levels. As a result his survey was of diminished value for those mineral proprietors whom the Dublin Society must have had in mind when it commissioned the survey in 1809.

With the coalfield survey completed, Griffith turned his attention to a far more ambitious project. In 1811, or perhaps even earlier, G. B. Greenough suggested to Griffith that he should compile a geological map of

Ireland as a companion to the sheet for England and Wales which had been engaging Greenough's own attention since 1808. Griffith accepted the proposal and work upon the new map started in earnest in 1813. An early draft of the map was used to illustrate a course of lectures that Griffith delivered at the Dublin Society in 1814, but a quarter of a century was to elapse before the map was finally ready for publication. In the meantime the Society required him to conduct a series of further surveys of mining districts. He surveyed the Connaught coalfield in 1814 and 1815, the Tyrone and Antrim coalfields between 1816 and 1818, and the Munster coalfield between 1818 and 1824, his report upon the Connaught region being published in 1819 (dated 1818) and that upon the Ulster coalfields in 1829. Unfortunately, the Munster survey was never completed, and another of his works which regretfully never reached the stage of publication was a geological section that he and his assistant John Kelly (1791–1869) surveyed across northern Ireland in 1816 from Newcastle, County Down, to the sea at the foot of Benbulbin, County Sligo.

The 1820s were a bad period for Irish geology. Perhaps there was some disillusionment with a science which had failed to conjure forth a mineral wealth sufficient to trigger off an Irish Industrial Revolution, but, for whatever reason, the decade yielded singularly few contributions towards a better understanding of the nation's geology. Even Griffith seems to have lost some of his fervour, but in his case two factors obviously contributed to the reduced level of his geological activity. Firstly, his efforts to compile a geological map of Ireland were being thwarted by the absence of any accurate base-map upon which to record his observations. Repeatedly he complained of the injury done to his geological lines as a result of his having to plot field work upon mis-shapen base-maps, and the situation drove him to such despair that in 1819 he resolved to compile his own topographical map of Ireland using triangulation methods. He began his triangulation in County Kerry, but the work was soon abandoned as there dawned upon him the full magnitude of the task he had so naively undertaken. Secondly, during the 1820s Griffith's time was increasingly taken up in the performance of a variety of onerous public duties. In 1822 he became Engineer of Public Works in the south-west, and in 1825 he received the additional appointment of Director of the General Boundary Survey, in which capacity he had to oversee the location of all Ireland's administrative boundaries so that they might be recorded upon the six-inch maps that the Ordnance Survey was to publish between 1833 and 1846. These responsibilities, together with his continuing duties at the Royal Dublin Society, left him little time for geological

synthesis, but throughout the decade his travels did afford him ample opportunity for adding to his store of geological experience, even if for the moment his interpretations had to remain buried in the pages of pocket-notebooks.

The 1830s saw a revival of interest in the geology of Ireland, seemingly stimulated in large measure by economic considerations. Between 1791 and 1831 Ireland's population had almost doubled but there had been no corresponding expansion of the nation's economy and population pressure was acute. Now more than ever before the obvious palliative seemed to be an Irish Industrial Revolution based upon native mineral resources. One sign of the times was the foundation in 1831 of the Geological Society of Dublin, which initially had hopes of employing surveyors to investigate areas of suspected mineral potential. The Society's finances never proved equal to such a task although its meetings and journal did greatly assist the national dissemination of geological information. From the very beginning Griffith was prominent in the affairs of the new Society and during the 1830s he certainly found more time for the pursuit of his favourite science. In 1829 he had resigned his post at the Royal Dublin Society, and in 1830, while retaining the Directorship of the Boundary Survey, he assumed the new office of Commissioner of the General Valuation of Rateable Property. In this capacity he was responsible for the valuation of all land and property for the purposes of rate-assessment, and for this task was provided with a staff of around one hundred valuators. The new post was of the greatest importance to Griffith because geology was a legitimate study for valuators seeking to assess soil quality. When the valuation commenced in County Londonderry in 1830 his men were under instruction to visit every quarry, to measure the dip there, and to collect a rock-sample. From that moment Griffith was running a rudimentary, if unofficial, geological survey of Ireland. Indeed, there is more than a suspicion that Griffith was guilty of misapplying public funds by employing his valuators upon geological investigations which had no purpose other than the refinement of his geological map. Some of his staff became very proficient field-geologists and, as Commissioner, Griffith found that his tours of inspection afforded ample opportunity for geological investigation. He was later to claim that during these years he had frequently travelled from the north to the south of Ireland up to 40 times per year, moving regularly by night in order to avoid the loss of a day in the field.

In 1835 Griffith was the President of the Geological Section when the British Association convened in Dublin for the first of what were eventually to total 10 Irish meetings. He proudly displayed his map of Ireland for the benefit of the visitors and it received universal praise, Adam Sedgwick considering it 'a thousand pities' that Griffith had failed to publish the map 14 years earlier. But the reason for that failure is clear enough: Griffith was still being haunted by the old base-map problem. The map exhibited in 1835 was founded upon Aaron Arrowsmith's map of Ireland at a scale of about one inch to four miles (1:235,400), and Griffith was at pains to apologise to the visitors for the topographical errors underlying his carefully plotted geological lines. The Ordnance Survey was of course busily publishing its magnificent six-inch maps, but there was still no small-scale Ordnance map depicting the whole of Ireland. Then suddenly the situation changed. In 1836 Griffith joined a four-man commission appointed to examine Irish railway development, and the commissioners persuaded the Ordnance Survey to compile for their use a quarter-inch topographical map of Ireland. But the new map was to be more than just a topographical sheet. The commissioners decided that it should carry Griffith's geological lines and that a geologically coloured version of the map should be published as a document vital not only to the railway engineer, but also to the railway economist. Were Ireland's limestone regions not both the seat of the country's richest agricultural land and the site of most of the major towns, and were they not therefore the areas that would generate most of the rail-traffic? Equally, were the regions of pre-Carboniferous rocks not areas of poor soils, low population densities, and subsistence agriculture? Railways were thus unlikely to be economic if they strayed down the stratigraphical column into systems of Devonian or earlier age.

Following the commissioners' decision, Griffith's map was published in two forms. It appeared first in 1838 in a simplified version at a scale of one inch to 10 miles (1:633,600) and contained in an atlas of six maps accompanying the second report of the commissioners. Then, in May 1839, the full map was published at a scale of one inch to four miles (1:253,440). This large map is a handsome production unequalled in either detail or beauty by any later small-scale geological map of Ireland. True, the map does have its geological weaknesses and it even bears trace of hasty compilation, the result, doubtless, of Griffith being caught unawares by the speed with which his long-standing base-map problem had suddenly evaporated. For example, there had not been time to introduce the tripartite division of the Carboniferous Limestone into Lower Limestone, Calp Beds, and Upper Limestone – a tripartite division which Griffith himself had announced in 1837 – and the earliest issues of the map depicted no Calp Beds whatsoever. Similarly, on the eve of the map's publication Griffith decided that large areas of West Cork and Kerry which he had represented as 'Transition

Clay Slate' were in reality underlain by Silurian strata and he therefore had affixed to the map a small addendum label to that effect. The map is nevertheless a remarkable achievement, not least because one third of Ireland had to all intents and purposes never before been represented upon any published geological map. As the first adequate geological map of Ireland, Griffith's masterpiece takes an honoured place alongside William Smith's pioneer map of England and Wales published in 1815 and John Macculloch's equivalent map of Scotland published in 1836.

Ordnance Survey geology 1824–1845

Although Griffith was conducting an unofficial geological survey of Ireland from 1830 onwards, his was by no means the first such geological survey to be undertaken. Here we must retrace our steps back to the 1820s because, despite Irish geology having been temporarily in the doldrums, that decade did witness the inauguration of Ireland's first national geological survey. The story began in 1824 when the Ordnance Survey entered Ireland to begin the production of a national coverage of six-inch topographical maps. The man in charge of the operation, Lieutenant-Colonel Thomas Colby (1784–1852), was himself a keen geologist, and he believed that as his men worked their way across Ireland they would be able to collect geological information as a by-product of their normal topographical duties. Indeed, writing in 1826, he looked forward to the completion in Ireland of 'the most minute and accurate geological survey ever published'. His initial plan was that his surveyors would collect geological samples, mark the collection sites upon maps, and then despatch both samples and maps to the Survey's Dublin headquarters where a geologist would identify the specimens and interpolate geological lines upon the maps. But the inadequacy of such random methods soon became apparent, and in 1826 Captain John Watson Pringle (c. 1793–1861), a former Freiberg student, was appointed to reshape the Survey's geological activities. Under his direction the field-parties were themselves instructed in the construction of geological maps and a few fruits of their geological labours in County Londonderry are still to be seen in the Dublin archives of both the Ordnance and Geological surveys. But Pringle's system was never accorded a fair trial; in September 1828 the economy axe fell. Colby's masters maintained that geology had been interfering with the Survey's more legitimate topographical duties and he was directed to cease all geological investigations forthwith. Failure though it was, Colby does deserve the credit for having inaugurated the earliest official geological survey of any part of the British Isles. Not until 1826 was Macculloch commissioned to complete a geological survey of Scotland and it was 1835 before the Geological Survey of England and Wales was formally established under Henry De La Beche (1796–1855). Colby's geological survey of Ireland commenced only three years after the Corps Royal des Mines had planned in France the earliest of all national geological surveys.

The 1828 prohibition of geology did nothing to extinguish Colby's personal concern for the science and he was allowed to revivify his geological survey just as soon as Irish interest in geology showed signs of revival in the 1830s. The new survey was placed under the charge of an enthusiastic Lieutenant named Joseph Ellison Portlock (1794–1864), and the earliest achievement of his regime was a geological map and memoir of the parish of Templemore, County Londonderry, published in 1837 as part of the first and only volume of the Ordnance Survey's projected series of parish inventories. Small though the Templemore map may be, it was the first official geological map published for any part of Ireland.

In 1837 Portlock extended his geological activities by opening in Belfast a geological survey office, a museum, and a soils laboratory. His staff was expanded to include eight civilian geologists, among them being men such as Thomas Oldham (1816–78) and George Victor Du Noyer (1817–69), both of whom were destined to make considerable reputations through their Irish geological researches. All seemed to be set fair when suddenly in February 1840 the activities of Portlock's department were brought to a shuddering halt by a second descent of the economy axe. He was ordered to terminate all his geological activities, to close his Belfast office, and to transfer the contents of the museum from Belfast to Dublin. This last must in itself have proved a formidable task; there had to be removed 1,900 minerals, 4,824 named fossils, 70 boxes of unnamed fossils, 13,580 rock samples, and 16 boxes of soil specimens.

This second suspension of the Ordnance Survey's geological investigations aroused considerable Irish protest and, as a sop to public opinion, it was agreed that Portlock might complete and publish a geological survey of Londonderry. In making this concession the authorities believed his survey of the county to be virtually finished, but Portlock was a perfectionist who refused to be hurried and his superiors were driven to despair by his repeated failure to meet deadlines. Finally, in February 1843, the report was published as a bulky octavo volume, dealing not only with Londonderry but also with large portions of the neighbouring counties of Fermanagh and Tyrone. Portlock had created a classic of Irish geology – a worthy companion to De La Beche's more famous sister work on south-western England published in

1839 – but commercially it was disappointing and barely a hundred copies were sold in the year of publication. Colby himself was certainly far from satisfied; he found the report too profuse, too pernickety, and too palaeontological. The volume sealed Portlock's fate. He was virtually dismissed from the Ordnance Survey and despatched to Corfu, there to return to the general duties of his corps.

Twice, in 1825 and 1830, Colby had initiated a geological survey of Ireland, and twice, in 1828 and 1840, the survey had come to an abrupt halt. Now Colby resolved to try yet again. His superiors were unenthusiastic, but in July 1844 he secured permission to proceed and at the head of the revived survey he placed Captain Henry James (1803–77). James prepared himself for his new duties by spending four months in Britain as a member of De La Beche's field-staff and late in 1844 he left for County Donegal, there to apply his freshly acquired geological expertise. Accompanying him were six soldiers to be trained as geologists, but from the outset it was a forlorn venture. The Dalradian rocks of Donegal are hardly a suitable training-ground for geological novices, and Colby's third essay in the geological mapping of Ireland had a life of barely three months. For Colby it was the end, but out of the Ordnance Survey's failure there was to develop the modern Geological Survey of Ireland.

The years of the Geological Survey 1845–1914

While James and his men swung their hammers in Donegal, the Government in London was having second thoughts about the geological mapping of Ireland. Ever since its inception in 1835 De La Beche's Geological Survey of England and Wales had been a department of the Ordnance Survey, but De La Beche had long been anxious to escape from Colby's suzerainty. He now found an ally in the Prime Minister, Sir Robert Peel, and the outcome was the foundation on 1 April 1845 of a new Geological Survey of Great Britain and Ireland under the independent control of De La Beche. The staff of the new Survey was to be entirely civilian although in Ireland, as a sweetener for Colby, James was seconded from the Royal Engineers to become the Local Director of the Survey's Irish branch. James was given a staff of five field-geologists, and, in addition, it was agreed that De La Beche himself would spend a part of each year working in Ireland, as also would Edward Forbes (1815–54) and Warington Wilkinson Smyth (1817–90) who were respectively the Survey's London-based Palaeontologist and

Mining Geologist. With this work-force at his disposal, De La Beche believed that the geological surveying of Ireland could be completed within only 10 years at the trifling cost of £15,000.

De La Beche's men of course possessed no monopoly of interest in Irish geology during the decades after 1845. Griffith remained active in Irish geological circles down to the 1860s (indeed he was aged 89 when he last occupied the chair at a geological assembly), and the members of the Geological Society of Dublin (it became the Royal Geological Society of Ireland in 1864) continued to do sterling work on behalf of their chosen science. In the universities, too, geology had taken firm root. John Phillips (1800–74) became the first Professor of Geology in the University of Dublin (Trinity College) in 1844, and in 1849 geology took its place in the newly-founded Queen's Colleges in Belfast, Cork, and Galway. Useful research was carried out by the geologists in most of these institutions and especially noteworthy are the mineralogical papers of Samuel Haughton (1821–97), who held the Trinity College chair from 1851 until 1881, and a group of studies in Irish regional geology by Robert Harkness (1816–78), who taught geology in Queen's College, Cork, between 1853 and 1878. William King (1809–86), the Professor in Galway from 1849 until 1883, is best remembered for his participation in the international debate over the character of the supposed Pre-Cambrian fossil *Eozoön canadense*. Only Queen's College, Belfast, failed to make much impact upon the geological scene. There the emphasis was upon natural history rather than geology, and as a result the northern city's chief preceptor of the earth-sciences was Ralph Tate (1840–1901), who from 1861 until 1864 was a Belfast-based lecturer for the Department of Science and Art. His local investigations resulted in an important series of papers on Ulster's Mesozoic and Tertiary strata.

Much though these and other geologists accomplished, it was unquestionably the staff of the Geological Survey who dominated the Irish geological world during the second half of the nineteenth century. The Survey 'broke ground' at Hook Head, County Wexford, in the summer of 1845 and from there the surveyors advanced northwards through Leinster, examining every outcrop and producing maps far more detailed than Colby or Griffith had ever dreamed of. All the field observations were plotted upon the splendid six-inch (1:10,560) Ordnance maps, the existence of which gave the Irish staff a distinct advantage over their British counterparts. In Britain there was as yet no six-inch survey and De La Beche's men had perforce to map upon the inadequate one-inch scale. But the Irish Survey had its own problems. After only a few weeks of work two members of the staff had to be dismissed, one for

incompetence and the other because he was anathema to James; and then in July 1846 James himself resigned because he found the Local Directorship insufficient to satisfy his ego. His successor was Thomas Oldham who is perhaps best remembered in Ireland for his discovery of *Oldhamia* in the Bray Group of County Wicklow. In 1845 Oldham had succeeded Phillips in the Trinity College chair of geology, but the authorities now agreed to his holding the academic and Survey appointments concurrently, and under his direction the Survey settled down to its appointed task. But that is not to suggest that all the Survey's problems dissolved with James's departure. Among Oldham's earliest tasks was the delivery of a reprimand to Frederick McCoy (1823–1899), one of the field-staff, for his slipshod mapping and the offender found it prudent to resign rather than face dismissal. (This was by no means the end of McCoy's career in science; in 1849 he became Professor of Mineralogy and Geology in Queen's College, Belfast, and in 1854 he moved to the chair of Natural Science in the University of Melbourne where he eventually became the doyen of Australian scientists). Finance was so tight that one of the two Fossil Collectors had to be discharged, and there was incessant friction between the Survey and the distinguished Irish chemist Sir Robert Kane (1809–90), who in 1845 had established in Dublin a government-financed Museum of Economic Geology (later known as the Museum of Irish Industry). It was unfortunate that the Survey and the Museum had to share the same premises at 51 St Stephen's Green East.

Perhaps the most serious problem facing Oldham was nevertheless an old and familiar one – that very same base-map problem as had plagued every previous Irish geologist. In Britain the Survey was both mapping and publishing upon the one-inch scale, but in Ireland there was as yet no one-inch map available and the six-inch scale, although admirable in the field, was clearly far too large for publication. Oldham was therefore forced to fall back upon the county index maps that accompanied the six-inch survey, most of the indexes being drawn to a scale of half an inch to the mile (1:126,720). It was absurd to map at the six-inch scale and then to lose all the carefully plotted detail during reduction to the half-inch scale, but Oldham had no alternative. The first county map, that for Wicklow, was published in July 1848, to be followed in 1849 by companion maps of counties Carlow and Kildare. Leaving aside their overly small scale, the three maps may be hailed as accurate and very handsome examples of geological cartography, although the problem of representing both solid and drift geology upon the same sheet had yet satisfactorily to be solved.

In 1850 Oldham resigned both his chair and the

Local Directorship in order to become the first Superintendent of the Geological Survey of India and by 1855 five other members of the Irish Survey's staff had left to join Oldham's team in the east. Oldham's successor in Dublin was Joseph Beete Jukes (1811–1869), an officer of the British Survey since 1846 and one of the finest field-geologists of his day. In Ireland one of Jukes's earliest tasks was to oversee the publication of two more of the geological county maps, these being for Wexford and Dublin, both of which were published in 1851. The public took little interest in the county maps, however, and by May 1855 only 155 copies of the five sheets had been sold. The geologists themselves were certainly far from satisfied with the maps and Jukes repeatedly pressed the Ordnance Survey to produce a one-inch (1:63,360) map for geological use. Finally his wish was granted. In 1851 the Ordnance Survey was authorised to construct a one-inch map of Ireland and the first of the new one-inch geological sheets (the present sheets numbered 120, 121, 129, 130, 138, 148, 149) were published in December 1856 with the solid geology represented by the usual hand-applied colour washes and the Pleistocene drifts depicted by a fine stipple.

After 1856 the story of the Survey becomes the story of the one-inch geological map. Each year the surveyors examined about a thousand square miles* of country, moving first from Leinster into Munster and thence northwards on a broad front, so that by 1870 one-inch maps had been published for the whole of Ireland to the south of a line drawn from Galway Bay to Drogheda. With the passage of time the Survey grew in size. The turbulent George Henry Kinahan (1829–1908) was recruited in 1854, and in 1857 William Hellier Baily (1819–88) was brought over from England to become the Survey's Acting Palaeontologist. It was he who was responsible year after year for the identification of the thousands of fossils collected by the field-staff, although to his chagrin he never secured promotion beyond his 'acting' status. The chief expansion of the Survey occurred in 1867 when the establishment was raised to one Director (Jukes), one District Surveyor, four Senior Geologists, and some ten Assistant Geologists. It was a considerably larger establishment than that vouchsafed to the Scottish Survey which only began its independent existence in 1867. De La Beche had died in 1855 and the Director-General was now Sir Roderick Murchison (1792–1871), but a single visit of inspection in 1856 was sufficient to convince him first that 'the geology of Ireland is the dullest which I am acquainted with in Europe', and second that the Irish climate was quite unbearable. As a result he never returned to Ireland in his official capacity. This threw

an additional burden of responsibility upon Jukes (he too found life in Ireland distasteful), and in Ireland the chief legacy of Murchison's reign is the memoirs that accompany each one-inch geological sheet. The preparation of the memoirs was ordered by Murchison in December 1855 and by 1891 every Irish one-inch sheet had its descriptive memoir, a record achieved nowhere else in the British Isles. One noteworthy feature of the Irish memoirs is the fine landscape sketches contained therein (Fig. 75), many of them from the artistic pen of the District Surveyor, Du Noyer, whose death from scarlet fever at his Antrim field-station in January 1869 was a serious blow for the Survey.

Du Noyer's was not the only death to strike the Survey that year. During a tour of inspection in July 1864 Jukes had been injured in a fall at Kenmare, County Kerry, and there ensued a long period of ill-health that ended with his own death in July 1869. The new Director was Edward Hull (1829–1917), Antrim-born, a Dublin graduate, and a member of the Geological Survey of Great Britain since 1850. It was Hull who in 1870 supervised the transfer of the Survey from St Stephen's Green to number 14 Hume Street where the Survey was to have its headquarters for over a century. Sadly the air of Hume Street was soon poisoned by a personality clash between Hull and Kinahan, his newly-promoted District Surveyor. The frequent altercations between the two men became so heated that successive Directors-General had to visit Ireland to oil the troubled waters and both Hull and Kinahan allowed their personal animosities to cloud their scientific judgement. Field-mapping nonetheless continued, although progress was rather slower than hitherto because the surveyors were now tackling the complex Dalradian districts of the north-west. What was the relationship between the rocks of Ulster and those of Scotland? Was the granite of County Donegal igneous or metamorphic in origin? Did Laurentian rocks exist in Ireland? These were the questions that now taxed the geologists as the primary mapping of Ireland drew to its close.

The survey was completed in 1887 – the task that De La Beche had estimated would take 10 years had occupied almost half a century – and the final one-inch sheet was published in August 1890. Now the Survey was run down because the authorities believed its task to be completed. Joseph Nolan (1841–1902) was left in charge with a staff of four geologists to answer routine enquiries and to execute minor field-revision. During the primary mapping the Survey had given inadequate attention to the subdivision of what were then described as 'Upper Silurian' and 'Lower Silurian' rocks (the Ordovician system was not so

---

* It has not seemed appropriate to convert to the metric system in this particular chapter.

named upon an Irish Survey map until 1913) and
the first task awaiting Nolan in the field was a re-
examination of the Lower Palaeozoic districts – a
re-examination that resulted in the appearance of
some 30 revised one-inch sheets in 1900 and 1901.

Increasingly, however, the Survey's attention came
to focus upon drift rather than solid geology. In 1897,
for instance, James Robinson Kilroe (1848–1927)
was instructed to prepare a memoir upon Ireland's
agricultural geology and the resultant work was published in 1907, accompanied by a fine drift map at a
scale of one inch to 10 miles (1:633,600). Then in
1901 it was decided to undertake drift surveys of the
vicinities of Ireland's five major cities and, Nolan
having retired, George William Lamplugh (1859–
1926), an experienced drift man, was brought over
from England to take charge of the project. The outcome was a series of new one-inch, colour printed
drift maps and memoirs for Dublin (1903), Belfast
(1904), Cork (1905), Limerick (1907), and Londonderry (1908).

In April 1905 the link between the Irish Survey
and its parent body in Britain was severed and hence-
forth the Geological Survey of Ireland was a purely
Irish concern. Lamplugh returned to England and
Grenville Arthur James Cole (1859–1924) became
the new Director, having served since 1890 as Professor of Geology in the Royal College of Science for
Ireland. Under Cole one of the Survey's chief assignments was a re-examination of the interbasaltic beds
of counties Antrim and Londonderry to ascertain
whether there was sufficient bauxite present to meet
the needs of the rapidly developing British aluminium
industry. One other project of those pre-1914 years
nevertheless deserves mention. In 1910 Cole and
Thomas Crook (1876–1937) published a memoir on
the geology of the Irish continental shelf and, although
the work is slight, it can now be seen as representing
the Survey's earliest incursion into that realm of
marine geology which is today attracting so much
attention.

The Lean Years 1914–1947

Throughout the nineteenth century Ireland occupied
a leading position in the geological world. Her geologists were figures of international repute and no
foreign student of the science could afford to overlook
the geological publications emanating from the Royal
Dublin Society, the Royal Irish Academy, and the
Royal Geological Society. Many were the visitors
who came to Ireland to inspect localities made famous
by Irish geologists or to study such collections as the
Leskean mineral cabinet at the Royal Dublin Society,
the museum of fossil fish assembled at Florence Court,

County Fermanagh, by the third Earl of Enniskillen
(1807–86), or the fine geological exhibit that was
opened to the public in 1890 in the galleries of the
Dublin Science and Art Museum (later the National
Museum of Ireland). But now, in the twentieth century, all this was to change as Ireland sank to the
status of being little more than a geological back-
water.

A presage of what was in store was seen in the
1880s when the once-flourishing Royal Geological
Society became moribund before finally dying in
1890, and the collapse of most of the Irish mining
industry at about the same time certainly did nothing
to revive a flagging public interest in the geological
sciences. The run-down of the Geological Survey in
1890 was further evidence of the creeping geological
malaise, but it was after the First World War that the
decay really gathered pace. The government of the
newly independent Irish Free State in June 1922
swept the geological collections from the National
Museum to create working-space for civil servants,
and the specimens associated with men such as
Griffith, Portlock, and Jukes eventually came to rest
in packing-cases lying in the vaults of the former
Royal Hospital at Kilmainham. In 1921 William
Bourke Wright (1876–1939), the Survey's chief drift
geologist, felt disquiet at the political developments
taking place around him and obtained a transfer to
England. Three years later the Survey was left in a
still more perilous condition when Cole's death removed from the scene the last member of the Survey
to be possessed of an international reputation. For a
few years the occasional new publication did trickle
from the Survey, but a slow financial strangulation
was taking its effect. A series of excellent quarter-inch
(1:253,440) colour-printed geological maps was
abandoned in 1922 after publication of only four
sheets and between 1928 and 1943 the emaciated
Survey was unable to publish so much as one new
map or memoir. In Northern Ireland the situation was
even more deplorable because the partition of the
island had severed all cross-border links with Dublin,
and for a quarter of a century the Six Counties
languished devoid of a geological survey of any
description.

During the 1920s Ireland's political troubles were
sufficient to deter many a British geologist from
crossing the Irish Sea. Earlier in the century, for
instance, Sidney Hugh Reynolds (1867–1949) of
Bristol and Charles Irving Gardiner (1868–1940) of
Cheltenham had published a series of joint papers
dealing with the Irish Lower Palaeozoic rocks; but
after the First World War the pair felt it prudent to
abandon their Irish studies and instead to turn their
attentions to Scotland. Thus the birth pangs of an
independent Ireland tended to insulate her geologists

from scientific intercourse with visitors from overseas. Even within the universities the flame of Irish geology burned but dimly. The most renowned Irish earth-scientist of the period was undoubtedly that brilliant polymath John Joly (1857–1933) who held the Trinity College chair of Geology and Mineralogy from 1897 until his death, but his reputation lay in geophysics and he did little to further an understanding of Ireland's geological evolution. Perhaps the happiest academic event of these years was the decision of Queen's University, Belfast, to re-establish an independent chair of geology to which, in 1921, there was appointed that redoubtable student of the Irish Pleistocene, John Kaye Charlesworth (1889–1972).

During the lean years really significant advances were made in only two branches of Irish geology: first in our understanding of the igneous rocks of the north-east, and second in the decipherment of Ireland's ubiquitous Pleistocene deposits. In each of these branches there are two names deserving of particular mention. In the realms of igneous petrology are those of James Ernest Richey (1886–1968), who investigated the Mourne and Slieve Gullion ring complexes, and Doris Livesey Reynolds, who devoted 30 years to the study of the Newry Granite, Slieve Gullion, and the region's Tertiary dyke swarms. The two outstanding Pleistocene geologists were the aforementioned Professor Charlesworth, who spent half a century in the study of Ireland's glacial history, and Anthony Farrington (1893–1973), an amateur from whose pen there flowed a steady stream of memorable papers on the glacial geomorphology both of Leinster and of his native Munster. It was Farrington who in 1934 became Secretary to the newly-constituted Committee for Quaternary Research in Ireland, and as such played a part that year in bringing the Dane Knud Jessen to Ireland to train Irish students in the study of Quaternary deposits. One of those students was George Francis Mitchell, the author of the chapter on the Irish Quaternary in the present volume.

The revival since 1947

In April 1947 a branch of the Geological Survey of Great Britain was established in Belfast to begin the revision of the one-inch geological sheets of Northern Ireland. This event can now be seen as the beginning of a renaissance in Irish geology – a renaissance which has allowed the science to regain much of the vigour that it displayed in its Victorian heyday. Three factors have been instrumental in rescuing Irish geology from its long years in the doldrums.

First, the last few decades have seen a revived understanding of a simple fact, long forgotten but clear enough to the members of the Dublin Society in the late eighteenth century, that any nation aspiring to economic progress must possess a detailed inventory of its geological resources. Construction materials for civil engineering; mineral and groundwater supplies for industry; drift deposits for agriculture; fuel resources for a growing population; all are of vital national importance in our modern shrinking world. It was this revived understanding which brought a geological survey back to Northern Ireland in 1947, and from the outset that survey has been especially concerned with aspects of applied geology. Its publications have included, for example, a memoir on the sources of roadstones and aggregate in Northern Ireland and a map of the engineering geology of the Belfast district (page 273). In the Republic of Ireland this same revived interest in the nation's resources led to the establishment of a national Soil Survey in 1958 (it published the first modern soil map of Ireland in 1969) and to a remarkable rejuvenation which has transformed the Dublin-based Geological Survey in the years since 1967, so that today the Survey is both larger and far better equipped than at any time since its foundation in 1845.

Second, the last two decades have witnessed a boom in Irish mining (Chapter 18). Modern methods of geophysical and geochemical prospecting have shown the island to possess that mineral wealth which Griffith and his contemporaries dreamed of, but a mineral wealth which their primitive prospecting methods were quite incapable of locating. Since the earliest of the modern mineral strikes at Tynagh, County Galway, in 1961, a number of other important mineral bodies have been located, each of them stimulating public interest in the geological sciences and bringing into the country further professional geologists in search of yet more riches. To cater for the widespread public interest in geology there have been established two new societies which are modern counterparts to the old Royal Geological Society of Ireland that went to its grave in 1890. The first of these is the Irish Geological Association founded in 1959 and offering an annual programme of events of interest alike to both the professional and the amateur, while the second body is the Irish Association for Economic Geology established in 1973 and conceived as a forum for those with a professional involvement in the economic aspects of the earth sciences.

The final reason for the revival of Irish geology in recent years is related to the fact that since the Second World War geology has flourished in institutes of higher learning throughout these islands with the result that large numbers of both staff and students have been scouring the maps, the literature, and the ground itself in a quest for worthwhile research problems. For many that hunt has come to a satisfying conclusion among the long-neglected rocks of Ireland, and the hundreds of modern researchers who have applied themselves to Irish geological problems are surely sufficient to gainsay Murchison's 1856 verdict that Ireland possessed the dullest geology in Europe. Many are the institutions which have sent geologists to test their intellectual mettle against Ireland's rocks, but three merit particular mention: Imperial College, London; King's College, London; and the University of Liverpool. Since 1948 members of these three institutions have made a detailed study of the finely-exposed granites of County Donegal with the prime intention of shedding light upon the nature and emplacement of granitic bodies. The programme was initiated by Harold Herbert Read (1889–1970) and by 1972 almost fifty other geologists had contributed to the project. Apart from achieving its primary objective of enhancing our understanding of granite, the investigations have shed significant new light upon the structure and history of the Irish Caledonides. Arising out of the project, Wallace Pitcher and Antony Berger were in 1972 able to publish a major new study of the geology of County Donegal – a study which now takes its worthy place alongside such other milestones of Irish geology as Griffith's great map of 1839 and that fine memoir of Portlock's which in 1843 earned him nothing more than a banishment to Corfu.

BIBLIOGRAPHY

COLBY, T. F. — 1837 *Ordnance Survey of the county of Londonderry. Volume the first. Memoir of the city and north western liberties of Londonderry. Parish of Templemore.* Dublin, pp. 363.

CONYBEARE, W. D. & BERGER, J. F. — 1816 On the geological features of the north-eastern counties of Ireland. *Trans. geol. Soc. Lond.*, 3, 121–222.

DAVIES, G. L. H. — 1978 The earth sciences in Irish serial publications 1787–1977. *J. Earth Sci. R. Dubl. Soc.*, 1, 1–23.

DAVIES, G. L. H. & MOLLAN, R. C. — 1980 *Richard Griffith 1784–1878.* Dublin, pp. vi + 221.

FRASER, R. — 1801 *General view of the agriculture and mineralogy, present state and circumstances of the county Wicklow, with observations on the means of their improvement.* Dublin, pp. xvi + 289.

GRIFFITH, R. J. — 1814 *Geological and mining report on the Leinster coal district.* Dublin, pp. xxiv + 135.

GRIFFITH, R. J. — 1818 *Geological and mining survey of the Connaught coal district in Ireland.* Dublin, pp. vii + 108.

GRIFFITH, R. J. — 1829 *Geological and mining surveys of the coal districts of the counties of Tyrone and Antrim in Ireland.* Dublin, pp. ix + 77.

GRIFFITH, R. J. — 1838 'Geological map of Ireland to accompany the report of the Railway Commissioners, 1837. Shewing the different lines laid down under the direction of the Commissioners and those proposed by joint stock companies' in *Atlas to accompany 2D. report of the Railway Commissioners Ireland 1838.*

GRIFFITH, R. J. — 1839 *A general map of Ireland to accompany the report of the Railway Commissioners shewing the principal physical features and geological structure of the country.* Dublin.

HAMILTON, W. — 1786 *Letters concerning the northern coast of the county of Antrim. Containing a natural history of its basaltes: with an account of such circumstances as are worthy of notice representing the antiquities, manners and customs of that country.* Dublin, pp. viii + 195.

KILROE, J. R.   1907 *A description of the soil-geology of Ireland, based upon Geological Survey maps and records, with notes on climate.* Dublin, pp. 300.

PORTLOCK, J. E.   1843 *Report on the geology of the county of Londonderry, and of parts of Tyrone and Fermanagh.* Dublin, pp. xxxii + 784.

SAMPSON, G. V.   1802 *Statistical survey of the county of Londonderry, with observations on the means of improvement.* Dublin, pp. xxv + 551.

TIGHE, W.   1802 *Statistical observations relative to the county of Kilkenny, made in the years 1800 & 1801.* Dublin, pp. xvi + 763.

TOWNSEND, H.   1810 *Statistical survey of the county of Cork, with observations on the means of improvement.* Dublin, pp. xx + 845.

WEAVER, T.   1819 Memoir on the geological relations of the east of Ireland. *Trans. geol. Soc. Lond.,* 5, 117–304.

WEAVER, T.   1838 On the geological relations of the south of Ireland. *Trans. geol. Soc. Lond.,* series two, 5, 1–68.

INDEX

Compiled by
ELIZABETH WILLIAMS
Department of Geology
Trinity College, Dublin

317